Exploring maths

Class Book

PEARSON Longman

Anita Straker, Tony Fisher, Rosalyn Hyde, Sue Jennings and Jonathan Longstaffe

6

Published and distributed by Pearson Education Limited, Edinburgh Gate, Harlow, Essex, CM20 2JE, England
www.longman.co.uk

First published 2009

ISBN-13 978-1-405-84422-2

Typeset by Tech-Set, Gateshead

Printed and bound in Great Britain at Scotprint, Haddington

The publisher's policy is to use paper manufactured from sustainable forests.

Picture credits

The publisher would like to thank the following for their kind permission to reproduce their photographs:

(Key: b-bottom; c-centre; l-left; r-right; t-top)

Alamy Images: Peter Barritt 222t; Brotch Travel 112b; Bubbles Photolibrary 238, 341, 393; Rob Crandall 135b; Editorial Image, LLC 265; Melanie Eldred Photography 108cl; Jeff Greenberg 136t; Chris Howes/Wild Places Photography 108b; icpix_uk 35c; INTERFOTO Pressebildagentur 299; Matthew Jackson 216; JUPITERIMAGES/ Comstock Images 180l; Denis Kennedy 217r; Picture Partners 109t; PCL 392b; PHOTOTAKE Inc 96; John Powell Photographer 304; Purestock 225; Radius Images 309; Nigel Reed QEDimages 33; Ian Shaw 54; StockImages 57; Jack Sullivan 187; The London Art Archive 230r; Glyn Thomas 108t; Zig Urbanski 217l; Libby Welch 29l; Jim West 97t; **Bodleian Library:** Erich Lessing 226; **Corbis:** Bettmann 88; Myron Jay Dorf 180r; Julie Fisher/zefa 343l; Patrik Giardino 40bc; Eddy Lemaistre/For Picture 188b; Wally McNamee 183, 222b; Reuters 40bl; Charlotte Wood/Arcaid 392t; **DK Images:** 66, 336; Paul Bricknell 6; Andy Crawford 112t; Paul Harris 121; Nick Hewetson 52; Dave King 25b, 31b, 37t; David Murray and Jules Selmes 45; Charles Schiller 189; Neil Setchfield 193; Karl Shone 44c; Steve Shott 160l; Roger Smith 37b; Matthew Ward 32; Steven Wooster 273c; **Getty Images:** Jeffrey Coolidge/Iconica 194; Getty Images Sport 219, 343c; Petr Svarc/Iconica 169; Alvis Upitis/The Image Bank 40br; Roger Viollet 335; **Robert Harding World Imagery:** Nick Wood 227; **iStockphoto:** 8t, 25t, 51, 60, 113, 115t, 116, 176c, 197, 204, 236, 255, 257, 316; Judy Allan 268; Santino Ambrogio 130, 177l; Alexandr Anastasin 24t; Chad Anderson 10; Leonid Anfimov 160r; Adrian Assalve 8b; Galina Barskaya 210; Don Bayley 70; Mike Bentley 234r; Juergen Bosse 323; Ian Bracegirdle 318; Nihtyan Chilingirov 188t; Andrew Cribb 92l; Luke Daniek 24b; Winston Davidian 202; Matthew Dixon 374; Dan Driedger 162; Stephen Finn 322; David Franklin 29r; Mark Goddard 208b; Andy Green 35r; Joanne Green 342; José Luis Gutiérrez 288r; Long Ha 184, 372; Alexander Hafemann 288c; Ian Hamilton 177r; Dieter Hawlan 176l, 191; Laurin Johnson 231; Carri Keill 190; Murat Koc 44l; Olessya Laskova 273l; Tobias Lauchenauer 42; Sean Locke 46, 53; Jonathan Maddock 26; René Mansi 208t; Malgorzata Maryniak 243; Tim McCaig 234c; Alan McCredie 48; Andrei Merkulov 343r; Aldo Murillo 240; Petr Nad 289; Patricia Nelson 346r; David Nigel Owens 40t; Guillermo Perales 273r; Tatiana Popova 63; Michael Powers 346l; Dave Raboin 115b; Rick Rhay 272; Amanda Rohde 31t; Marco Rosario Venturini Autieri 92c; Kriss Russell 206; Chris Schmidt 35l, 108cr, 211; Olga Shelego 92r; Harris Shiffman 321; Jeffrey Smith 138b; Anna Solovei 39; Steven Allan 97b; Nicholas Sutcliffe 201; Rob Sylvan 235; Julie Vader 347; Lisa Valder 234l; Michael Valdez 317; Maurice van der Velden 50; Dave White 288l; Natthawat Wongrat 195b; Forest Woodward 149t; **Jupiter Unlimited:** BananaStock 283; Photos.com 373; Stockxpert 135t; **PA Photos:** AP 258; AP Photo/Ben Margot 4; David Eulitt/Landov 389; **Pearson Education Ltd:** Collection of The New York Public Library, Astor, Lenox and Tilden Foundation 1; Library of Congress 230l; PH College 348l, 348r; Prentice Hall School Division 44r; Silver Burdett Ginn 3; **Photofusion Picture Library:** Trevor Perry 67; John Powell 242; **Photolibrary.com:** 81A Productions 112cl; 307; Brand X Pictures 112cr; Photodisc/Steve Cole 185; Izzy Schwartz /Photodisc 109b; C Squared Studios /Photodisc 43; **Rex Features:** Sipa Press 176r; **Science Photo Library Ltd:** 98, 110, 296; KENNETH LIBBRECHT 163c, 163r; CLAUDE NURIDSANY & MARIE PERENNOU 163l; **Anita Straker:** 195t; **Texas Instruments:** Suzie Williams Photography 100, 105, 148, 149; **TopFoto:** 328; **www.spidron.hu:** 77

Cover images: *Front:* **Corbis:** Gianni Dagli Orti

All other images © Pearson Education

Picture Research by: Louise Edgeworth

Every effort has been made to trace the copyright holders and we apologise in advance for any unintentional omissions. We would be pleased to insert the appropriate acknowledgement in any subsequent edition of this publication.

Contents

Power and roots

This unit will help you to:

- ⊙ use 'trial and improvement' to estimate square roots and cube roots;
- ⊙ use facts that you know to work out new facts;
- ⊙ multiply and divide positive and negative integer powers;
- ⊙ write numbers in standard form.

1 Squares, cubes and roots

This lesson will help you to estimate square roots and cube roots using 'trial and improvement'.

Did you know that...?

The Whetstone of Witte

The English word with more Zs than any other word is *zenzizenzizenzic*. It means the eighth power of a number, so the zenzizenzizenzic of 2 is $2^8 = 256$.

The word was suggested in 1557 in *The Whetstone of Witte*, by **Robert Recorde**. Recorde was a 16th-century Welsh writer of popular mathematics textbooks, born in Tenby in 1510.

The word is based on the German word *zenzic*, which means 'squared'. The eighth power, or the square of the square of the square, is *zenzizenzizenzic*. Similarly, the sixth power, which is the square of a cube, is *zenzicube*.

Exercise 1

$\sqrt[3]{n}$, the **cube root** of n, is positive for a positive number and negative for a negative number.

Some calculators have a cube root key $\boxed{\sqrt[3]{}}$.

For example:

- ⊙ to find $\sqrt[3]{64}$, press: $\boxed{6}\,\boxed{4}\,\boxed{\sqrt[3]{}}$, or $\boxed{\sqrt[3]{}}\,\boxed{6}\,\boxed{4}$ to get $\boxed{\qquad\qquad 4}$

- ⊙ to find $\sqrt[3]{-64}$, press: $\boxed{6}\,\boxed{4}\,\boxed{+/-}\,\boxed{\sqrt[3]{}}$, or $\boxed{\sqrt[3]{}}\,\boxed{-}\,\boxed{6}\,\boxed{4}$ to get $\boxed{\qquad\qquad -4}$

You can **estimate the cube root** of a number that is not a perfect cube.

Example 1

Estimate the value of $\sqrt[3]{70}$.

Since 70 lies between 4^3 and 5^3, $4 < \sqrt[3]{70} < 5$.

Since 70 is closer to 64 than to 125, $\sqrt[3]{70}$ is likely to be closer to 4 than to 5. An estimate is 4.2.

```
      ³√64   ³√70                              ³√125
       |      |                                  |
       4      ↑                                  5
```

You can estimate the value of a root more accurately by using trial and improvement.

Example 2

Solve $a^3 = 240$.

Value of a	Value of a^3
6	216
7	343
6.2	238.328
6.3	250.047
6.22	240.641 848
6.21	239.483 061
6.215	240.061 988 4

too small
too big a is between 6 and 7
too small a is between 6.2 and 7
too big a is between 6.2 and 6.3
too big a is between 6.2 and 6.22
too small a is between 6.21 and 6.22
too big a is between 6.210 and 6.215

So a must lie on the number line between 6.21 and 6.215.

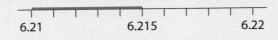

```
        |‾‾‾‾‾‾‾‾‾|
        6.21      6.215      6.22
```

Numbers between 6.21 and 6.215 round down to 6.21 to 2 d.p.

$a = 6.21$ to 2 d.p.

You will need a scientific calculator.

1   Solve each equation **without using a calculator**.

   a $x^3 = 64$ b $x^3 = -27$ c $x^3 = 125$ d $x^3 = -1$

(2) **Use a calculator** to find the value of each expression correct to two decimal places.

a $\sqrt{5}$ b $\sqrt[3]{100}$ c $\sqrt[3]{(-80)}$ d $\sqrt{0.9}$

(3) Estimate the integer that is closest to the value of each of these.

a $\sqrt[3]{40}$ b $\sqrt[3]{85}$ c $\sqrt[3]{550}$ d $\sqrt[3]{900}$

(4) **Use a calculator** to find the cube roots in question 3 correct to two decimal places.

(5) Solve these equations by using trial and improvement.
Make a table to help you.
Give your answers correct to one decimal place.

a $a^3 = 14$ b $a^3 = 7000$

(6) This Indian box is in the shape of a cube.
Its volume is 800 cm³.

Use trial and improvement to find the length of a side correct to two decimal places.

(7) Any positive whole number can be written as the sum of four square numbers.
For example:

$$23 = 1 + 4 + 9 + 9$$

Investigate different ways of writing 150 as the sum of four square numbers.
How many different ways can you find?

Can you write 150 as the sum of three square numbers?

Extension problems

(8) I am an odd two-digit number but I am not a prime number.
If you reverse me and add me to myself, you get a square number.
If you reverse me and subtract me from myself, you get another square number.
Who am I?

(9) Solve the equation $a(a + 2) = 10$ by using trial and improvement.
Make a table to help you.
Give your answer correct to one decimal place.

Points to remember

⊙ $\sqrt{n}$ is the **square root** of n and $\sqrt[3]{n}$ is the **cube root** of n.

⊙ When n is positive, $\sqrt{n}$ can be positive or negative.

⊙ When n is positive, $\sqrt[3]{n}$ is positive and when n is negative, $\sqrt[3]{n}$ is negative.

⊙ You can estimate square roots and cube roots using **trial and improvement**.

2 Equivalent calculations using powers of 10

This lesson will help you to use facts you know to work out new facts.

Did you know that...?

A **googol** is 10 to the power 100, or 10^{100}. This is 1 with one hundred zeros.

A **googolplex** is 10 to the power googol.

The headquarters of Google, the Internet search engine, at Mountain View, California, is called **Googleplex**, named using a variation of googol.

Sergey Brin and Larry Page, of Google

Exercise 2

When you multiply, or divide, both numerator and denominator of a calculation by the same number, the answer does not change.

Example 1

Given that $\dfrac{16.3}{2.5} = 6.52$, work out the value of $\dfrac{16.3}{250}$.

$$\frac{16.3}{250} = \frac{16.3 \div 100}{250 \div 100} = \frac{16.3 \div 100}{2.5} = 6.52 \div 100 = 0.0652$$

Example 2

Given that $\dfrac{3.46 \times 25.5}{3.4} = 25.95$, work out the value of $\dfrac{34.6 \times 2.55}{0.34}$.

$34.6 \times 2.55 = (34.6 \div 10) \times (2.55 \times 10) = 3.46 \times 25.5$, so the two numerators are equivalent.

$$\frac{34.6 \times 2.55}{0.34} = \frac{34.6 \times 2.55 \times 10}{0.34 \times 10} = \frac{3.46 \times 25.5 \times 10}{3.4} = 25.95 \times 10 = 259.5$$

Do these questions **without using a calculator**. Show your working.

1. Given that $5.5 \times 6.6 = 36.3$, work out:

   a 5.5×66
   b 0.55×0.66
   c 55×0.66
   d 550×0.066

2. Given that $18.3 \div 3.75 = 4.88$, work out:

   a $183 \div 3.75$
   b $1.83 \div 3.75$
   c $0.183 \div 3.75$
   d $0.183 \div 37.5$

3. Given that $23 \times 56 = 1288$, work out:

   a 0.23×560
   b $1288 \div 5.6$
   c $12.88 \div 0.23$
   d 0.023×0.56

4. Given that $1512 \div 72 = 21$, work out:

   a $15.12 \div 7.2$
   b $1.512 \div 0.072$
   c $15.12 \div 21$
   d $1.512 \div 2.1$

5. Given that $442 \div 34 = 13$, work out:

   a $4.42 \div 340$
   b $442 \div 1.3$
   c $4.42 \div 130$
   d $44.2 \div 0.34$

6. Given that $\dfrac{46.4 \times 5.1}{3.4} = 69.6$, work out:

   a $\dfrac{46.4 \times 51}{34}$
   b $\dfrac{464 \times 51}{3400}$
   c $\dfrac{0.464 \times 510}{3.4}$
   d $\dfrac{4.64 \times 5.1}{0.34}$

7. Given that $\dfrac{72 \times 56}{42} = 96$, work out:

   a $\dfrac{7.2 \times 56}{0.42}$
   b $\dfrac{0.72 \times 5.6}{420}$
   c $\dfrac{7.2 \times 5.6}{9.6}$
   d $\dfrac{7200 \times 560}{9600}$

◉ Points to remember

- ⊙ When you multiply, or divide, both numerator and denominator of a calculation by the same number, the answer does not change.
- ⊙ If you multiply the numerator by a number, the answer is multiplied by the same number.
- ⊙ If you divide the numerator by a number, the answer is divided by the same number.
- ⊙ If you multiply the denominator by a number, the answer is divided by the same number.
- ⊙ If you divide the denominator by a number, the answer is multiplied by the same number.

3 Standard form

This lesson will help you to use the index laws and express numbers in standard form.

Did you know that...?

This puzzle was invented by the ancient Egyptians and recorded on the **Rhind Papyrus** nearly 4000 years ago.

A wealthy Egyptian farmer owned seven barns.
Each of the barns housed seven cats.
Each of the cats caught seven mice.
Each of the mice would have eaten seven sheaves of wheat.
Each sheaf of wheat produced seven measures of flour.
How many measures of flour did the farmer's cats save?

$7 \times 7 \times 7 \times 7 \times 7 = 7^5 = 16\,807$

A similar puzzle exists today in the traditional English rhyme: 'As I was going to St Ives ...'

Exercise 3A

$10\,000 = 10 \times 10 \times 10 \times 10$, which is 10^4 or '10 to the power 4'.
The small number 4 is called the **index**.

An index can be negative as well as positive. For example, $10^{-2} = \dfrac{1}{10^2} = \dfrac{1}{100}$.

To **multiply** two numbers in index form, **add** the indices, so $10^m \times 10^n = 10^{m+n}$.
For example, $10^4 \times 10^2 = 10^{4+2} = 10^6$.

To **divide** two numbers in index form, **subtract** the indices, so $10^m \div 10^n = 10^{m-n}$.
For example, $10^3 \div 10^2 = 10^{3-2} = 10^1 = 10$.

Example

Work out the value of $(4^2)^3$.

$(4^2)^3 = 4^2 \times 4^2 \times 4^2 = 4^{2+2+2} = 4^6 = 4096$

① Work out the value of each expression.

    a 2^{-1} b 3^{-2} c 10^{-3} d 2^0

② Simplify these.

    a $3^2 \times 3^{-3}$ b $4^{-2} \times 4$ c $10^4 \times 10^{-2}$ d $2 \times 2^2 \times 2^{-5}$

    e $4^{-2} \div 4^3$ f $3^2 \div 3^{-1}$ g $5^4 \div 5^{-3}$ h $10^{-2} \div 10^{-3}$

③ Simplify these.

a $\dfrac{2^4}{2^7 \times 2^{-2}}$　　　b $\dfrac{5^{-2} \times 5^4}{5}$　　　c $\dfrac{4^{-3} \times 4^3}{4^{-2}}$　　　d $\dfrac{2^4 \times 2^2}{2^7 \times 2^{-1}}$

④ Find the value of n in each equation.

a $32 = 2^n$　　　b $2^n = 2^2 \div 2^5$　　　c $2^n = 4^3$　　　d $100 = 2^2 \times 5^n$

Exercise 3B

A number written in **standard form** has the form $A \times 10^n$, where A is a number between 1 and 10 and n is an integer.

For example, the age of the Earth is about 4.6 thousand million years.
In full, this is 4 600 000 000 years. In standard form, the age of the Earth is 4.6×10^9 years.

Example 1

Write 9000 in standard form.

$9000 = 9 \times 1000 = 9 \times 10^3$ in standard form

9 is the number between 1 and 10, so A = 9 and n = 3.

The 9 has moved three places to the left because it has been multiplied by 10^3.

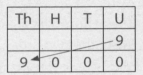

Th	H	T	U
			9
9	0	0	0

Numbers in standard form can be written as ordinary numbers.

Example 2

Write 8×10^6 as an ordinary number.

$8 \times 10^6 = 8\ 000\ 000$

The 8 moves six places to the left from the units place to the millions place.

① Write each number in standard form.

a 58 000 000　　　b 0.000 37　　　c 225 000　　　d 49 300

e 0.0002　　　f 26 789　　　g 0.0043　　　h 0.000 000 15

② Write each standard form number as an ordinary number. You may **use your calculator**.

a 8.6×10^4　　　b 4.21×10^{-3}　　　c 7.8×10^3　　　d 3.25×10^{-2}

e 7×10^9　　　f 4.13×10^{-4}　　　g 6.9×10^6　　　h 2.01×10^{-1}

③ Write each number in standard form.

a 26×10^3　　　b 47.2×10^{-5}　　　c 0.33×10^{-3}　　　d 28×10^{-4}

4   Rewrite these sentences using numbers in standard form.

   a   The diameter of the Earth is approximately 12 735 km.

   b   The diameter of the Sun is approximately 1 392 000 km.

   c   The Sun is about 150 000 000 km from the Earth.

5   Rewrite these sentences using ordinary numbers.

   a   A grain of pollen is about 1×10^{-2} mm in diameter.

   b   A virus is about 1×10^{-4} mm in diameter.

   c   The radius of a hydrogen atom is about 5×10^{-8} mm.

6   These numbers are in standard form.
   Write them in order, starting with the smallest.

   1.6×10^{4} 3.7×10^{-1} 4.6×10 1.9×10^{-2} 2.3×10^{2}

Extension problems

7   Show that $(7 \times 10^{6}) \times (6 \times 10^{4}) = 4.2 \times 10^{11}$.

8   Write each expression as a number in standard form.

   a $(4 \times 10^{8}) \times (2 \times 10^{3})$ b $(6 \times 10^{5}) \times (1.5 \times 10^{3})$

   c $(4 \times 10^{2}) \times (3 \times 10^{5})$ d $(6 \times 10^{7}) \times (3 \times 10^{6})$

   e $(6 \times 10^{9}) \times (5 \times 10^{3})$ f $(5 \times 10^{8}) \times (2 \times 10^{-6})$

◉ Points to remember

⊙ To **multiply** two numbers in index form, add the indices,
   so $a^{m} \times a^{n} = a^{m+n}$.

⊙ To **divide** two numbers in index form, subtract the indices,
   so $a^{m} \div a^{n} = a^{m-n}$.

⊙ A number in **standard form** is of the form $A \times 10^{n}$,
   where $1 \leqslant A < 10$ and n is an integer.

How well are you doing?

Can you:

- estimate and calculate square roots and cube roots?
- multiply and divide positive and negative integer powers?
- use facts that you know to work out new facts?
- write numbers in standard form?

Powers and roots (no calculator)

1 Work out the value of each expression correct to two decimal places.

   a $\sqrt{19}$ b $\sqrt[3]{400}$ c $\sqrt[3]{(-150)}$ d $\sqrt{0.08}$

2 *1999 level 6*

The length of one side of a rectangle is y.

This equation shows the area of the rectangle:

$$y(y + 2) = 67.89$$

Find the value of y. Show your working.   You may find the following table helpful.

y	$y + 2$	$y(y + 2)$	
8	10	80	too large

3 *1999 level 7*

   a Write the values of k and m.

$$64 = 8^2 = 4^k = 2^m$$

   b Here is some information.

$$2^{15} = 32\,768$$

What is the value of 2^{14}?

4 *2005 level 7*

Here is an equation.

$$x^y = 64$$

Give four different pairs of values for x and y that satisfy this equation.

5 *2007 level 7*

Work out the values of m and n.

$$5^8 \times 5^4 = 5^m$$

$$\frac{5^8}{5^4} = 5^n$$

6 *2005 level 8*

What is $(4 \times 10^8) \div (8 \times 10^4)$?
Write your answer in standard form.

7 *2007 level 8*

One light year is approximately 9 430 000 000 000 kilometres.
Write this distance in standard form.

Expressions and formulae

> **This unit will help you to:**
>
> - simplify algebraic fractions;
> - solve linear equations;
> - expand brackets;
> - factorise expressions;
> - recognise identical expressions;
> - change the subject of a formula.

1 Algebraic fractions

This lesson will help you to add, subtract and simplify algebraic fractions.

 Did you know that...?

The word **fraction** comes from the Latin word *fractus* meaning broken, but fractions as we know them today come from Indian civilisation.

Exercise 1

To add or subtract fractions with the same denominator, add or subtract the numerators and leave the denominator the same. For example:

$$\frac{3}{5} + \frac{1}{5} = \frac{4}{5} \qquad \frac{6}{a} + \frac{4}{a} = \frac{10}{a}$$

To add or subtract fractions with different denominators, find the **lowest common multiple (LCM)** of the denominators.

Example 1

Denominators with no common factors

a Work out $\frac{2}{3} + \frac{3}{4}$.

The LCM is $3 \times 4 = 12$.

$$\frac{2}{3} + \frac{3}{4} = \frac{8 + 9}{12} = \frac{17}{12} = 1\frac{5}{12}$$

b Simplify $\frac{2}{a} + \frac{7}{b}$.

The LCM is $a \times b = ab$

$$\frac{2}{a} + \frac{7}{b} = \frac{2b + 7a}{ab}$$

Example 2

Denominators with common factors

a Work out $\dfrac{5}{6} + \dfrac{2}{15}$.

The LCM is $2 \times 3 \times 5 = 30$.

$$\frac{5}{6} + \frac{2}{15} = \frac{25 + 4}{30} = \frac{29}{30}$$

b Simplify $\dfrac{3}{a} + \dfrac{5}{ab}$.

The LCM is $a \times b = ab$.

$$\frac{3}{a} + \frac{5}{ab} = \frac{3b}{ab} + \frac{5}{ab} = \frac{3b + 5}{ab}$$

To simplify a fraction, divide the numerator and denominator by common factors.

Example 3

a Simplify $\dfrac{8}{20}$.

Divide the numerator and denominator by the common factor 4.

$$\frac{8}{20} = \frac{8 \div 4}{20 \div 4} = \frac{2}{5}$$

b Simplify $\dfrac{3a}{5ab}$.

Divide the numerator and denominator by the common factor a.

$$\frac{3a}{5ab} = \frac{3a \div a}{5ab \div a} = \frac{3}{5b}$$

1
  a $\dfrac{4}{7} + \dfrac{5}{7}$
    b $\dfrac{17}{13} - \dfrac{9}{13}$
    c $\dfrac{10}{b} + \dfrac{3}{b}$

  d $\dfrac{8}{a} + \dfrac{6}{a}$
    e $\dfrac{15}{x} - \dfrac{12}{x}$
    f $\dfrac{29}{y} - \dfrac{16}{y}$

  g $\dfrac{5}{ab} + \dfrac{9}{ab}$
    h $\dfrac{16}{xy} - \dfrac{9}{xy}$
    i $\dfrac{14}{pqr} + \dfrac{6}{pqr}$

2
  a $\dfrac{5}{9} + \dfrac{3}{4}$
    b $\dfrac{1}{2} - \dfrac{3}{11}$
    c $\dfrac{3}{a} + \dfrac{4}{b}$

  d $\dfrac{13}{c} + \dfrac{15}{d}$
    e $\dfrac{8}{a} - \dfrac{3}{b}$
    f $\dfrac{5}{c} - \dfrac{9}{d}$

  g $\dfrac{5}{xy} + \dfrac{6}{wz}$
    h $\dfrac{4}{pq} - \dfrac{3}{rs}$
    i $\dfrac{8}{ab} - \dfrac{7}{cd}$

3
  a $\dfrac{2}{3} + \dfrac{4}{6}$
    b $\dfrac{3}{10} + \dfrac{2}{15}$
    c $\dfrac{6}{7} - \dfrac{3}{14}$

  d $\dfrac{2}{3} - \dfrac{1}{9}$
    e $\dfrac{5}{a} + \dfrac{7}{ab}$
    f $\dfrac{6}{xy} - \dfrac{5}{y}$

  g $\dfrac{1}{2ab} + \dfrac{3}{4b}$
    h $\dfrac{3}{5a} - \dfrac{2}{10ab}$
    i $\dfrac{2}{3pqr} + \dfrac{1}{9p^2}$

④ Simplify these expressions by dividing the numerator and denominator by common factors.

a $\dfrac{26}{32}$ b $\dfrac{20}{55}$ c $\dfrac{7a}{14b}$ d $\dfrac{3a}{5a}$

e $\dfrac{4ab}{6ac}$ f $\dfrac{7ad}{8a^2c}$ g $\dfrac{9xy}{12xz}$ h $\dfrac{14x^2}{7xy}$

⑤ The expression or number in each cell is the result of adding the expressions or numbers in the two cells beneath it.

Copy the diagrams and fill in the missing expressions.

a
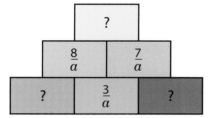

b
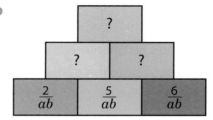

c
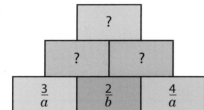

d

⑥ In a magic square the sum of the expressions in each row, column and diagonal is the same.

Copy and complete these magic squares.

a

b

Extension problem

7

a $\dfrac{5}{x^2} + \dfrac{9}{x^2}$

b $\dfrac{12}{y^2} - \dfrac{8}{y^2}$

c $\dfrac{a}{x} - \dfrac{b}{y}$

d $\dfrac{c}{p} + \dfrac{d}{q}$

e $\dfrac{m}{xy} + \dfrac{n}{yz}$

f $\dfrac{p}{qx} + \dfrac{r}{sx}$

g $\dfrac{9}{ax^2} + \dfrac{12}{bx^2}$

h $\dfrac{6}{abx} + \dfrac{8}{acx} - \dfrac{4}{adx}$

i $\dfrac{3}{a^2bc} - \dfrac{5}{ab^2c} + \dfrac{2}{abc^2}$

Points to remember

- The rules for adding and subtracting algebraic fractions are the same as for numerical fractions.
- You can only add and subtract fractions with the same denominator. If the denominators are different, first convert them to the same denominator.
- You can simplify a fraction by dividing the numerator and denominator by common factors.

2 Linear equations

This lesson will help you to solve linear equations.

Exercise 2

To solve a simple linear equation, use inverse operations. This means that what you do to one side of the equation you must do to the other to keep the equation in balance.

Example 1

Solve $2x + 5 = 11$.

$$2x + 5 = 11 \qquad x \to \boxed{\times 2} \to \boxed{+5} \to 11$$

subtract 5 $\qquad 2x = 6 \qquad\quad 3 \leftarrow \boxed{\div 2} \leftarrow \boxed{-5} \leftarrow 11$

divide by 2 $\qquad \underline{x = 3}$

When there are x terms on both sides, first rearrange to get all the x terms on one side.

Example 2

Solve $3x - 4 = 2x - 2$.

subtract $2x$ $\qquad x - 4 = -2 \qquad x \to \boxed{-4} \to -2$

add 4 $\qquad\qquad \underline{x = 2} \qquad\qquad 2 \leftarrow \boxed{+4} \leftarrow -2$

When the equation has one or more brackets, first work out the brackets and simplify the algebraic expression.

Example 3

Solve $2(3x - 1) = 28$.

$$2(3x - 1) = 28$$

multiply out $\qquad\qquad 6x - 2 = 28$

add 2 $\qquad\qquad\qquad 6x = 30$

divide by 6 $\qquad\qquad\quad x = 5$

$x \rightarrow \boxed{\times 6} \rightarrow \boxed{- 2} \rightarrow 28$

$5 \leftarrow \boxed{\div 6} \leftarrow \boxed{+ 2} \leftarrow 28$

Example 4

Solve $6(4x + 2) + 5(2x - 7) = 79$.

multiply out $\quad 24x + 12 + 10x - 35 = 79$

simplify $\qquad\qquad\qquad 34x - 23 = 79$

add 23 $\qquad\qquad\qquad\quad 34x = 102$

divide by 34 $\qquad\qquad\qquad x = 3$

$x \rightarrow \boxed{\times 34} \rightarrow \boxed{- 23} \rightarrow 79$

$3 \leftarrow \boxed{\div 34} \leftarrow \boxed{+ 23} \leftarrow 79$

When there are fractions first multiply through the equation by the lowest common denominator.

Example 5

Solve $\frac{1}{5}(x + 29) = 7$.

$$\frac{1}{5}(x + 29) = 7$$

multiply by 5 $\qquad x + 29 = 35$

subtract 29 $\qquad\qquad x = 6$

$x \rightarrow \boxed{+ 29} \rightarrow \boxed{\div 5} \rightarrow 7$

$6 \leftarrow \boxed{- 29} \leftarrow \boxed{\times 5} \leftarrow 7$

Example 6

Solve $\frac{3}{5}x + 2 = \frac{1}{5}x + 6$.

multiply by 5 $\qquad 3x + 10 = x + 30$

subtract x $\qquad\quad 2x + 10 = 30$

subtract 10 $\qquad\qquad 2x = 20$

divide by 2 $\qquad\qquad\quad x = 10$

$x \rightarrow \boxed{\times 2} \rightarrow \boxed{+ 10} \rightarrow 30$

$10 \leftarrow \boxed{\div 2} \leftarrow \boxed{- 10} \leftarrow 30$

Check your solution to each equation by substituting the value of x back into the equation.

(1) Find the value of x in each equation.

a $6x + 17 = 35$

b $8x - 11 = 37$

c $7x - 8 = 69$

d $5x + 62 = 112$

(2) Find the value of x in each equation.

a $7(3x + 4) = 133$

b $6(9x + 7) = 150$

c $5(4x - 19) = 45$

d $4(3x + 2) = 80$

(3) Find the value of x in each equation.

a $5(4x + 6) + 3(2x + 7) = 77$

b $3(6x + 2) + 4(5x + 3) = 170$

c $8(6x - 2) - 4(3x + 6) = 68$

d $3(2x + 8) + 4(3x - 5) = 94$

(4) Find the value of x in each equation.

a $8x + 2 = 5x + 23$

b $9x - 14 = 5x + 2$

c $12x - 15 = 4x + 9$

d $6x - 21 = 4x - 11$

e $7x + 35 = 10x + 17$

f $3x + 41 = 10x - 15$

g $9x + 45 = 15x - 21$

h $14x + 33 = 19x - 17$

(5) Find the value of x in each equation.

a $\frac{x}{9} + 15 = 19$

b $\frac{x}{5} - 2 = 8$

c $\frac{x}{3} + 21 = 30$

d $\frac{1}{8}(x - 5) = 2$

e $\frac{1}{4}(x + 3) = 3$

f $\frac{1}{3}(x - 2) = 5$

(6) Find the value of x in each equation.

a $\frac{2}{3}x + 5 = \frac{1}{3}x + 8$

b $\frac{4}{5}x + 7 = \frac{2}{5}x + 13$

c $\frac{3}{4}x + 9 = \frac{1}{4}x + 15$

d $\frac{6}{7}x - 5 = \frac{3}{7}x + 1$

e $\frac{7}{5}x - 6 = \frac{9}{5}x - 16$

f $\frac{3}{8}x + 19 = \frac{7}{8}x + 11$

(7) Find the value of x in each equation.

a $\frac{1}{3}(x + 10) + \frac{1}{3}(x + 16) = 10$

b $\frac{1}{3}(x - 1) + \frac{1}{3}(x - 4) = 3$

c $\frac{1}{5}(2x + 38) - \frac{1}{5}(x + 19) = 5$

d $\frac{1}{7}(3x + 8) - \frac{1}{7}(2x - 4) = 3$

Extension problem

 Find the value of x in each equation.

  a $\frac{2}{3}x + 5 = \frac{3}{4}x + 4$ **b** $\frac{4}{5}x + 9 = \frac{1}{3}x + 16$ **c** $\frac{3}{4}x + 7 = \frac{5}{7}x + 8$

  d $\frac{3}{2}x - 14 = \frac{5}{8}x + 14$ **e** $\frac{6}{5}x - 16 = \frac{4}{9}x + 18$ **f** $\frac{5}{6}x - 13 = \frac{2}{5}x + 13$

 Points to remember

- A **coefficient** of x can be a whole number or a fraction.
- You can use inverse operations to solve simple **linear equations**.
- If there are brackets, multiply them out first.
- If the unknown letter is on both sides of the equation, rearrange the equation so the unknown letter is on one side only.
- If there are fractions, multiply through by the lowest common denominator.

3 Expanding brackets

This lesson will help you to work out the product of two linear expressions.

Exercise 3

Writing $6(9x + 3)$ as $54x + 18$ is called **expanding brackets** or **multiplying out brackets**.

Example 1

Expand and simplify $2(5a + 7b) + 4(3a + 6b)$.

$2(5a + 7b) + 4(3a + 6b) = 10a + 14b + 12a + 24b = 22a + 38b$

The product of two expressions is normally written without the $\times$ sign, e.g. as $(a + 5)(a + 7)$.

To expand a pair of brackets, each term in the first bracket is multiplied by each term in the second bracket. You can use a multiplication grid to help you to do this.

Example 2

Multiply out $(a + 5)(a + 7)$.

$\times$	a	$+ 7$	
a	a^2	$+ 7a$	$a^2 + 7a$
$+$			$+$
5	$5a$	$+ 35$	$5a + 35$
			$a^2 + 12a + 35$

1. Multiply out the brackets.

   a $11(x + 9)$

   b $7(y - 6)$

   c $8(x + 10)$

   d $5(x + 9)$

   e $7(8x - 6)$

   f $12(4a + 3)$

   g $4(11 + 9t)$

   h $15(4x - 3)$

   i $4(5p - 8q + 5r)$

2. Expand and simplify.

   a $5(x + 8) + 4(x + 6)$

   b $7(y + 6) + 5(y + 10)$

   c $9(s + 7) + 11(s + 3)$

   d $4(p + 12) + 6(p + 8)$

   e $7(8a + 9) + 8(a - 5)$

   f $6(9x - 4) + 10(5x + 6)$

   g $\frac{1}{5}(4x + 3) + \frac{3}{5}(7x - 6)$

   h $\frac{2}{3}(b + 8) + \frac{1}{3}(10b - 4)$

   i $\frac{3}{4}(9x - 2) + \frac{1}{4}(5x + 2)$

3. Find the five matching pairs.

   A $6(x + 2) + 4(3x - 1)$

   B $2(10x + 7) - 5(3x + 4)$

   D $6(2x + 3) + 5(4x - 1)$

   E $7(2x + 6) - 3(3x + 16)$

   C $4(5x + 6) - 5(2x + 4)$

   F $2(4x + 1) - 3(2x - 3)$

   G $3(6x + 1) - 4(4x - 2)$

   H $3(4x + 6) + 2(3x - 5)$

   J $8(3x + 1) - 2(7x + 2)$

   I $5(6x + 3) + 2(x - 1)$

4. Use a multiplication grid to expand and simplify.

   a $(x + 3)(x + 4)$

   b $(y + 8)(y + 5)$

   c $(s + 6)(s + 7)$

   d $(p + 9)(p + 8)$

   e $(a + 10)(a + 8)$

   f $(x + 4)(x + 11)$

   g $(t + 5)(t + 17)$

   h $(x + 7)^2$

   i $(y + 5)^2$

Extension problem

5. Expand and simplify.

   a $(2x + 5)(3x + 4)$

   b $(6y + 8)(7y + 2)$

   c $(9x + 5)(5x + 3)$

   d $(4y + 3)(6y + 8)$

   e $(7a + 2)(3a - 2)$

   f $(6x - 3)(4x + 7)$

   g $(5b - 1)(3b - 1)$

   h $(8x + 3)^2$

   i $(7x - 2)^2$

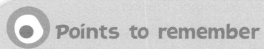

Points to remember

- Writing $6(9x + 3)$ as $54x + 18$ is called **expanding the brackets** or **multiplying out the brackets**.
- Each term inside the bracket is multiplied by the number or letter outside. e.g. $4(a + 7) = 4a + 28$ or $a(a + 5) = a^2 + 5a$.
- The product of two expressions is normally written without the $\times$ sign, e.g. as $(a + 5)(a + 7)$.
- To expand a pair of brackets, each term in the first bracket is multiplied by each term in the second bracket.
  e.g. $(a + 3)(a + 5) = a^2 + 3a + 5a + 15 = a^2 + 8a + 15$
- You can use a multiplication grid to help you to do this.

$\times$	a	$+ 3$
a	a^2	$+ 3a$
$+$		
5	$5a$	$+ 15$

$a^2 + 3a$
$+$
$5a + 15$
$a^2 + 8a + 15$

4 Factorising expressions

This lesson will help you to factorise algebraic expressions.

Exercise 4

A factor of an expression is a number, letter or expression that divides exactly into the expression. The number 1 is a factor of any term or expression.

Example 1

a What are all the factors of 12?

1, 2, 3, 4, 6 and 12 are all the numbers that divide exactly into 12.

b What are all the factors of $6a$?

1, 2, 3, 6, a, $2a$, $3a$ and $6a$ are all the factors of $6a$.

c What is the highest common factor of 12 and $6a$?

6 is the highest common factor of 12 and $6a$.

d Use your answer to part **c** to factorise $6a + 12$.

$6a + 12 = 6(a + 2)$

A6.1 *Expressions and formulae* | **19**

Factorising is the reverse process of expanding brackets.

Expanding $3(2b + 5)$ gives $6b + 15$. So factorising $6b + 15$ gives $3(2b + 5)$.

Example 2

Factorise $a^2 + 5a + 6$.

You are asked to find a pair of factors $(a + ?)(a + ?)$.

Use a multiplication grid to help you.

×	a	$+$	$?$	
a	$a^2 + ?$			$a^2 + ?$
$+$				$+$
$?$	$? + 6$			$? + 6$
				$a^2 + 5a + 6$

To find the missing numbers consider the pairs of factors of 6, which are 1, 6 and 2, 3.

The factor pair with a sum of 5 is 2 and 3.

So $a^2 + 5a + 6 = (a + 2)(a + 3)$.

×	a	$+$	3	
a	$a^2 + 3a$			$a^2 + 3a$
$+$				$+$
2	$2a + 6$			$2a + 6$
				$a^2 + 5a + 6$

(1) Write all the factors.

    a 8   **b** 50   **c** $2a$ **d** $10b$ **e** ab

    f $3ab$ **g** $26m$ **h** abc **i** $17xy$ **j** $2a^2$

(2) Factorise by taking out common factors.

    a $10x + 25$ **b** $26y + 18$ **c** $12a + 21$

    d $18b - 24c$ **e** $20p - 12q$ **f** $6a + 8b + 14c$

    g $14x + 21y - 28z$ **h** $25x^2 + 30x$ **i** $2b^2 - 10b$

(3) Find the matching pairs.

A $(a + 3)(a + 8)$

B $a^2 + 10a + 24$

C $a^2 + 14a + 24$

D $(a + 1)(a + 24)$

E $a^2 + 11a + 24$

F $(a + 2)(a + 12)$

G $(a + 6)(a + 4)$

H $a^2 + 25a + 24$

4 Factorise these expressions.

a $a^2 + 6a + 8$ b $a^2 + 9a + 18$ c $a^2 + 8a + 15$

d $a^2 + 11a + 18$ e $a^2 + 8a + 12$ f $a^2 + 11a + 28$

g $a^2 + 12a + 35$ h $a^2 + 14a + 49$ i $a^2 + 9a + 8$

Extension problem

5 Factorise these expressions.

a $a^2 + 6a + 9$ b $a^2 + 2a + 1$ c $2a^2 + 11a + 12$

d $3a^2 + 5a + 2$ e $4a^2 + 13a + 3$ f $6a^2 + 5a + 1$

 Points to remember

- A factor of an algebraic expression divides exactly into each term of the expression.
- You can take a common factor of each term of an expression outside a bracket, e.g. $6b + 10ab = 2b(3 + 5a)$, because $2b$ is a factor of $6b$ and a factor of $10ab$.
- A quadratic expression can be written as the product of two linear expressions, e.g. $a^2 + 3a + 1 = (a + 2)(a + 1)$.

5 Identities

This lesson will help you to recognise when two algebraic expressions are identical.

Did you know that...?

Diophantus of Alexandria, who lived around 200 BC, has been called the 'father of algebra'.

His main work was a set of 13 books called *Arithmetica*. The six of them that have survived show that Diophantus was interested in solving equations that had whole-number solutions and that he introduced a symbol to stand for the unknown he was trying to find.

His books are the oldest known publications to focus on algebra.

Not much is known about Diophantus apart from a puzzle said to be on his tombstone.

> *His boyhood lasted one sixth of his life; he married after one seventh more; his beard grew after one twelfth more, and his son was born 5 years later. The son lived to half his father's age, and the father died 4 years after the son.*

If the puzzle is correct, and it may not be, then Diophantus lived to the age of 84. He married at 26 and had a son 12 years later, at the age of 38.

Exercise 5

When two algebraic expressions can be expanded to produce exactly the same combination of terms they are said to be **identical**.

The symbol $\equiv$ is used to show when two expressions are identical.

Example

Prove that $(x + 4)(x + 2) \equiv x^2 + 6x + 8$.

Show that the left-hand side of the equation is identical to the right-hand side using the areas of rectangles in the diagram.

Area of the whole shape $= (x + 4)(x + 2)$ square units

Area of the whole shape is also equal to the sum of the areas of the four smaller rectangles, which is:

$x^2 + 4x + 2x + 8 = x^2 + 6x + 8$ square units

Therefore $(x + 4)(x + 2) \equiv x^2 + 6x + 8$

	x	$+4$
x	x^2	$+4x$
$+2$	$+2x$	$+8$

1. Use the diagram on the right to prove that:

   $(x + 4)(x + 5) \equiv x^2 + 9x + 20$

   a Write an expression for the area of the rectangle.

   b Write an expression for the sum of the four shapes inside the rectangle then simplify it.

   c Explain why the two expressions are equal.

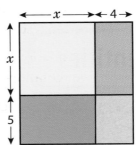

2. Use the diagram on the right to prove that:

   $(x + 7)^2 \equiv x^2 + 14x + 49$

   a Write an expression for the area of the square.

   b Write an expression for the sum of the four shapes inside the square then simplify it.

   c Explain why the two expressions are equal.

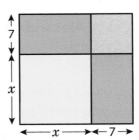

3. Draw a diagram and use it to prove that:

   $(x + 1)(x + 9) \equiv x^2 + 10x + 9$

4 **a** Copy and complete this table.

a	b	$a^2 - b^2$	$(a - b)(a + b)$
5	3	$25 - 9 = 16$	$2 \times 8 = 16$
8	2		
6	3		
4	1		
5	2		
7	6		
10	5		
8	4		
7	5		
4	3		

b What do you notice about the two columns on the right?

5 Use the diagram on the right to prove that:

$$x^2 - a^2 = (x - a)(x + a)$$

a Write an expression for the shaded area of the shape on the right as the area of the large square of side x minus the area of the small square of side a.

b Write an expression for the shaded area as the sum of the area of two rectangles.

c Explain why the two expressions are equal.

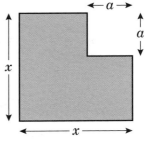

6 The identity $x^2 - y^2 \equiv (x - y)(x + y)$ is called the difference of two squares.
Use this identity to calculate these differences.

a $8^2 - 3^2$ **b** $14^2 - 4^2$ **c** $23^2 - 7^2$ **d** $89^2 - 11^2$ **e** $78^2 - 22^2$

Extension problem

7 Write an expression for the shaded area of the square on the right in two different ways.

Use this to prove that $(a - 5)^2 \equiv a^2 - 10a + 25$.

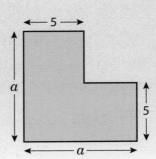

6 Changing the subject of a formula

This lesson will help you to change the subject of a formula.

Exercise 6

A **formula** is a way of expressing a relationship using symbols.

Example 1

The voltage V in an electrical circuit, with current I and resistance R is given by the formula $V = IR$.

The **subject** of the formula is the voltage V.

$$V = IR$$

To **change the subject** of the formula to the current I:

Divide by R $\dfrac{V}{R} = I$

Turn around $I = \dfrac{V}{R}$

Example 2

Here is a formula for calculating the velocity of a moving object travelling at constant acceleration.

final velocity = initial velocity + acceleration × time

$$v = u + at$$

The final velocity v is the **subject** of the formula. To make the acceleration a the subject, rearrange the formula:

Subtract u $v - u = at$

Divide by t $\dfrac{v - u}{t} = a$

Turn around $a = \dfrac{v - u}{t}$

1 Which of these formulae match the formula $p = q + r$?

A $q = p + r$ **B** $r = p + q$ **C** $q = p - r$

D $r = q - p$ **E** $q = r - p$ **F** $r = p - q$

2 Which of these formulae match the formula $m = st$?

A $s = \dfrac{t}{m}$ **B** $s = \dfrac{m}{t}$ **C** $t = \dfrac{s}{m}$

D $m = \dfrac{t}{s}$ **E** $t = \dfrac{m}{s}$ **F** $m = \dfrac{s}{t}$

3 Make the letter in brackets the subject of each formula.

  a $A = 2\pi r$ (r) **b** $V = lwh$ (h)

  c $p = qr + s$ (s) **d** $p = qr + s$ (r)

  e $m = np - r$ (r) **f** $m = np - r$ (n)

  g $w = \dfrac{xy}{z}$ (x) **h** $w = \dfrac{xy}{z}$ (z)

  i $V = x^3$ (x) **j** $V = x^2h$ (x)

4 **a** Batya wants to know the temperature in degrees Fahrenheit.

     She is given the formula to change the temperature from degrees Fahrenheit (F) to degrees Celsius (C):

$$C = \frac{5}{9}(F - 32)$$

     Rearrange the formula to make F the subject.

     b Ramesh is making cylindrical cartons with card.

        He wants to work out the radius of the circular base of the cylinder for a given height (h) and volume (V).

        Rearrange the formula $V = \pi r^2 h$ to make r the subject.

     c Angelica is investigating the height h of trapeziums given the area A and the lengths of the parallel sides a and b. She is using the formula $A = \frac{1}{2}(a + b)h$.

        Rearrange the formula to make h the subject.

d Tom is doing some experiments.

He is trying to work out the time t it takes in seconds for a car to accelerate from one velocity u to velocity v.

Rearrange the formula $v = u + at$ to make t the subject.

(5) The formula $C = \dfrac{11R}{8} + 50$ is used to calculate the cost in pounds of making a boiler of radius R cm.

a Make R the subject of the formula.

b Use this formula to find the radius of a boiler that cost £150 to make.

Extension problems

(6) I think of two numbers, x and y.

$x - y$ is one third of $x + y$.

Write x in terms of y.

(7) Two numbers, x and y, are related by the formula $x + y = xy$.

a Rearrange the formula to make x the subject.

b Explain why y cannot equal the number 1.

c What is the value of x when $y = 2$?

d What is the value of x when $y = 6$?

⊙ Points to remember

- ⊙ A **formula** is a way of expressing a relationship using symbols.
- ⊙ When a formula is written as $d = st$, then d is the **subject** of the formula.
- ⊙ You can rearrange a formula to make a different letter the subject, for example $s = \dfrac{d}{t}$ or $t = \dfrac{d}{s}$.

How well are you doing?

Can you:

- simplify algebraic fractions?
- solve linear equations?
- expand brackets?
- factorise expressions?
- recognise identical expressions?
- change the subject of a formula?

Expressions and formulae (no calculator)

1 *2005 level 6*

Look at this equation.

$$14y - 51 = 187 + 4y$$

a Is $y = 17$ a solution to this equation?

b Show how you know.

2 *2005 level 6*

Solve this equation.

$75 + 2t = 100 - 2t$

3 *2005 level 7*

Multiply out the brackets in these expressions.

a $y(y - 6)$

b $(k + 2)(k + 3)$

4 *2004 level 7*

a Which of the expressions below is the same as $y^2 + 8y + 12$?

     A $(y + 3)(y + 4)$ **B** $(y + 7)(y + 1)$ **C** $(y + 2)(y + 6)$

     D $(y + 1)(y + 12)$ **E** $(y + 3)(y + 5)$

b Multiply out the expression $(y + 9)(y + 2)$. Write your answer as simply as possible.

Doctors sometimes use this formula to calculate how much medicine to give a child.

$$c = \frac{ay}{12 + y}$$

c is the correct amount for a child, in ml

a is the amount for an adult, in ml

y is the age of the child, in years

A child who is 4 years old needs some medicine.
The amount for an adult is 20 ml.

Use the formula to work out the correct amount for this child.
You must show your working.

Proportional reasoning

This unit will help you to:

- multiply and divide fractions;
- recognise and use reciprocals;
- work out rates of interest;
- calculate reverse percentage changes;
- use direct and inverse proportion;
- use measures of rate and speed.

1 Fraction calculations

This lesson will help you to calculate with fractions.

Exercise 1

When you **add or subtract mixed numbers**, deal with whole numbers first.

Example 1

Work out $5\frac{5}{8} + 2\frac{7}{12}$.

$5\frac{5}{8} + 2\frac{7}{12} = 7 + \frac{5}{8} + \frac{7}{12}$ First add the whole numbers.

$= 7 + \frac{15}{24} + \frac{14}{24}$ Change the fractions to a common denominator.

$= 7 + \frac{29}{24}$ Add the two fractions.

$= 8\frac{5}{24}$ Change the improper fraction to a mixed number.

Example 2

Work out $7\frac{5}{12} - 4\frac{3}{4}$.

$7\frac{5}{12} - 4\frac{3}{4} = 3 + \frac{5}{12} - \frac{3}{4}$ First subtract the whole numbers.

$\phantom{7\frac{5}{12} - 4\frac{3}{4}} = 3 + \frac{5}{12} - \frac{9}{12}$ Change the fractions to a common denominator.

$\phantom{7\frac{5}{12} - 4\frac{3}{4}} = 2 + \frac{17}{12} - \frac{9}{12}$ As you can't take 9 from 5, change 1 whole to 12 twelfths.

$\phantom{7\frac{5}{12} - 4\frac{3}{4}} = 2\frac{8}{12}$ Subtract the fractions.

$\phantom{7\frac{5}{12} - 4\frac{3}{4}} = 2\frac{2}{3}$ Simplify the fraction by cancelling.

When you **multiply or divide** mixed numbers, first write them as **improper fractions**.

Example 3

Work out $1\frac{3}{5} \times 2\frac{1}{8}$.

$1\frac{3}{5} \times 2\frac{1}{8} = \frac{\overset{1}{\cancel{8}}}{5} \times \frac{17}{\underset{1}{\cancel{8}}}$ Change mixed numbers to improper fractions. Cancel.

$\phantom{1\frac{3}{5} \times 2\frac{1}{8}} = \frac{17}{5}$ Multiply the numerators and multiply the denominators.

$\phantom{1\frac{3}{5} \times 2\frac{1}{8}} = 3\frac{2}{5}$ Change the improper fraction to a mixed number.

Example 4

Work out $1\frac{1}{2} \div 2\frac{3}{8}$.

$1\frac{1}{2} \div 2\frac{3}{8} = \frac{3}{2} \div \frac{19}{8}$ Change mixed numbers to improper fractions.

$\phantom{1\frac{1}{2} \div 2\frac{3}{8}} = \frac{3}{2} \times \frac{8}{19}$ Turn the divisor upside down and multiply.

$\phantom{1\frac{1}{2} \div 2\frac{3}{8}} = \frac{3}{\underset{1}{\cancel{2}}} \times \frac{\overset{4}{\cancel{8}}}{19}$ Cancel where possible.

$\phantom{1\frac{1}{2} \div 2\frac{3}{8}} = \frac{12}{19}$ Multiply the numerators and multiply the denominators.

Do questions 1–3 **without using your calculator**.
Show your working. Give each answer in its simplest form.

①   a $\frac{4}{5} + \frac{6}{15}$ b $\frac{5}{6} - \frac{3}{4}$ c $3\frac{3}{5} + 5\frac{2}{9}$

     d $4\frac{7}{12} - 1\frac{3}{8}$ e $6\frac{4}{5} + 2\frac{1}{2}$ f $3\frac{4}{9} - 1\frac{2}{3}$

     g $2\frac{7}{8} + 5\frac{3}{4}$ h $4\frac{1}{3} - 1\frac{3}{5}$ i $2\frac{3}{8} + 3\frac{2}{3} - 1\frac{5}{6}$

②   a $\frac{3}{5} \times \frac{20}{27}$ b $3\frac{1}{2} \times \frac{8}{25}$ c $2\frac{1}{8} \times 1\frac{3}{5}$ d $3\frac{1}{5} \times 2\frac{3}{4}$

     e $1\frac{3}{5} \times 2\frac{1}{2}$ f $\frac{5}{11} \times \frac{33}{15}$ g $2\frac{2}{7} \times 2\frac{4}{5}$ h $2\frac{1}{5} \times 1\frac{7}{8}$

3 **a** $\frac{5}{8} \div \frac{25}{32}$ **b** $\frac{9}{14} \div \frac{18}{21}$ **c** $1\frac{1}{4} \div \frac{5}{6}$ **d** $3\frac{1}{2} \div 1\frac{3}{5}$

   e $\frac{7}{8} \div 2\frac{3}{4}$ **f** $7 \div \frac{3}{4}$ **g** $4\frac{1}{2} \div \frac{8}{9}$ **h** $2\frac{1}{12} \div 2\frac{2}{9}$

You may **use your calculator** to answer questions 4–8.

4 Copy and complete this magic square.

$\frac{1}{3}$		
$\frac{3}{4}$	$\frac{5}{12}$	
		$\frac{1}{2}$

5 **a** At the party, all the pizzas were the same size.
   Leroy ate $\frac{5}{6}$ of a pepperoni pizza.
   John ate $\frac{1}{10}$ of a sausage pizza.
   How much more pizza did Leroy eat?

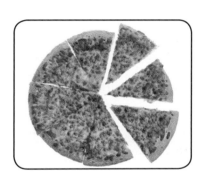

   b A baby weighed $4\frac{3}{8}$ pounds at birth.
   In the next 6 weeks, she gained $2\frac{3}{4}$ pounds.
   How much does she weigh now?

   c In a bag of cubes, $\frac{1}{6}$ are green, $\frac{1}{12}$ are yellow, $\frac{1}{2}$ are white and $\frac{1}{5}$ are blue.
   What fraction of the cubes are other colours?

   d A rectangular patio measures $3\frac{1}{8}$ m by $4\frac{2}{5}$ m.
   What is its area in square metres?

   e There are $24\frac{3}{4}$ cupfuls of flour in a bag.
   A cake recipe uses $2\frac{1}{4}$ cupfuls of flour.

   How many cakes can be made from the flour
   in the bag?

   f A teapot is four fifths full.
   Two thirds of the tea in the pot is poured out.
   How full is the teapot now?

   g Two fifths of the pupils in a class go home by car.
   Two thirds of those who are left go home by bus.
   The remaining six pupils walk home.

   How many pupils are in the class?

6 Play **Capture** with a partner.
You need some 2 cm squared paper.
Each of you will need a different coloured pen.

Draw a 6 by 6 grid of dots with fractions like this.

$+\frac{1}{2}$	$-\frac{5}{6}$	$+\frac{1}{3}$	$-\frac{1}{12}$	$+\frac{1}{4}$
$-\frac{3}{8}$	$+\frac{7}{12}$	$-\frac{1}{2}$	$+\frac{5}{8}$	$+\frac{2}{3}$
$+\frac{3}{4}$	$-\frac{5}{8}$	$+\frac{5}{12}$	$-\frac{3}{4}$	$-\frac{1}{2}$
$-\frac{1}{3}$	$+\frac{1}{2}$	$-\frac{7}{8}$	$+\frac{5}{6}$	$-\frac{5}{12}$
$+\frac{7}{8}$	$-\frac{1}{4}$	$+\frac{3}{8}$	$-\frac{2}{3}$	$+\frac{1}{6}$

Rules

- Take turns.

- Join two neighbouring dots with a line.
  Diagonal lines are not allowed.

- If you complete a small square of dots, you capture the fraction inside.
  Ring the fraction with your coloured pen, then have another turn.

- The winner is the player with the highest total when all the squares are completed.

Extension problems

7 The weight of a tin of paint is the weight of the paint plus the weight of the tin.

A tin of paint weighs 5 kg when it is half full of paint.
It weighs 4 kg when it is one third full.

What is the weight of a full tin of paint?

8 Use each of the digits 1, 2, 3, 4, 5, 6, 7, 8 and 9.
Write one digit in each box to make this addition correct.

$$\boxed{}\boxed{} + \boxed{}\frac{\boxed{}}{\boxed{}} = \boxed{}\boxed{}\frac{\boxed{}}{\boxed{}}$$

Points to remember

⊙ To add and subtract fractions, change them to the same denominator.

⊙ If there are whole numbers, deal with them first.

⊙ To multiply fractions, cancel, then multiply the numerators and multiply the denominators.

⊙ To divide fractions, turn the divisor upside down and multiply by it.

⊙ To multiply or divide mixed numbers, first change them to improper fractions.

2 Reciprocals

This lesson will help you to find and use reciprocals.

Did you know that...?

The word **fraction** is from the Latin *fractus*, broken. The numerator and denominator of a fraction are separated by a horizontal line called a **vinculum**, for example: $\frac{3}{4}$.

The separator can also be a slanting line called a **solidus** or **slash**, for example $^3/_4$.

The slash is sometimes omitted from the slanting style (e.g. $^3{}_4$) when space is short and the meaning is obvious, as in this road sign to Come-to-Good, in Cornwall.

Exercise 2

Because it is impossible to divide something into zero equal parts, zero can never be the denominator of a fraction.

The **reciprocal** of a number is 1 divided by the number, e.g. the reciprocal of 3 is $\frac{1}{3}$.

The reciprocal of a fraction is another fraction with the numerator and denominator swapped.

The reciprocal of $\frac{3}{7}$, for instance, is $1 \div \frac{3}{7}$, which is $1 \times \frac{7}{3} = \frac{7}{3}$.

The reciprocal key of a calculator is usually $\boxed{\frac{1}{x}}$ or $\boxed{x^{-1}}$.

Example

Find the reciprocal of 0.625.

Use the reciprocal key, or divide 1 by 0.625, to get the reciprocal 1.6.

1 a Write as a decimal the reciprocal of each of the integers from 1 to 20.

   b Which of the integers have reciprocals that are terminating decimals?

   c What do all these integers have in common?

2 Write the reciprocal of each of these numbers.

   a 100   b 0.4   c 40   d 0.05

   e 400   f 0.002   g 30   h 0.001 25

   i $\frac{2}{3}$ j $\frac{4}{7}$ k $2\frac{2}{5}$ l $6\frac{1}{8}$

3 Is there a reciprocal for zero?

4 The powers of 2 are 2, 2^2, 2^3, 2^4, ..., which are equal to 2, 4, 8, 16, ...

   a Work out the values of the negative powers of 2, namely 2^{-1}, 2^{-2}, 2^{-3}, 2^{-4}, ...

   b Use your calculator to investigate the relationship between the reciprocals of positive powers of 2 and negative powers of 2.

5 Write the reciprocal of each of these numbers.

   a 10^4 b 2^6 c 4^{-3} d 3^{-2}

6 **Without using a calculator**, work out the fraction that is equivalent to the reciprocal of each decimal.

   a 0.4   b 0.75   c 1.6   d 0.28

   e 5.2   f 20.125   g $0.\dot{6}$ h $0.\dot{2}$

7 Try this investigation.

   ⊙ Choose any positive integer.
   ⊙ Write down its reciprocal and subtract it from 1.
   ⊙ Write down the reciprocal of your answer and subtract it from 1.
   ⊙ Keep repeating this process.

   What happens?
   What happens with other positive integers?

Extension problem

 You will need some graph paper.

a Draw the graph of the reciprocal function $\frac{1}{x}$ from $x = -6$ to $x = 6$.

b Where does the line $y = x$ meet $y = \frac{1}{x}$?

c The line $y = x$ is a line of symmetry of the graph $y = \frac{1}{x}$.

What is the equation of the other line of symmetry?

d Draw the line $y = 2x$.

Where does this line meet $y = \frac{1}{x}$?

⊙ Points to remember

- ⊙ The **reciprocal** of a is $1 \div a$.
- ⊙ The reciprocal of $\frac{a}{b}$ is $\frac{b}{a}$.
- ⊙ The reciprocal of a^n is a^{-n} for any power n.

---

3 Percentage increases and decreases

London Stock Exchange

Interest rates

£20 notes

This lesson will help you to work out percentage increases and decreases, including working out the interest on an amount of money after a period of time.

Sometimes **simple interest** is paid on an amount of money. The interest is not added to the amount in the account, and the same amount of interest is paid each year.

Example 1

An investment of £500 has a simple interest rate of 4% per annum.
How much interest will be paid after 3 years?

The interest for 1 year is 4% of £500, which is £500 × 0.04 = £20.

The interest for 3 years is £20 × 3 = £60.

Banks and building societies usually pay **compound interest**. At the end of a year, interest is paid on the money in an account. It is then added to the account.

At the end of the next year interest is paid on the **total amount in the account**. This means that interest is paid on the original amount of money **plus** the previous interest earned.

Example 2

£200 is invested in a bank account for one year and the interest rate is 5%.
Find the amount in the account after 3 years.

Using the multiplier 1.05:

after 1 year there will be £(200 × 1.05) = £210 in the account

after 2 years there will be £((200 × 1.05) × 1.05) = £220.05 in the account

after 3 years there will be £(((200 × 1.05) × 1.05) × 1.05) = £231.53 in the account.

To find the amount in the account after 3 years the original £200 has been multiplied by 1.05 × 1.05 × 1.05, which is equivalent to 1.05^3.

1 Is 7% the same as 0.7? Explain your answer.

2 Give the multiplier for:

   a an increase of 60%   b a decrease of 60%

3 Write down multipliers to increase an amount by:

   a $\frac{1}{5}$ b $\frac{1}{2}$ c $\frac{1}{10}$ d $\frac{1}{3}$

4 Write down multipliers to decrease an amount by:

   a $\frac{1}{5}$ b $\frac{1}{2}$ c $\frac{1}{10}$ d $\frac{1}{3}$

5. How much will you have in the bank if you invest at these annual rates of **simple interest**?

    a £1000 at 5% for 2 years
    b £200 at 2% for 4 years
    c £150 000 at 3% for 5 years

6. How much will you have in the bank if you invest at these annual rates of **compound interest**?

    a £1000 at 5% for 2 years
    b £3000 at 4.5% for 7 years
    c £200 at 2% for 4 years
    d £12 000 at 6% for 10 years
    e £75 at 2.5% for 3 years

7. £3000 is invested for 4 years at 7% per annum compound interest.
   Work out the total interest earned over the 4 years.

8. A motorbike was worth £7500.
   Each year its value went down by 25%.
   Work out the value of the motorbike at the
   end of 3 years.

9. The population of Andover is 32 000.
   The population is increasing at an approximate rate of 4% per year.
   Estimate the population of Andover in 4 years' time.

10. During the hot spell in June, there was a hosepipe ban.
    At the start of the hot spell, 4 m² of my lawn had turned brown.
    The brown area increased by 20% each day.

    What area of my lawn was brown at the end of 5 days?
    Give your answer to two decimal places.

11. At the start of the hot spell, there were 550 litres of water in my garden pond.
    Every day 6% of the pond water evaporated.
    How many days did it take to reduce the amount of water in the pond to less than 400 litres?

12. A house is worth £145 000. Its value goes up by 6% each year.
    Work out the value of the house to the nearest pound after:

    a 10 years
    b 25 years

Extension problem

 a John invested £500 in a savings account.
His investment gained 10% each year.
The interest was added to his account at the end of each year.
How many years will John's investment take to double in value?

b Nasreen invested £500 in the stock market.
Her investment went down in value by 10% each year.
How long will it take until only half of her original investment remains?

Points to remember

- Percentage increases and decreases can be calculated using **decimal multipliers**.
- **Simple interest** is paid on the original investment.
  The same amount of interest is paid each year.
- **Compound interest** is paid on the original investment plus any previous interest. The amount of interest paid increases each year.

---

4 Reverse percentages

This lesson will help you to work out a percentage rate and to use a multiplier to calculate reverse percentage changes.

Exercise 4

The price of a new washing machine is £376.
This price includes Value Added Tax (VAT) at 17.5%.
Work out the cost of the washing machine before VAT was added.

Method 1: Unitary method

£376 represents 117.5%.   Find the value of 1%.

£376 ÷ 117.5 = £3.20 represents 1%.   Find the value of 100%.

100% = £3.20 × 100 = £320

Method 2: Using a multiplier

A 17.5% increase is represented by the multiplier 1.175.   Divide £376 by 1.175 to find the original amount.

£376 ÷ 1.175 = £320

1. Peter bought a bicycle for £205.
He sold it to a friend for £165.
What is his percentage loss?
Give your answer to one decimal place.

2. Janet had £245 in savings at the start of the year.
She now has £327.
What is the percentage gain in her savings?
Give your answer to one decimal place.

3. A packet of dishwasher tablets claims to be 24% bigger.
It now contains 52 tablets.
How many tablets did it have before the increase?

4. After a 10% price decrease, a hi-fi system costs £279.
How much was it before the decrease?

5. a A skiing holiday is advertised at a price of £403.
   Last year the same holiday cost £390.
   What is the percentage increase in the cost?

   b The cost of the skiing holiday for an adult is £403.
   This is a 35% saving on the brochure price.
   What is the brochure price of the holiday?

   c This year, the cost of the skiing holiday for a child is
   70% of the adult price.
   What is the discounted cost for a child?

   d The ski shop has a sale.
   All prices are reduced by 15%.
   A pair of skiing gloves costs £38.25 in the sale.
   What did the gloves cost before the sale?

6. 14 076 people visited the Tower of London on Saturday.
This was an increase of 2% on the Friday.
How many visitors were there on the Friday?

7. Linda has had a pay increase of 4%.
After the increase, she is earning £24 960 per year.
What did she earn before the pay increase?

8. Ajit pays tax at 22%.
After tax, he earns £117 per week.
How much does Ajit earn each week before tax?

9 This table shows the cost of some items after 17.5% VAT has been added.
Work out the cost of each item before VAT.

Item	Cost inc. VAT
Microwave	£112.80
Food processor	£131.60

Item	Cost inc. VAT
Freezer	£329
Cooker	£376

Extension problems

10 The length of a rectangle is increased by 20%.
The width is decreased by 20%.
By what percentage is the area changed?

11 A farmer bought two pedigree cows.
Later he sold them for £6000 each.
He made a loss of 20% on one cow.
He made a profit of 20% on the other cow.
Did he make a profit or loss on the whole deal?

Points to remember

- The **unitary method** involves finding the size of one part as an intermediate step.
- Percentage increases and decreases, and **reverse percentages**, can be calculated using the unitary method or by using **decimal multipliers**.

5 Rate, speed and density

This lesson will help you to use compound measures such as rate, speed and density.

Speed

A car travelled 200 kilometres in 4 hours.
If it had travelled the 200 km at the same speed for the whole 4 hours, then the car would travel 50 km each hour.
50 kilometres per hour (km/h) is the average speed of the car.

So $\quad$ average speed $= \dfrac{\text{total distance travelled}}{\text{total time taken}}$

Speed can be measured in kilometres per hour, miles per hour or metres per second.

If a car travels at an average speed of 40 km/h, the car travels:

40 km in 1 hour
$40 \times 2 = 80$ km in 2 hours
$40 \times 3 = 120$ km in 3 hours, and so on.

So $\quad$ distance $=$ average speed $\times$ time

The time the car takes to travel 120 km at 40 km/h is $\dfrac{120}{40} = 3$ hours.

So $\quad$ time $= \dfrac{\text{distance}}{\text{average speed}}$

This triangle diagram is a way to remember the formulae, where D stands for distance, S for average speed and T for time.

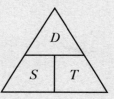

Example 1

Jean drove 100 miles from Andover to Bristol in $2\frac{1}{2}$ hours.
What was her average speed for the journey?

Average speed $= \dfrac{\text{distance}}{\text{time}} = \dfrac{100}{2.5} = 40$ mph

The distance is in miles and the time is in hours, so the speed is miles per hour.

Example 2

The distance from Glasgow Airport to Liverpool Airport is 345 km.
An aeroplane flew the distance at an average speed of 300 km/h.
Work out the flight time, in hours and minutes.

Time $= \dfrac{\text{distance}}{\text{average speed}} = \dfrac{345}{300} = 1.15$ hours, which is 1 hour 9 minutes.

To change 0.15 hours to minutes, multiply by 60, as there are 60 minutes in 1 hour.

1. A journey of 65 km takes $2\frac{1}{2}$ hours.
   What is the average speed for the journey?

2. Hilary jogged 3.8 km in 40 minutes.
   Work out her average speed in km/h.

3. An athlete runs a 1000 m race in
   3 minutes 20 seconds.
   Find his average speed in metres per second.

4. Harry drove 275 km from London to Hull at an
   average speed of 50 km/h.
   Work out the time his journey took.

5. A train journey covered 205 km at an average speed of 100 km/h.
   Find the time taken in hours and minutes.

6. Jade drove 85 miles from Bristol to Bournemouth at an average speed of 51 mph.
   In hours and minutes, how long did her journey take?

7. Bader rode his bike for 4 hours 15 minutes at an average speed of 20 km/h.
   What distance did he ride?

8. A car is travelling at an average speed of 85 m/s.
   Work out the distance that the car travels in 0.4 seconds.

9. The flight time from London Gatwick to Atlanta in the USA is 8 hours 20 minutes.
   The average speed of a jumbo jet is 540 mph.
   What is the distance between Gatwick and Atlanta Airport?

Extension problems

10. Ruth drove 150 km from Reading to Bristol at an average speed of 60 km/h.
    She then drove 50 km from Bristol to Weston-super-Mare at an average speed of 80 km/h.
    Work out her average speed for the whole journey.

11. John drove from his home to visit a friend.
    He drove the first 3 hours at an average speed of 40 km/h.
    He then drove the remaining 60 km at an average speed of 30 km/h.
    Work out John's average speed for his whole journey.

12. Change a speed of 85 m/s to km/h.

Density

The density of a substance is its mass divided by its volume.

So $\boxed{\text{density} = \dfrac{\text{mass}}{\text{volume}}}$

This triangle diagram is a way to remember the formulae, where M stands for mass, D for density and V for volume.

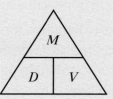

So $\boxed{\text{mass} = \text{density} \times \text{volume}}$ and $\boxed{\text{volume} = \dfrac{\text{mass}}{\text{density}}}$

When the mass is measured in kg and the volume in cubic metres or m^3, density is measured in kg per m^3 or kg/m^3.
Density can also be measured in g/cm^3.

Example

The density of silver is $10.5\,g/cm^3$.
A silver bangle has volume of $4\,cm^3$. What is its mass?

Mass = density $\times$ volume = $10.5 \times 4 = 42\,g$

The density is in g/cm^3 and the volume is in cm^3, so the mass is in grams.

1. $14.7\,g$ of sulphur has a volume of $7.5\,cm^3$. Work out the density of sulphur.

2. a A gold ring has a mass of $9.65\,g$ and a volume of $0.5\,cm^3$. What is its density?

   b The gold in a ring has a mass of $15.44\,g$. Work out the volume of the gold in the ring.

3. Cork has a density of $0.2\,g/cm^3$. What volume of cork has a mass of $1\,kg$?

4. The density of a model made from balsa wood is $0.2\,g/cm^3$.
   Its volume is $70\,cm^3$.
   Work out the mass of the model.

5. The density of tin is $7300\,kg/m^3$. Work out the mass of $1.25\,m^3$ of tin.

6. Petrol has a density of $0.8\,g/cm^3$. What is the mass of 4 litres of petrol?

7. The density of sea water is $1.05\,g/cm^3$.
   A bucket with a capacity of 5 litres is filled with sea water.
   Find the mass in kilograms of the water in the bucket.

Points to remember

⊙ A **compound measure** involves more than one unit. Examples are:

average speed $= \dfrac{\text{distance}}{\text{time}}$ and density $= \dfrac{\text{mass}}{\text{volume}}$

⊙ **Per** in a measure such as miles per hour means 'for every'.

⊙ These diagrams for speed, distance and time and density, mass and volume can help you to solve problems.

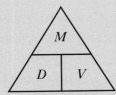

6 Proportionality

This lesson will help you to use direct and inverse proportion in different contexts.

Exercise 6

Two quantities a and b are **directly proportional** if their ratio $a : b$ stays the same as the quantities increase or decrease:

$\dfrac{a}{b} = k$, where k is constant

You can use the **unitary method** to solve direct proportion problems.

Example 1

Three books cost £10.50.
How much do five books cost?
One book costs £10.50 ÷ 3 = £3.50.
Five books cost £3.50 × 5 = £17.50.

Two quantities a and b are **inversely proportional** if a increases as b decreases at the same rate, so their product is constant:

$ab = k$, where k is constant

You can also use the **unitary method** to solve inverse proportion problems.

Example 2

A large bag of dog food can feed 3 puppies for 6 days.
For how many days will the same-sized bag feed 2 of the puppies?

A bag will feed 1 puppy for $3 \times 6 = 18$ days.

A bag will feed 2 puppies for $18 \div 2 = 9$ days.

1. Karen buys 3 files. The total cost of the 3 files is £5.40.
   Work out the cost of 7 of the files.

2. A piece of wire is 25 cm long and has a weight of 6 grams.
   Another piece of the same wire is 30 cm long. Calculate its weight.

3. The exchange rate for Swiss francs is £1 = 2.10 francs.
   Meg changed £450 into francs. How many francs did she get?

4. It takes 4 builders 6 days to build a wall.
   To build the same wall, how long will it take:

   a 2 builders   b 8 builders?

5. It takes 6 technicians 8 hours to enter data into a computer.
   How long would it take 4 technicians to enter the data?

6. It takes 3 combine harvesters 6 days to harvest a crop.
   How long would it take 2 combine harvesters to harvest the same crop?

7. This recipe for Tuna Bake is for 4 people.

Tuna Bake (for 4 people)

400 g of tuna
300 g of mushroom soup
100 g of grated cheddar cheese
4 spring onions
250 g of pasta

Work out the amounts needed to make Tuna Bake for 10 people.

(8) In 2008 in Spain, a hat cost 24 euros.
In England, the identical hat cost £15.50.
The exchange rate was £1 = 1.6 euros.
In which country was the hat cheaper and by how much?

(9) Bob earns £8 an hour.
It took him 12 hours to earn enough to buy a guitar.
If Bob earned only £6 an hour, how long would it take him to earn the money?

Extension problems

(10) 3 sewing machines are used to make 1000 T-shirts in 15 hours.
Two extra machines are used.
How long will it take to make 500 T-shirts?

(11) 12 tins of dog food will feed 6 dogs for 3 days.

How many tins of dog food will be needed for:

a   6 dogs for 2 days   b   3 dogs for 1 day   c   1 dog for 3 days?

⦿ Points to remember

⊙ a and b are **directly proportional** if their ratio $a : b$ stays the same as a and b increase or decrease:
$\frac{a}{b} = k$, where k is constant

⊙ a and b are **inversely proportional** if a increases as b decreases at the same rate:
$ab = k$, where k is constant

⊙ When you solve problems involving direct or inverse proportion:
   – use the unitary method;
   – make sure that corresponding quantities are in the same units;
   – ask yourself whether the answer should be larger or smaller.

How well are you doing?

Can you:

- multiply and divide fractions?
- recognise and use reciprocals?
- work out rates of interest?
- calculate reverse percentage changes?
- use direct and inverse proportion?
- use measures of rate and speed?

Proportional reasoning (no calculator)

1 *2004 level 7*

The table shows a recipe for a fruit drink.

Type of juice	Amount
Orange	$\frac{1}{2}$ litre
Cranberry	$\frac{1}{3}$ litre
Grape	$\frac{1}{6}$ litre
	Total 1 litre

I want to make $1\frac{1}{2}$ litres of the same drink.

Copy and complete the table below to show how much of each type of juice to use. Show your working.

Type of juice	Amount
Orange	... litre
Cranberry	... litre
Grape	... litre
	Total $1\frac{1}{2}$ litres

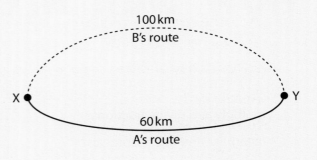

② *2004 level 7*

Two people, A and B, travel from
X to Y along different routes.
Their journeys take the same amount
of time.

B travels at an average speed of 40 km/h.
What is A's average speed?
Show your working.

Proportional reasoning (calculator allowed)

③ *2004 level 7*

The heights of Russian dolls are in
the ratio 7 : 6 : 4.

a In a set of dolls, the height of the
middle doll is 9 cm.
What are the heights of the other
dolls?

b In another set of dolls, the height of
the tallest doll is 9 cm.
What are the heights of the other dolls?
Show your working, and give your answers to 1 decimal place.

④ *2002 level 7*

a One calculation below gives the answer to the question:

What is 70 increased by 9%?

Write the correct calculation.

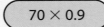 70 × 0.9   70 × 1.9   70 × 0.09   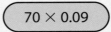 70 × 1.09

b Choose one of the other calculations. Write it down.
Write a question about percentages that this calculation represents.

c Now do the same for one of the remaining two calculations.

d Copy and complete this sentence with the missing decimal number.

To decrease by 14%, multiply by ....

(5) *1996 level 7*

A clothes shop had a closing-down sale.
The sale started on Tuesday and finished on Saturday.
For each day of the sale, prices were reduced by 15% of the prices on the day before.

A shirt had a price of £19.95 on Monday.
Kevin bought it on Wednesday.

How much did he pay? Show your working.

(6) *2003 level 7*

A cup of coffee costs £1.75.
The diagram shows how much money different people get when you buy a cup of coffee.

Cup of coffee costs **£1.75**

Retailers get 44p
Growers get 5p

Others get £1.26

Not drawn accurately

Copy and complete the table to show what percentage of the cost of a cup of coffee goes to retailers, growers and others. Show your working.

Retailers	... %
Growers	... %
Others	...%

(7) *2006 level 8*

Since 1952 the total number of people living in Wales has increased by about one eighth.
The total number of people living in Wales now is about 3 million.
About how many people lived in Wales in 1952?

Money, money, money

This group activity will help you to:

- make an initial model of a situation using suitable forms of representation;
- adjust relationships to see the effects on answers in the model;
- consider how appropriate and accurate your results and conclusions are.

Background

Here are the sizes of UK bank notes.

Bank note	Length (mm)	Width (mm)
£5	135	70
£10	142	75
£20	149	80
£50	156	85

Watch a webcast of Andrew Bailey, Chief Cashier of the bank of England, talking about the new-style £20 note (www.bankofengland.co.uk/banknotes/newtwenty/index.htm).

Problem 1

Work in a small group.
Suppose your classroom is 7 m long and 6 m wide.

1. How many £5 notes would you need to cover the floor with a single layer of notes?

2. If you covered the floor with £50 notes, how much money would you need?

3. Each of these lines of notes is 1 km long. Which line has the greatest value?
   - **A** £10 notes laid side-by-side with their long sides touching
   - **B** £20 notes laid side-by-side with their short sides touching

Here are the sizes of UK coins.

Coin	Diameter (mm)	Thickness (mm)	Mass (g)
1p	20.03	1.65	3.56
2p	25.90	1.85	7.12
5p	18.00	1.70	3.25
10p	24.5	1.85	6.5
20p	21.4	1.7	5
50p	27.3	1.78	8
£1	22.5	3.15	9.5
£2	28.4	2.5	12

4 Imagine you had a bag containing £1000 in 1p coins.

   a How much would the coins weigh? Do you think you could lift the bag?

   b If you piled up all the 1p coins to make a tower, how high would the tower be?

   c How much money in 1p coins would you need to cover your classroom floor?

5 A survey in 2005 found that:

> About £1bn is lost or lying idle in the UK's 24.7 million households.
>
> An overwhelming 88% of the 1500 people surveyed said at least £10 was lost in small change throughout their home.
>
> A further 62% estimated they had at least £56 in loose change in jars, pots, pockets, purses and down the back of sofas.
>
> Londoners were the country's biggest losers, with £121 worth of redundant cash at home, whereas people in Birmingham had £61.

   a How much in loose change do you think there is in your house?
Write down the coins that could make up this amount.

   b Work out how much your coins would weigh.

   c Work out how high the tower would be if your coins were stacked in a tower.

Be prepared to present your solutions to other groups.

Enquiry 1

This unit will help you to:

- ⊙ understand the terms population and sample;
- ⊙ appreciate that a sample of data must be chosen fairly;
- ⊙ represent and interpret grouped data in a frequency polygon;
- ⊙ estimate measures of average and spread for grouped data and use them to compare sets of grouped data;
- ⊙ carry out a statistical investigation involving grouped data;
- ⊙ draw and interpret scatter graphs and lines of best fit.

1 Representative samples

This lesson will help you to understand that a sample of data must be chosen fairly.

 Did you know that...?

In 1936, a magazine in the USA predicted a Republican win in the election for President. This was based on a survey of a sample of more than one million people, whose names and addresses were chosen from magazine subscription lists and telephone directories.

However, the easy winner of the election was Franklin D. Roosevelt, who was a Democrat.

The magazine was wrong because its sample of one million people did not represent the nation as a whole.

In 1936, people who had a telephone or who subscribed to a magazine tended to be richer and more likely to vote Republican.

Exercise 1

It is difficult to ask every person in a large town what their favourite TV programme is. It is easier to ask a small number of people. This is called a **sample**.

A sample has to be chosen carefully so that it represents the whole **population**, that is, all the people who live in the town. It should not be **biased** towards any group of people – for example, children only or males only. A sample that represents a population fairly and is not biased is called a **representative sample**.

A **random sample** is one in which each person has an equal chance of being chosen. For example, if 5 out of 30 pupils are needed for a sample,

- ◎ each pupil could be allocated a number from 1 to 30, and then five random numbers from 1 to 30 chosen by using a calculator;

- ◎ or the names of the pupils could be placed in a box and a name selected then replaced in the box, which continues until 5 different names are chosen.

Example

A school plans to carry out a survey on pupil attitudes to school uniform.
Explain whether each of the following samples is likely to be biased or not.

a The headteacher asks a sample of 30 pupils in the school library at lunchtime.

This sample is likely to be **biased** as many groups are not included, e.g. pupils who go home for lunch and pupils who don't visit the library.

b The deputy headteacher asks a sample of 30 boys in his Year 8 PE lesson.

This sample is **biased** as girls and pupils of different ages are not included.

c A teacher asks one boy and one girl chosen at random from each class in the school.

This sample is likely to be **representative** as pupils from the two main groups – boys and girls and different ages – are selected randomly.

1 Petra is investigating people's shopping habits.

She plans to ask 100 women to complete a questionnaire at her local supermarket on Sunday morning.

Why is this sample likely to give biased results? Give at least three reasons.

2 In an opinion poll, 50 women in Newcastle are asked how they are going to vote in a national election.

a Why is this an unreliable way of predicting the result of the election?

b Suggest how the opinion poll could be improved.

(3) Some pupils do a survey to test this hypothesis.

> Most pupils in our school do more than 30 minutes homework a night.

They ask pupils in their class this question during their Wednesday morning maths lesson.

> How much homework did you do last night?

a What is the population for the survey?

b What is the sample?

c List ways in which the sample is **not** representative of the population.

d Describe how the sampling method could be improved.

(4) A magazine publishes a questionnaire about attitudes to fox hunting.
They ask their readers to complete the questionnaire and send it to them.

a Explain why the results are likely to be biased.

b Describe a better method of asking people to complete the questionnaire.

(5) a Bill is taking a sample of balls from a large box of small coloured balls.
Some of the balls are metal and some are plastic.
Bill uses a magnet to select his sample.
Bill notices that all the balls in his sample are metal.

What conclusion is Bill likely to make about the balls in the box?
How reliable is this conclusion?
Explain your answer.

b Explain why biased samples generally lead to unreliable conclusions.

(6) Explain why a **random** sample might not give a **representative** sample.

(7) A questionnaire asks people what they think about increasing Value Added Tax on computers and spending the money raised on computers in schools.

The survey is carried out by sending out random emails.

Explain why this is likely to produce a biased sample.

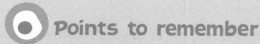

Points to remember

- The whole set of people or items that might be part of a study is called a **population**.
- A **sample** is used when it would be too difficult to study every person or item in the population.
- A **representative sample** represents a population fairly. It is not biased towards any group in the population.
- In a **random sample** each person or item has an equal chance of being chosen. A random sample may not be representative.

2 Frequency polygons

This lesson will help you to draw and interpret frequency polygons.

Exercise 2

Frequency polygons can be drawn for discrete or continuous grouped data.

To draw a frequency polygon:

- plot points at the midpoints of the class intervals;
- connect the points with straight lines.

For example, the heights of 42 pupils at Wellfield School are shown in the frequency table and represented in a frequency polygon.

Height (h, cm)	Frequency
$160 \leqslant h < 165$	10
$165 \leqslant h < 170$	14
$170 \leqslant h < 175$	8
$175 \leqslant h < 180$	5
$180 \leqslant h < 185$	3
$185 \leqslant h < 190$	2

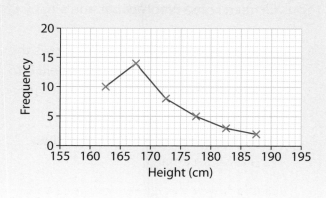

Example

This frequency polygon shows the heights of a sample of boys at Wellfield School.
A zigzag in the height axis is used to show that the scale does not start at 0.

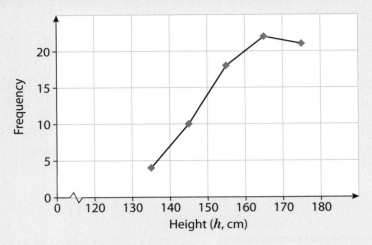

a How many boys were included in the sample?

There were 4 + 10 + 18 + 22 + 21 = 75 boys in the sample.

b How many boys had a height of less than 150 cm?

4 + 10 = 14 boys had a height of less than 150 cm.

c Draw a grouped frequency table for the data in the frequency polygon.

Height (h, cm)	Frequency
$130 \leqslant h < 140$	4
$140 \leqslant h < 150$	10
$150 \leqslant h < 160$	18
$160 \leqslant h < 170$	22
$170 \leqslant h < 180$	21

You will need some graph paper and a copy of **S6.1 Resource sheet 2.2** for this exercise.

1 The grouped frequency table shows the distribution of the distances travelled to work by employees at an office.

On graph paper, draw a frequency polygon to represent this set of data.

Distance (d, km)	Frequency
$0 \leqslant d < 2$	3
$2 \leqslant d < 4$	4
$4 \leqslant d < 6$	8
$6 \leqslant d < 8$	4
$8 \leqslant d < 10$	1

2 50 boys and 50 girls take part in an experiment to test their reaction times. The results are shown in this grouped frequency table.

On graph paper, draw a frequency polygon to represent each set of data.

Reaction time (t, milliseconds)	Boys	Girls
$20 \leqslant t < 30$	4	6
$30 \leqslant t < 40$	12	8
$40 \leqslant t < 50$	19	26
$50 \leqslant t < 60$	11	9
$60 \leqslant t < 70$	4	1

3 You will need **S6.1 Resource sheet 2.2**.

You are going to test the hypothesis:

> Male smokers smoke for longer each day than female smokers.

This data has been collected from representative samples of 100 male and 100 female smokers in each of two different age groups.

Number of hours h spent smoking each day	Smokers aged 15 to 25		Smokers aged 26 to 40	
	Male	Female	Male	Female
$0 < h \leqslant 1$	28	40	21	48
$1 < h \leqslant 2$	44	39	52	42
$2 < h \leqslant 3$	14	12	12	5
$3 < h \leqslant 4$	11	6	8	4
$4 < h \leqslant 5$	3	3	7	1

Start testing the hypothesis.
Draw frequency polygons for this data on **Resource sheet 2.2**.

Extension problem

4 A supermarket manager measures waiting times in the checkout queue for a representative sample of customers.

The frequency polygon represents the results.

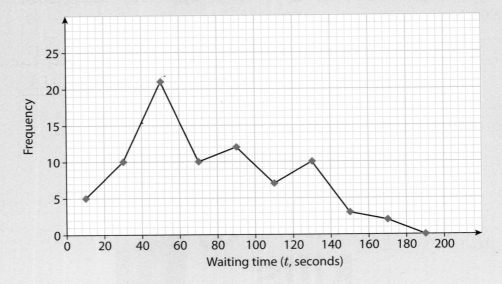

a How many customers are included in the sample?

b How many customers waited for between 40 and 60 seconds?

c How many customers waited for less than two minutes?

d The manager selects a customer at random.
What is the probability that the customer will have to wait at the checkout queue for less than one minute?

⊙ Points to remember

- ⊙ A **frequency polygon** is a statistical diagram used to represent discrete or continuous grouped data. It shows the shape of a distribution more clearly than a frequency diagram drawn with bars.
- ⊙ To draw a frequency polygon:
  - plot the frequencies against the midpoints of the class intervals;
  - join the points with straight lines.

3 Average and range of grouped data 1

This lesson will help you to find the modal class and estimate the mean of a set of grouped data.

Exercise 3

You cannot estimate the exact mean of a set of grouped data because you do not know what the individual data items are, but you can **make an estimate of the mean**.

Example

The table represents the heights in centimetres of 51 pupils.

Height (h cm)	Frequency (f)
$140 \leqslant h < 150$	5
$150 \leqslant h < 160$	17
$160 \leqslant h < 170$	20
$170 \leqslant h < 180$	9

a What is the modal class?

The modal class is the class interval with the highest frequency.

The modal class is $160 \leqslant h < 170$.

b Estimate the mean.

To estimate the mean, assume that the mean of the values in each class interval is the value of the midpoint of the class interval.

Midpoint of class (H)	$H \times f$
145	$145 \times 5 = 725$
155	$155 \times 17 = 2635$
165	$165 \times 20 = 3300$
175	$175 \times 9 = 1575$

Estimated sum of heights = 725 + 2635 + 3300 + 1575 = 8235

Number of heights = 5 + 17 + 20 + 9 = 51

Estimated mean height = 8235 ÷ 51 = 161.47…,
so the mean height is approximately 161 cm.

1. Work out the modal class and calculate an estimate of the mean for each set of data.

a The actual time, t, that 31 students took to estimate the length of two minutes

Time (t, seconds)	Frequency
$60 \leqslant t < 80$	2
$80 \leqslant t < 100$	6
$100 \leqslant t < 120$	10
$120 \leqslant t < 140$	9
$140 \leqslant t < 160$	3
$160 \leqslant t < 180$	1

b The time that 75 junior runners took to run 200 metres

Time (t, seconds)	Frequency
$30 \leqslant t < 35$	28
$35 \leqslant t < 40$	40
$40 \leqslant t < 45$	5
$45 \leqslant t < 50$	2

2. 50 boys and 50 girls take part in an experiment to test their reaction times. The results are shown in this grouped frequency table.

Work out the modal class and calculate an estimate of the mean for the boys' and girls' reaction times.

Reaction time (t, milliseconds)	Boys	Girls
$20 \leqslant t < 30$	4	6
$30 \leqslant t < 40$	12	8
$40 \leqslant t < 50$	19	26
$50 \leqslant t < 60$	11	9
$60 \leqslant t < 70$	4	1

3. You will need **S6.1 Resource sheet 3.1**.

Continue testing the hypothesis:

> Male smokers smoke for longer each day than female smokers.

Use the data from Exercise 2, question 3, to write down the modal class and estimate the mean of each distribution.

Complete the appropriate parts of the table on **Resource sheet 3.1**.

Extension problems

 4 Work out the modal class and calculate an estimate of the mean for the sets of data represented in each frequency polygon.

a The number of hours a group of pupils spent watching TV in one week

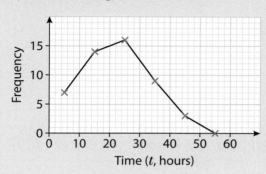

b The weights of 35 boys

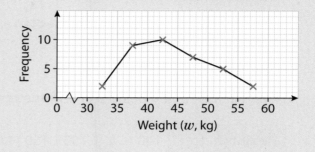

5 A supermarket manager measures waiting times in the checkout queue for a representative sample of customers. The frequency polygon represents the results.

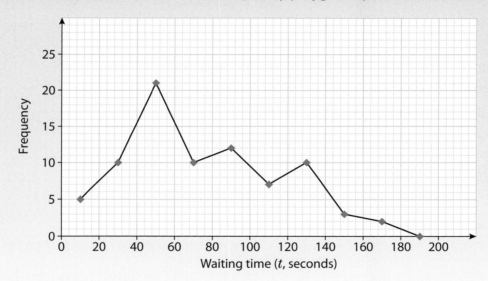

Work out the modal class and calculate an estimate of the mean for the data shown in the frequency polygon.

Points to remember

⊙ The **modal class** of a set of grouped data is the class interval with the greatest frequency.

⊙ To calculate an estimate of the **mean** of a set of grouped data, work out:

$$\frac{\text{the sum of (midpoints of class intervals} \times \text{frequency)}}{\text{the sum of the frequencies}}$$

4 Average and range of grouped data 2

This lesson will help you to estimate the range and median of a set of grouped data.

Exercise 4

It is also possible to estimate the **median** and **range** of a set of grouped data.

Example

Here is a table of the heights in centimetres of 51 pupils.

Height (h, cm)	$140 \leqslant h < 150$	$150 \leqslant h < 160$	$160 \leqslant h < 170$	$170 \leqslant h < 180$
Frequency	5	17	20	9

a Estimate the range of the heights.

The minimum possible height is 140 cm.
The maximum possible height is 180 cm.

Estimated range = 180 – 140 = 40 cm

b Estimate the median height.

In a set of 51 heights the median is the 26th height.

Height (h, cm)	Number of pupils	
< 150	5	The shortest 5 heights are less than 150 cm.
< 160	5 + 17 = 22	The shortest 22 heights are less than 160 cm.
< 170	22 + 20 = 42	The shortest 42 heights are less than 170 cm.

The 26th height is in the class interval $160 \leqslant h < 170$.
So the median height lies between 160 cm and 170 cm.

To estimate the median, assume that the 20 pupils in the class interval $160 \leqslant h < 170$ are evenly spread throughout the interval.

So 20 heights are evenly spread over 10 cm.
So there is one height every $10 \div 20 = 0.5$ cm.

The 26th height is the 4th height in the interval, and $4 \times 0.5 = 2$ cm.

So an estimate of the median = 160 + 2 = 162 cm.

So the median is approximately 162 cm.

1   Estimate the range and median for the sets of data represented in the grouped frequency tables in Exercise 3, question 1.

2   The numbers of half-day absences for each of 29 pupils in a class are given below.

0	0	0	0	2	3	5	5	6	6
7	9	9	10	10	10	12	12	15	18
18	20	20	21	23	26	28	31	33	

a   Work out the range and the median of the number of half-day absences.

b   Copy and complete each of these grouped frequency tables for the half-day absences.

No. of half-day absences	Frequency
0 to 4	
5 to 9	
10 to 14	
15 to 19	
20 to 24	
25 to 29	
30 to 34	

No. of half-day absences	Frequency
0 to 9	
10 to 19	
20 to 29	
30 to 39	

c   Use each of the frequency tables you completed in part b to estimate the range and the median of the grouped data for number of absences.

d   Compare the estimates you worked out in part c with the actual values you worked out in part a. What do you notice?

3   You will need your copy of **S6.1 Resource sheet 3.1**.
Continue testing the hypothesis:

> Male smokers smoke for longer each day than female smokers.

Use the data from Exercise 2, question 3, to estimate the range and the median for each grouped frequency distribution.

Complete the table on **Resource sheet 3.1**.

④ Estimate the range and median for the sets of data represented in the frequency polygons in Exercise 3, question 4.

⦿ **Points to remember**

⊙ For a set of grouped data, **the estimated range** is:

maximum possible value – minimum possible value

The maximum possible value is the highest value in the highest class interval.
The minimum possible value is the lowest value in the lowest class interval.

⊙ To **estimate the median**, assume that the data is evenly spread throughout the class interval in which the median occurs.

5 Comparing sets of grouped data

This lesson will help you to compare two sets of grouped data.

Exercise 5

You can compare two or more sets of grouped data by:

◎ comparing **average** values (the modal class or the estimated mean or median);

◎ comparing the **spread** of values (the estimated range);

◎ comparing the **shapes** of frequency polygons.

Example

These frequency polygons show the high jump heights for some Year 8 and Year 9 pupils.

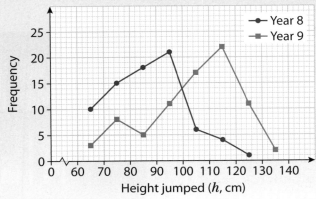

Compare the two sets of data.

Year 9 pupils jumped a greater number of higher heights.
The modal class is also greater.
So on average Year 9 pupils jumped higher.

The lowest height for both Year 8 and Year 9 occurs in the class interval $60 \leqslant h < 70$.
The greatest height for Year 9 pupils occurs in the class interval $130 \leqslant h < 140$.
For Year 8 pupils it occurs in the class interval $120 \leqslant h < 130$.

So the spread of heights is greater for Year 9 pupils.
This means that Year 9 pupils vary more in their ability to high jump.

This is confirmed by the measures of average and spread shown in this table.

	Modal class	Estimate of the mean	Estimate of the median	Estimate of the range
Year 8	$90 \leqslant h < 100$	87	87	70
Year 9	$110 \leqslant h < 120$	104	107	80

You will need some graph paper.

1 Three classes in Year 7 take a maths test.
The frequency polygons represent the scores out of 50.

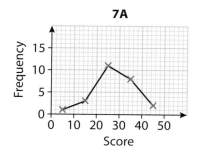
7A

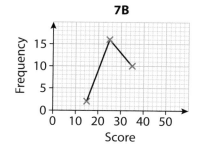
7B

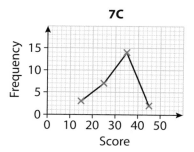
7C

a In which class do the scores vary the least?
Explain your answer.

b In which class do the scores vary the most?
Explain your answer.

c Which class, on average, obtained the highest scores?
Explain your answer.

d Which class, on average, obtained the lowest scores?
Explain your answer.

② The table shows the best distances thrown by competitors in discus competitions in 2006 and 2007.

Distance thrown (d, metres)	Number of competitors in 2006	Number of competitors in 2007
10 ⩽ d < 20	0	1
20 ⩽ d < 30	3	4
30 ⩽ d < 40	23	17
40 ⩽ d < 50	12	13
50 ⩽ d < 60	2	3
60 ⩽ d < 70	0	2

a On the same set of axes, draw a frequency polygon for each set of results. Use graph paper.

b Comment on the results.

③ You will need your copies of **S6.1 Resource sheets 2.2 and 3.1**.

Continue testing the hypothesis:

> Male smokers smoke for longer each day than female smokers.

Compare the numbers of hours spent smoking for male and female smokers. Use the diagrams and statistics that you have completed on **Resource sheets 2.2 and 3.1**.

Comment on the validity of the hypothesis.

Look at the data handling cycle and identify which parts of it have been covered in your work on **Resource sheets 2.2 and 3.1**.

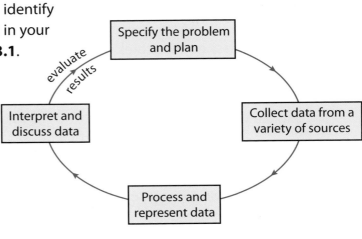

Extension problem

 4 Natasha investigated the distances travelled to school by representative samples of pupils at an inner-city school and pupils at a rural school.

The table shows her results.

Distance travelled (d, km)	Inner-city school Frequency	Rural school Frequency
$0 \leqslant d < 2$	12	4
$2 \leqslant d < 4$	15	5
$4 \leqslant d < 6$	13	9
$6 \leqslant d < 8$	6	12
$8 \leqslant d < 10$	3	8
$10 \leqslant d < 12$	1	5
$12 \leqslant d < 14$	0	3
$14 \leqslant d < 16$	0	2
$16 \leqslant d < 18$	0	2

Compare the distances that pupils from each school travel.
Give evidence to support your conclusions.

 Points to remember

- You can compare two or more sets of grouped data by comparing:
  - **average** values (the modal class or the estimated mean or median);
  - the **spread** of values (the estimated range);
  - the **shapes** of frequency polygons.
- Statistical investigations are based on the data handling cycle.

6 Scatter graphs and lines of best fit

This lesson will help you to draw and use scatter graphs and lines of best fit.

Exercise 6

Scatter graphs are used to investigate whether there is a relationship or a link between two variables.

For example, this scatter graph shows the number of cold drinks sold at a cafe in a local park plotted against the temperature.

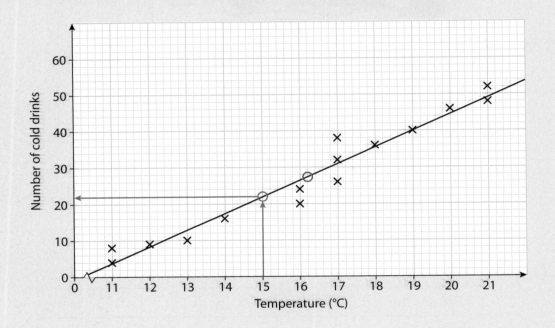

The scatter graph shows a link between the number of cold drinks sold and the temperature: as the temperature increases so does the number of drinks sold.

The line on the scatter graph is called a **line of best fit**.
This is a line drawn so that it lies as close as possible to the points on the scatter graph.

- When you draw a line of best fit, use a ruler.
- Draw a line that has roughly equal numbers of points on each side of it.
- Aim to keep all the points as close to the line as possible.

The line of best fit should pass through the **mean point**:

Mean temperature = 16.2°C
Mean number of cold drinks sold = 27.3

The mean point is (16.2, 27.3) – the blue circled point on the scatter graph.

The line of best fit can be used to make predictions.

Example

How many drinks might be sold when the temperature is 15°C?

The scatter graph passes through the point (15, 22) – the red circled point on the scatter graph. This shows that approximately 22 drinks might be sold when the temperature is 15°C.

You will need graph paper.

1 Some students took a Spanish test and a French test.
The marks scored are shown in the table.

Spanish	10	18	16	24	28	25	32	38	36	46	38	42	53	56	52
French	14	15	20	22	26	30	30	32	36	38	40	44	45	47	54

a Copy and complete this scatter graph to represent this information.
The first five points have been added to help you.

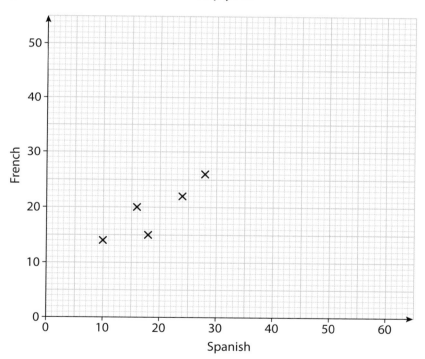

b Draw a line of best fit.

c Describe the relationship between the Spanish and French scores.

d Tania scored 27 in the Spanish test but missed the French test. Use your line of best fit to estimate the mark that Tania might have scored in the French test.

e Oki scored 27 in the French test but missed the Spanish test.
Estimate the mark that Oki might have scored in the Spanish test.

2 The table shows the scores of some students in a music exam and in a maths exam.

Student	A	B	C	D	E	F	G	H	I	J
Music	35	48	72	23	76	51	45	60	88	17
Maths	42	57	80	32	65	69	50	71	94	25

a Plot the data on a scatter graph. Use the horizontal axis for the music exam scores from 0 to 100, and the vertical axis for the maths exam scores from 0 to 100.

b Draw a line of best fit.

c One person did not do quite as well as expected on the maths test. Who do you think it was? Give a reason.

3 The table shows the ages of some children and the number of hours of sleep they had last night.

Age (years)	1	2	3	4	5	6	7	10	11	12	13
Hours of sleep	15	14	14	13	12	12.5	12	11	10	10.5	9.6

a Plot the data on a scatter graph. Use the horizontal axis for age from 0 to 14, and the vertical axis for hours of sleep from 8 to 16.

b Describe the relationship between the age of the children in years and the number of hours of sleep they had last night.

c Draw a line of best fit.

d Use your line of best fit to estimate the number of hours sleep for an 8-year-old child.

4 Describe the relationship you would expect between each of these pairs of variables.
Give a reason for each of your answers.

a Ice cream sales and temperature

b Shoe size and scores in an English test

c Average speed on a journey and the time that the journey takes

d Weight and height of adults

e Weight and height of children

f The time spent revising and the marks in a test

g The size of a family and the weekly shopping bill

Extension problems

Example

If the points on a scatter graph are clustered around the line of best fit there is a **correlation** between the variables. The closer they are to the line of best fit the stronger the correlation.

If an increase in one variable results in an increase in the other then the correlation is **positive**.

This scatter graph shows that there is a positive correlation between the length and weight of some dogs.
As the length increases, so does the weight.

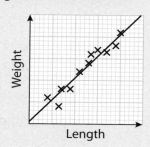

If an increase in one variable results in a decrease in the other then the correlation is **negative**.

This scatter graph shows that there is a negative correlation between the age and value of some cars.
As the age increases the value decreases.

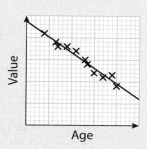

If there is no clear relationship between the two variables there is **no correlation**.

This scatter graph shows that there is no correlation between the age and weight of adults.
It is not possible to draw a line of best fit.

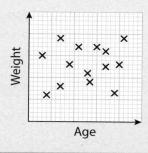

 5 The table shows the maximum air temperature and the number of people who used an outdoor pool on ten Saturdays in the summer.

Temperature (°C)	19	22	24	28	28	28	29	31	33
Number of people	750	1000	1500	1200	1750	2600	2350	2650	2850

a Plot the data on a scatter graph.

b Describe the correlation between the maximum temperature and the number of people who used the pool.

c Draw a line of best fit.

d The weather forecast for next Saturday gives a maximum temperature of 27°C.
Use your line of best fit to estimate the number of people who will use the pool.

6 The table shows the marks given by two different judges in a competition.

Judge A	33	30	29	38	43	45	40	50	44	52
Judge B	29	31	34	34	40	42	42	44	48	46

a Draw a scatter graph for this data.

b Draw a line of best fit.

c Use your line of best fit to:

   i describe the correlation between the judges' scores;

   ii decide which judge awarded the better scores.

d A late entry was awarded 65 marks by Judge A.

   Estimate the mark that might have been given by Judge B.
   Is this a reliable estimate?
   Explain your answer.

e i Work out the mean of Judge A's scores.

   ii Work out the mean of Judge B's scores.

   iii Plot the point represented by these mean scores on your scatter graph.

   What does this tell you about your line of best fit?

Points to remember

⊙ A **scatter graph** is used to show whether there is a relationship between two variables.

⊙ A **line of best fit** is a straight line that represents the best estimate of the relationship between the two variables on a scatter graph.

⊙ To draw the line of best fit, draw a straight line so that there are roughly equal numbers of points of the scatter graph on each side of it.

How well are you doing?

Enquiry 1 (calculator allowed)

1 These frequency polygons show the distribution of the amounts of rainfall per day in two different months.

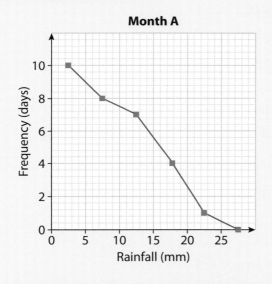
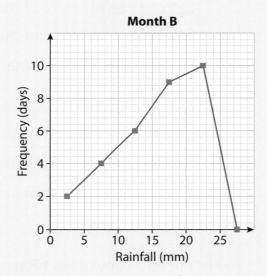

a Which month has 30 days? Explain how you know.

b In which month were there more days with rainfall between 10 mm and 20 mm?

c In which month was there more rain? Explain how you know.

d Petra says that the frequency polygon for Month B shows that it rained more towards the end of the month. Explain why Petra is wrong.

e For each month, estimate:

   i the range   ii the median   iii the mean

f Compare the frequency distributions for the two months.

2 This grouped frequency table shows the time taken for 100 pupils to travel to school.

Time (t, minutes)	Frequency
$0 \leqslant t < 5$	2
$5 \leqslant t < 10$	14
$10 \leqslant t < 15$	28
$15 \leqslant t < 20$	35
$20 \leqslant t < 25$	20
$25 \leqslant t < 30$	1

a Draw a frequency polygon to represent this data.

b i   Write down the modal class of the data.

   ii   Calculate an estimate of the mean.

   iii Calculate an estimate of the median.

c Estimate the range of the data.

3 Jon wanted to find out if people liked a new biscuit.
He decided to give a questionnaire to a sample of 50 pupils in his school.

a Explain why Jon's sample is biased.

b Describe how Jon could obtain more reliable results from his survey.

4 *1997 level 7*

You will need a copy of **S6.1 Resource sheet 6.1**.

The scatter diagram on the resource sheet shows the total amounts of sunshine and rainfall for 12 seaside towns during one summer.

Each town has been given a letter.

The dashed lines drawn go through the mean amounts of sunshine and rainfall.

a Which town's rainfall was closest to the mean?

b On the scatter graph on the resource sheet, draw a line of best fit.

c Use your line of best fit to find an estimate of the hours of sunshine for a seaside town that had 30 cm of rain.

Geometrical reasoning

This unit will help you to:

- ⊙ solve problems involving angles, tangents and chords;
- ⊙ solve problems involving congruent triangles and similar shapes;
- ⊙ use geometrical reasoning;
- ⊙ appreciate the difference between evidence and proof.

1 Isosceles triangle problems

This lesson will help you to solve angle problems involving isosceles triangles.

Exercise 1

You can use the properties of triangles and regular polygons to find unknown angles.

Example

A regular hexagon is joined by an edge to a regular pentagon ABCDE. O is the centre of the pentagon.

a Calculate each angle in triangle OBD.

OB = OD, so triangle OBD is isosceles.

angle BOC = angle COD = 360° ÷ 5 = 72°
(angle at centre of pentagon)

angle BOD = angle BOC + angle COD = 72° + 72° = 144°

angle OBD = angle ODB = (180° − 144°) ÷ 2 = 18°
(sum of angles in a triangle)

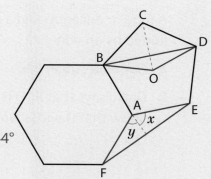

b Calculate each angle in triangle AEF.

AF = AE, so triangle AFE is isosceles.

angle EAF is the sum of the exterior angles
of the pentagon (x) and the hexagon (y).

angle EAF = $\dfrac{360}{5} + \dfrac{360}{6}$ = 72° + 60° = 132°

angle AFE = angle AEF = (180° − 132°) ÷ 2 = 24°

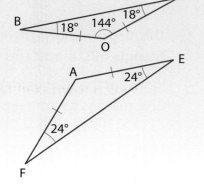

Diagrams in this exercise are not drawn accurately. Remember to give reasons for your answers.

① The diagram shows a regular dodecagon with centre O.

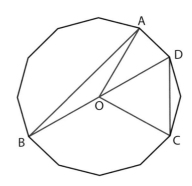

   a Calculate angle AOD, the angle at the centre of the dodecagon.

   b Calculate all the angles in triangle OAB.

   c Show that triangle OCD is equilateral.

② A regular hexagon and a regular octagon are joined by an edge.

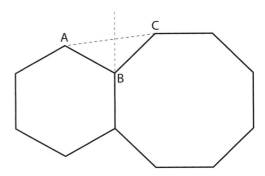

   a Sketch the diagram.

     Mark the exterior angle of the regular hexagon as x.

     Mark the exterior angle of the regular octagon as y.

   b Work out angles x and y.

   c Work out all the angles in triangle ABC.

③ A regular decagon and a square are joined by an edge.

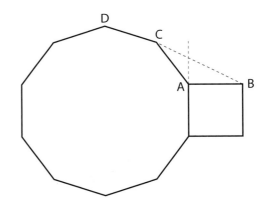

   a Calculate angle BAC.

   b David says that BCD is a straight line. Show that David is wrong.

④ The diagram shows triangle ABC. Triangle ABD is isosceles with AB = AD.

Work out the sizes of angles x, y and z. Give reasons for your answers.

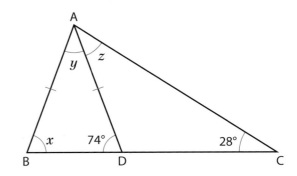

5 The diagram shows a circle with centre O.
OA, OB and OC are radii of the circle.

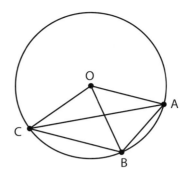

a Explain whether or not each of these triangles is isosceles.

   i triangle OAB   **ii** triangle ABC

   iii triangle OBC   **iv** triangle OAC

d Angle OAB is 70° and angle OBC is 50°.
Show that angle OAC is 30°.

Extension problem

Did you know that...?

In the early 1970s, the Hungarian industrial designer and artist **Dániel Erdély** experimented with a regular hexagon to create a 'sea-horse like' shape that he called a 'spidron'.

To create the spidron, a hexagon is split into equilateral and isosceles triangles as shown in the diagram. A hexagon contains six 'half-spidrons'.

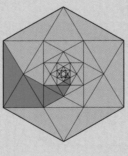

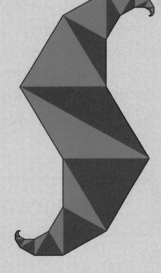

The pictures below show a polyhedron made from 120 spidrons and a structure made from 24 spidrons in a park near Leeuwarden in the Netherlands.

6 The diagram shows part of a spidron.
Calculate angle x.

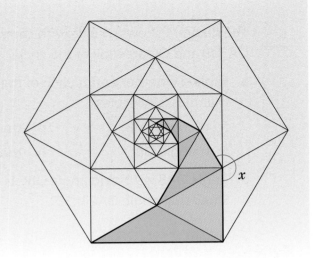

2 Evidence or proof?

This lesson will help you to appreciate the difference between evidence and proof.

Exercise 2

You can use the properties of triangles and parallel lines to find unknown angles.

Example 1

Triangle ABC is isosceles.
DC is parallel to AB.
Show that when angle $x = 50°$, angle $y = 80°$.

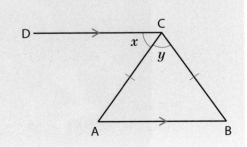

Angle CAB $= 50°$ (alternate angles)

Angle CBA $=$ angle CAB $= 50°$ (triangle CAB is isosceles)

Angle $y = 180 - 2 \times 50 = 80°$ (angle sum of triangle)

We have shown that, in the particular case when angle $x = 50°$, angle $y = 180 - 2 \times x = 80°$.

You could repeat this for some other values of angle ACD and complete this table.

angle ACD	40°	45°	50°	55°	60°
angle y	100°	90°	80°	70°	60°

Each pair of values of x and y provides **evidence** to **demonstrate** that values of x are connected to values of y by the general rule: angle $y = 180 - 2 \times$ angle x.

You can **prove** that these general results hold for all values of x and y, not just for the particular cases in the table. In a proof, the steps should follow each other in a logical order and you should give a reason or explanation for each step.

Example 2 is a **proof** to show that angle y is always equal to $180 - 2 \times$ angle x.

Example 2

Triangle ABC is isosceles.
DC is parallel to AB.
Prove that angle $y = 180 - 2 \times$ angle x.

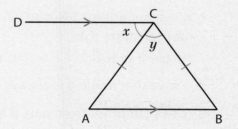

Angle CAB = angle ACD = x (alternate angles)

Angle CBA = angle CAB (triangle CAB is isosceles)

Angle $y = 180 - 2 \times x$ (angle sum of triangle)

① Triangle ABC is isosceles.

a Angle x is 120°. Show that angle $y = 60°$.

b Prove that angle y is always equal to $\frac{1}{2} \times$ angle x.

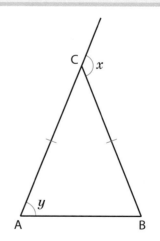

② AB and CD are parallel lines.
AB = BC

a Angle $x = 50°$.
Show that angle $y =$ angle $z = 50°$.

b Prove that angle y is always equal to angle z.

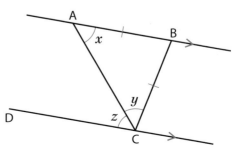

3 ABC, DEF and GHI are parallel lines.
Angle BHE = z.

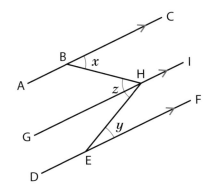

  a Choose values of x and y to show that
  angle z = angle x + angle y.

  b Prove that angle z = angle x + angle y.

4 AB and CD are parallel lines.
AB = BC and AD = AC.

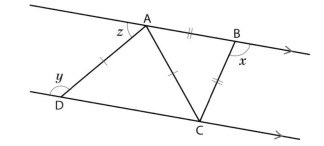

  a Show that when angle $x = 100°$,
  angle $y = 130°$.

  b Calculate angle y when angle $x = 60°$.

  c Use your answers to parts **a** and **b** to
  demonstrate that
  angle $y = 180 - \frac{1}{2} \times$ angle x.

  d Prove that angle y is always equal to $180 - \frac{1}{2} \times$ angle x.

  e Use your proof from part **d** to prove that angle $z = \frac{1}{2} \times$ angle x.

5 ABCD is a kite.
AD = BD = CD

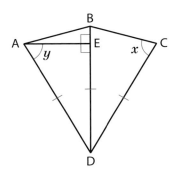

  a Show that when angle $x = 75°$, angle $y = 60°$.

  b **Prove** that angle $y = 2 \times$ angle $x - 90$.

Extension problem

6 ABC is a triangle.
D is a point on AC such that AD = BD = DC.

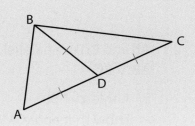

  a Show that when angle BAD is $60°$, angle ABC = $90°$.

  b Prove that angle ABC is always a right angle.

Points to remember

- The angles in geometrical shapes are often connected by simple rules.
- A **proof** is a logical, step-by-step procedure with reasons and explanations given for each step.
- A proof shows that a rule works for all values.
- You can **demonstrate** that a rule works by testing it with particular values.

3 Congruent triangles

This lesson will help you to prove that triangles are congruent.

Exercise 3

Two triangles are **congruent** if they have exactly the same shape and size. To prove that two triangles are congruent, one of these four conditions must be shown for the two triangles:

SSS

ASA

SAS

RHS

Three sides are equal.

Two angles and the included side are equal.

Two sides and the included angle are equal.

A right angle, the hypotenuse and one other side are equal.

To prove that two triangles are congruent:

- mark equal lengths and equal angles on the diagram;
- explain each step in the proof with reasons;
- state which of the four conditions for congruency is satisfied.

Example

In a quadrilateral ABCD, AB = AD. AC bisects angle BAD.
Prove that triangles ABC and ADC are congruent.

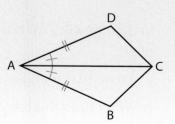

AB = AD (given)

angle BAC = angle CAD (given)

AC is common.

So triangles ABC and ADC are congruent (SAS).

You need **G6.1 Resource sheet 3.1**.

1 **Resource sheet 3.1** shows a hexagon split into half-spidrons. On the resource sheet:

   a Shade all the triangles that are congruent to the shaded isosceles triangle. Explain how you know that they are congruent.

   b Shade all triangles that are congruent to the shaded equilateral triangle. Explain how you know that they are congruent.

2 The diagram shows triangle ABC and triangle DEC.

   Prove that triangles ABC and DEC are congruent.

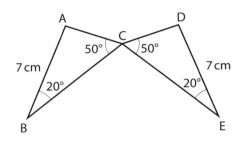

3 The diagram shows triangle ABC and triangle ABD.

   Prove that triangles ABC and ABD are congruent.

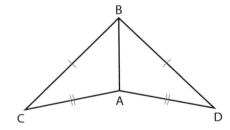

4 ABCD is a quadrilateral.
AB = AD
Angle ABC = angle ADC = 90°

   Prove that triangles ABC and ADC are congruent.

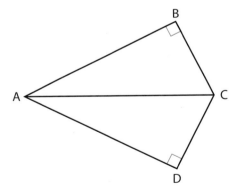

5 In triangle ABC, AD is the perpendicular bisector of BC.

   a Prove that triangles ABD and ACD are congruent.

   b What does this tell you about triangle ABC? Explain your answer.

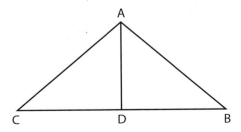

6 AED and CEB are straight lines.
AE = CE and BE = DE.

Explain why triangles ABE and CDE are congruent.

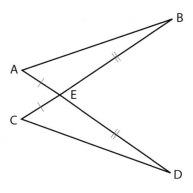

7 In this diagram AB is parallel to DE.
C is the midpoint of BD.

Prove that triangles ABC and EDC are congruent.
Explain each step of your proof.

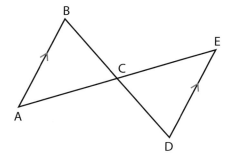

Extension problem

8 WXYZ is a quadrilateral.
WY is perpendicular to WX and ZY.
WZ = XY

a Prove that triangles WYZ and WXY are congruent.

b What does this tell you about quadrilateral WXYZ?
Give reasons for your answer.

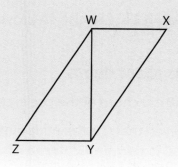

⊙ Points to remember

- Congruent shapes are identical; they have the same shape and size.
- Two triangles are **congruent** if:
  SSS three sides are equal;
  SAS two sides and the angle between them are equal;
  ASA two angles and the side between them are equal;
  RHS a right angle, the hypotenuse and one other side are equal.
- To prove that two triangles are congruent, show that one of the four conditions above is true.

4 Radii, chords and tangents

This lesson will help you to learn more properties of circles relating to tangents, chords and radii.

Exercise 4A

Two facts about tangents

1 A is a point on the circumference of a circle, centre O.

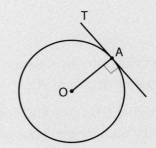

OA is a radius.
TA is the tangent to the circle at A.

OA is perpendicular to TA.

Question 1 in Exercise 4A demonstrates this fact.

2 T is a point outside the circle.

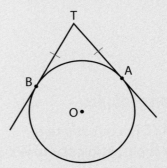

TA is the tangent to the circle at A.
TB is the tangent to the circle at B.

TA = TB

Question 2 in Exercise 4A proves this fact.

Facts about chords

3 AB is a chord of the circle, centre O.

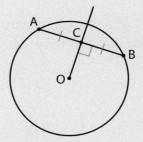

Given that C is the midpoint of AB, then
OC is perpendicular to AB.

Given that OC is perpendicular to AB, then
C is the midpoint of AB.

Question 3 in Exercise 4A proves this fact.

You can use **G6.1 Resource sheet 4.1** to remind you how to do the construction in question 1.

1 Draw a line about 6 cm long. Label the line AB.
   Mark a point P about 5 cm from the line.

   a Construct the perpendicular from the point P to the line.
      Label the intersection of the perpendicular and the line T.

   b Draw a circle with centre P and radius PT.
      What do you notice?

2 The diagram shows a circle with centre O.
A and B are points on the circumference of the circle.
AT and BT are tangents to the circle.

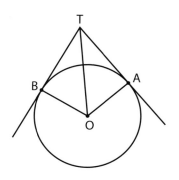

    a Prove that triangle OAT is **congruent** to triangle OBT.

    b Explain why this proves that AT = BT.

3 The diagram shows a circle with centre O.
AB is a chord.
C is the midpoint of AB.

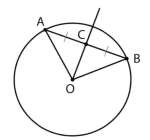

    a Prove that triangle OAC is **congruent** to triangle OBC.

    b Explain why this proves that OC is perpendicular to AB.

Exercise 4B

You can use properties of tangents, chords and radii to find unknown angles and lengths.

Example

TA and TB are tangents to a circle with centre O.
C is the midpoint of the chord AB.
Angle TBC = 68°.

Work out angle x, angle y and angle z.

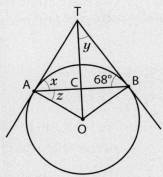

    a Find the size of angle x.

        AT = BT (equal tangents to a circle)

        So triangle ATB is isosceles.

        So angle x = angle TBA = 68°

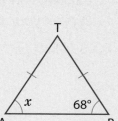

    b Find the size of angle y.

        Angle TCB = 90° (the line from the centre to the midpoint of
        a chord is perpendicular to the chord)

        So angle y + 68 + 90 = 180° (angles in a triangle)

        So angle y = 22°

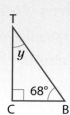

c Find the size of angle z.

OB is a radius and BT is a tangent.
So angle OBT = 90°
(the tangent at a point is perpendicular to the radius)

angle OBT = 90° = angle x + angle z

So angle z = 90° − 68° = 22°

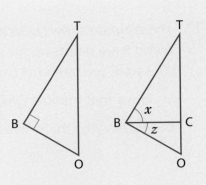

1 Each diagram shows a circle with centre O.
A, B and C are points on the circumference.
TA and TB are tangents.

a Angle ABC = 60°

Calculate angle a.
Explain your answer.

b Angle ATB = 50°

Calculate angle b and angle c.
Explain your answers.

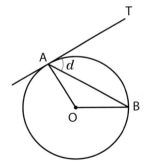

c Angle ABO = 20°

Calculate angle d.
Explain your answer.

2 PA is a tangent at A to a circle, centre O.
B is a point on the circumference.
POB is a straight line.

Find the size of angle y.
Give reasons for your answer.

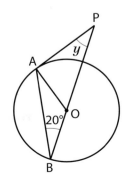

(3) AB, BC and CA are tangents to the circle at D, E and F.
AD = 3 cm
BE = 5 cm
CF = 8 cm

Work out the perimeter of triangle ABC.

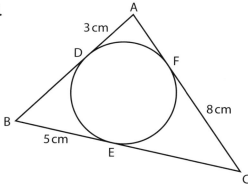

(4) XY, YZ and ZX are tangents to a circle at L, M and N.
YL = 5 cm
MZ = 7 cm
The perimeter of triangle XYZ is 38 cm.

Show that triangle XYZ is isosceles.

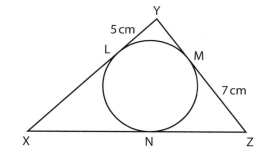

Extension problem

(5) The diagram shows a circle centre O.
A and B are points on the circumference of the circle.
CA is a tangent to the circle at A.
OBC is a straight line.

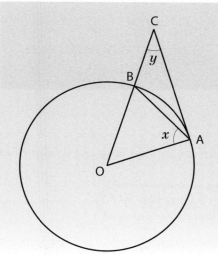

a   Calculate angle y when angle $x = 50°$.
Explain each step of your calculation.

b   Show that when triangle OAB is equilateral,
triangle ABC is isosceles.

c   Prove that angle $y = 2 \times$ angle $x - 90$.

Points to remember

⊙ The tangent at a point on a circle is **perpendicular to the radius** at the point.

⊙ The tangents to a circle from a point outside the circle are **equal in length**.

⊙ The perpendicular from the centre of a circle to a chord **bisects the chord**.

⊙ The line joining the midpoint of a chord to the centre of the circle is **perpendicular to the chord**.

5 Similar shapes

Did you know that...?

Sir Bertrand Russell (1881–1972) was famous for his contributions to mathematical logic. Here are some copies of a photograph of him.

This lesson will help you to identify similar shapes and use their properties.

Exercise 5

Congruent shapes are the same shape and size. **Similar shapes** are the same shape but are different sizes. The photographs of Sir Bertrand Russell above are **similar rectangles**.

Similar shapes are enlargements of each other. If shapes are similar:

- corresponding sides are **in the same ratio**, so they are connected by a scale factor;

- angles at corresponding vertices are **equal**.

Triangle ABC and triangle A'B'C' are **similar triangles**. They have the same shape but they are not the same size.

The angles in triangle ABC are the same as the angles in triangle A'B'C'.

The lengths of corresponding sides are in the same ratio, so:

$$\frac{AB}{A'B'} = \frac{BC}{B'C'} = \frac{CA}{C'A'}$$

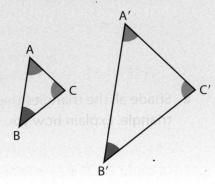

Example 1

Explain why rectangles R and S are **similar**.

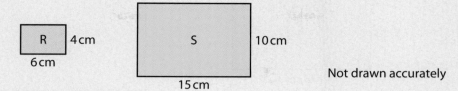

Not drawn accurately

Rectangles R and S are similar because:

⊙ corresponding angles are equal because, in a rectangle, all angles are right angles;

⊙ $\frac{10}{4} = \frac{15}{6}$, so corresponding sides are in the same ratio.

Example 2

Triangles A and B are similar right-angled triangles.

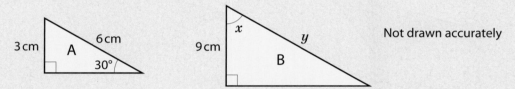

Not drawn accurately

a Work out the size of angle x.

In similar shapes, corresponding angles are equal.

So the angles in triangle B are equal to the corresponding angles in triangle A.

So angle $x + 90 + 30 = 180$

So angle $x = 60°$

b Work out the length of the side marked y.

In similar shapes, corresponding lengths are connected by a scale factor.
The scale factor $= 9 \div 3 = 3$

So lengths in triangle B are three times the corresponding lengths in triangle A.

So $y = 3 \times 6 = 18$ cm

You will need a copy of **G6.1 Resource sheet 3.1**.

① **Resource sheet 3.1** shows a hexagon split into half-spidrons. On the resource sheet:

a Shade all the triangles that are similar but **not** congruent to the shaded isosceles triangle. Explain how you know that they are similar.

b Shade all the triangles that are similar but **not** congruent to the shaded equilateral triangle. Explain how you know that they are similar.

2 Rectangles A and B are not drawn to scale.

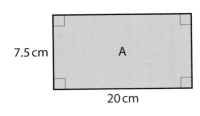

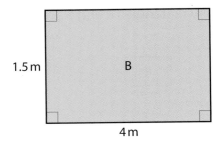

Explain why they are **similar**.

3 The diagram shows two triangles, triangle ABC and triangle XYZ.

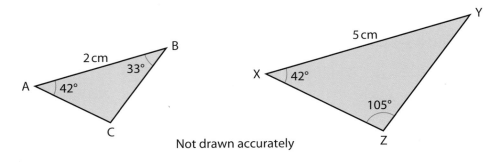

Not drawn accurately

a Show that triangle ABC is similar to triangle XYZ.

b How can you tell that AB and XY are corresponding sides?

c Write down the ratio of the length of AC to the length of XZ.

d What is the scale factor connecting the lengths of corresponding sides in triangle ABC and triangle XYZ?

4 Triangles ABC and DEF are similar.

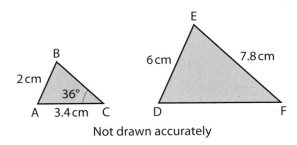

Not drawn accurately

a Find the size of angle DFE.

b Work out the length of:

   i DF   **ii** BC

5 Triangles PQR and STU are similar.

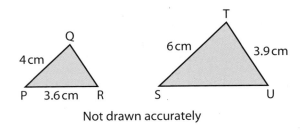

Not drawn accurately

Calculate the length of:

a SU

b QR

6 Trapezium ABCD is similar to trapezium WXYZ.

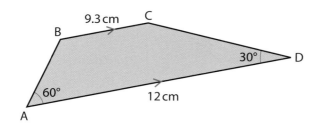
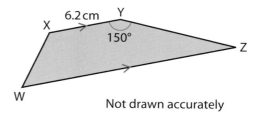

Not drawn accurately

a Work out angle WXY.
Explain each step of your working.

b Work out the ratio of the lengths of corresponding sides in its simplest form.

c Calculate the length of WZ.

Extension problems

 Here is a **scale drawing** of the London Eye.

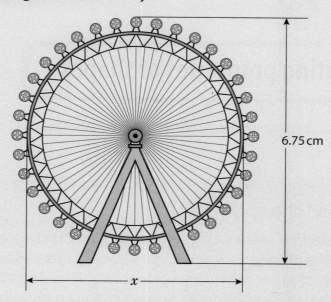

a Explain why the drawing is **similar** to the actual London Eye.

b The actual height of the London Eye is 135 m.
Show that the ratio of the height in the scale drawing to the actual height is 1 : 2000.

c Measure the length x on the scale drawing.
Work out the actual diameter of the wheel of the London Eye.

d The London Eye is supported by concrete piles that are 33 m deep.
How long would these be if they were shown on the scale drawing?

e 64 spoke cables, similar to bicycle spokes, stretch across the wheel.
What is the angle between these spokes at the centre of the wheel?
Explain why this is the same as the angle on the scale drawing.

8 AB is parallel to DE.

ACE and BCD are straight lines.

Calculate the length of:

  a CE

  b BC

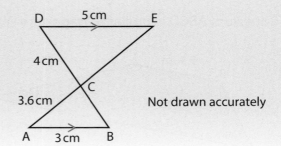

Not drawn accurately

Points to remember

When two shapes are **similar**:

⊙ each shape is an **enlargement** of the other;

⊙ **corresponding sides** are in the same ratio, so they are connected by a scale factor;

⊙ angles at **corresponding** vertices are equal.

6 Investigating properties of shapes

This lesson will help you to recognise the properties of different shapes and use them to make mathematical arguments.

Did you know that...?

Origami is the ancient Japanese art of paper folding, practised since around 1650. The aim is to make a 2D or 3D object using a single piece of paper and geometric folds, without gluing or cutting the paper. Origami uses only a small number of different folds but they can be combined in a variety of ways to make intricate designs.

Origami has many connections with mathematics. To make a model successfully you need to be familiar with the properties of shapes and to have good spatial skills.

Exercise 6

Circular pinboards have a number of dots equally spaced on their circumference.

This one has six pins.

You can make polygons by joining the dots with straight lines.

Three different types of triangle are shown on the six-pin board.

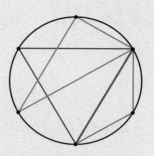

You will need a copy of **G6.1 Resource sheet 6.1**.

Your task is to investigate the polygons that you can make on circular pinboards and to find out about their properties. Here are some things you might like to try:

1. How many different sizes of triangles can you find on a circular nine-pin board?
   How many of each size can you find?
   How can you be sure when you have found them all?
   Calculate the angles in each different triangle.
   Remember to explain how you worked them out.

2. Make some different quadrilaterals on a circular nine-pin board.
   Calculate their angles.

3. How many pins must a circular pinboard have so that you can make a right-angled triangle?
   Explain your reasoning.

4. When do you get obtuse-angled triangles on a circular pinboard?
   What about acute-angled triangles?
   Explain your reasoning.

5. How many different triangles can you get on a circular n-pin board?

Extension problem

6. Now extend the problem. For example, sketch your own circular pinboards with different numbers of dots and look for polygons.

⦿ Points to remember

- ⊙ You can use properties of angles and shapes to solve geometrical problems.
- ⊙ You can solve multi-step problems by making decisions and explaining your reasoning.

How well are you doing?

Geometrical reasoning (no calculator)

1 *2006 level 7*

This shape is made of four congruent kites meeting at a point.

Calculate the size of angle k.

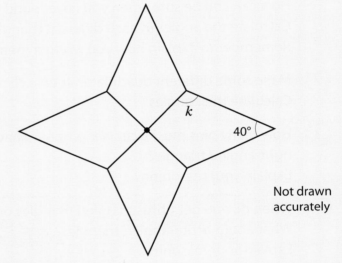

Not drawn accurately

2 ABC is a triangle.
D is a point on AC.
AB = BD = DC

Angle x is 35°.

Show that angle $y = 70°$.

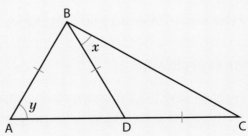

3 The diagram shows triangle ABC and triangle ABD.

AD = BC and angle DAB = angle ABC.

Prove that triangle ABC is congruent to triangle BAD.

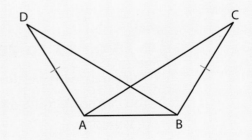

4 The diagram shows a circle with centre O.
B and C are points on the circumference of a circle.
AB and AC are tangents.

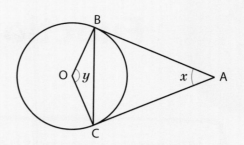

a Explain why triangle ABC is isosceles.

b Explain why triangle OBC is isosceles.

c Work out angle OBA and angle OCA.

d Show that angle $y = 140°$ when angle $x = 40°$.

e Prove that angle $x +$ angle y is always equal to 180°.

5 *2008 level 7*

Tom's height is 1.8 m. He stands near a tree.

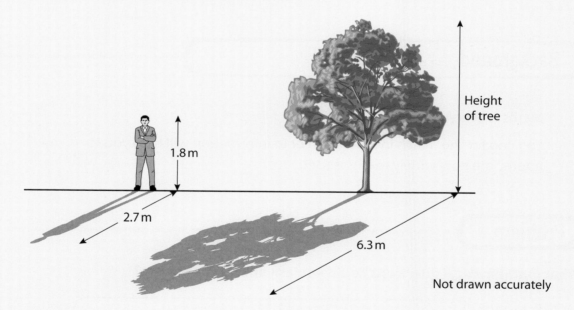

1.8 m

2.7 m

Height of tree

6.3 m

Not drawn accurately

At 4:00 pm, the length of Tom's shadow is 2.7 m.

At 4:00 pm, the length of the tree's shadow is 6.3 m.

What is the height of the tree?

Where is the mathematics?

This group activity will help you to:

- identify the mathematics in a situation;
- identify mathematical questions to ask;
- choose appropriate language and forms of presentation to communicate conclusions.

Background

Maths is everywhere.

Looking for the maths in a situation or in information will help you to appreciate how widely maths is used.

Problem 1

What mathematical questions could you ask about this picture?

What answers to your questions would you give?

Problem 2

What mathematical questions could you ask about this picture?

What answers to your questions would you give?

Problem 3

What mathematical questions could you ask about this picture?

What answers to your questions would you give?

Be prepared to discuss your questions and answers with other groups.

Linear graphs and inequalities

This unit will help you to:

- ⊙ sketch and draw linear graphs and their inverses;

- ⊙ use properties of linear graphs;

- ⊙ solve simultaneous linear equations;

- ⊙ solve linear inequalities.

1 Sketching and drawing linear graphs

 Did you know that...?

The French mathematician **Pierre de Fermat** (1601–1665), found graphical methods of looking at relationships between two variables.

His work was overshadowed by that of **Descartes**, with whom he argued over mathematical ideas for much of his life.

This lesson will help you to visualise and sketch the graph of a linear equation.

Exercise 1

The **normal form** of a linear equation is $y = ax + b$. Its graph is a straight line. a is the gradient of the line graph and $(0, b)$ the intercept on the y-axis.

Example 1

What is the gradient and intercept on the y-axis of $y = 2x + 3$?

The gradient of the graph is 2.
The intercept on the y-axis is (0, 3).

To **sketch** the graph, make a neat drawing and mark the origin and the intercept on the y-axis.

To **draw** the graph, work out three points from the equation. Use a ruler and pencil to draw a neat line through the three points.

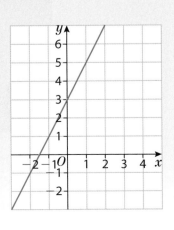

To work out the equation of a graph, find the gradient and the intercept on the y-axis.

Example 2

What is the equation of the graph?

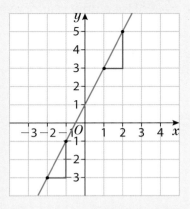

Work out the gradient of the graph by drawing right-angled triangles at any suitable points on the graph.

Gradient $a = \dfrac{\text{vertical distance}}{\text{horizontal distance}} = \dfrac{2}{1} = 2$

The intercept on the y-axis is (0, 1).

The equation of the graph is $y = 2x + 1$.

You will need graph paper.

1. Write the gradient and intercept for the graphs of these equations.
   Sketch the graphs, using a new grid for each graph.

   a $y = x + 10$ b $y = 2x - 5$ c $y = -x$

   d $y = 0.5x + 4$ e $y = -3x + 6$ f $y = -1.5x - 2.5$

2. Rearrange these equations into their normal form and write the gradient and intercept.
   Sketch the graphs, using a new grid for each graph.

   a $y - 3x = 4$ b $y + x = 2$ c $5x + y = 2$

   d $y - 3x + 8 = 0$ e $8 + 2y = 6x$ f $3y - 6x + 12 = 0$

3. Work out the equations of each of the graphs **a** to **e**.

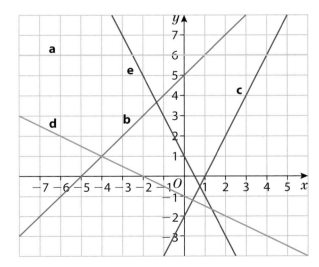

(4) On graph paper, draw an accurate graph of each equation.
Use a new pair of axes for each graph.

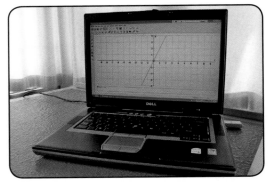

a $y = -x + 4$

b $y = x + 7$

c $y = -2x + 5$

d $y - 5x + 2 = 0$

e $3y - 15 = 12x$

f $3x + 5y = 6$

(5) The sum of two numbers x and y is 12.

a Write an equation to match this statement.

b Draw a graph to show the solutions of this equation.

c In this problem, x and y can only be positive whole numbers.
Give all the pairs of possible solutions.

Extension problem

(6) The difference between two numbers x and y is 4.

a Write two equations to match this statement.

b Explain why there are two equations that match the statement.

c Draw two graphs to show the solutions of this equation.

d In this problem, x and y can only be positive whole numbers less than 10.
Give all the pairs of possible solutions.

● Points to remember

⊙ The **normal form** of a linear equation is $y = ax + b$.

⊙ The graph of the equation $y = ax + b$ has **gradient** a and **intercept** on the y-axis at $(0, b)$.

⊙ When you **sketch** a linear graph, label the axes and mark the origin and the intercept on the y-axis.

⊙ To make an **accurate drawing** of a linear graph, calculate the coordinates of three points, plot them and draw a line through them using a ruler and sharp pencil.

2 Graphs of inverse functions

This lesson will help you to sketch and draw graphs of inverse functions.

Exercise 2

An **inverse function** does the reverse of the function.
It will use inverse operations to get you back to where you started.

Example 1

What is the inverse of $x + 7$?

The inverse of the function $x \rightarrow \boxed{+7} \rightarrow x + 7$ can be found by reversing the function.

$$x - 7 \leftarrow \boxed{-7} \leftarrow x$$

The inverse is $x - 7$.

Example 2

What is the inverse of $3x + 8$?

The inverse of the function $x \rightarrow \boxed{\times 3} \rightarrow \boxed{+8} \rightarrow 3x + 8$ can be found by reversing the function.

$$\frac{x - 8}{3} \leftarrow \boxed{\div 3} \leftarrow \boxed{-8} \leftarrow x$$

The inverse is $\dfrac{x - 8}{3}$.

The graph of the inverse of a function is a reflection in the line $y = x$.

Example 3

Draw the graph of the inverse of $y = 2x + 3$.

Draw the graph of $y = 2x + 3$.

Reflect the graph in the line $y = x$.

The equation of the graph of the inverse function is $y = \dfrac{x - 3}{2}$

or $y = 0.5x - 1.5$.

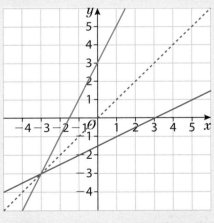

---

1   What's my number?

   a   I add 23 and get 68.   b   I subtract 19 and get 54.

   c   I multiply by 6 and get 174.   d   I divide by 8 and get 4.

   e   I subtract 20 and get −1.   f   I add −8 and get 39.

2 Match the functions **A** to **E** to their inverses **F** to **J**.

A $\quad x \rightarrow \boxed{+9} \rightarrow x + 9$

F $\quad x - 9 \leftarrow \boxed{-9} \leftarrow x$

B $\quad x \rightarrow \boxed{\times 34} \rightarrow 34x$

G $\quad x + 27 \leftarrow \boxed{+27} \leftarrow x$

C $\quad x \rightarrow \boxed{\div 12} \rightarrow \dfrac{x}{12}$

H $\quad 12x \leftarrow \boxed{\times 12} \leftarrow x$

D $\quad x \rightarrow \boxed{-27} \rightarrow x - 27$

I $\quad \dfrac{x}{34} \leftarrow \boxed{\div 34} \leftarrow x$

E $\quad x \rightarrow \boxed{\div 52} \rightarrow \dfrac{x}{52}$

J $\quad 52x \leftarrow \boxed{\times 52} \leftarrow x$

3 Sketch the graphs of the function and its inverse.
Use a different grid for each pair of graphs.
Label the lines with their equations.

a $\quad x \rightarrow \boxed{+5} \rightarrow x + 5$
b $\quad x \rightarrow \boxed{\times 2} \rightarrow 2x$
c $\quad x \rightarrow \boxed{\div 4} \rightarrow \dfrac{x}{4}$

d $\quad x \rightarrow \boxed{-1.5} \rightarrow x - 1.5$
e $\quad x \rightarrow \boxed{\times 8} \rightarrow 8x$
f $\quad x \rightarrow \boxed{\div 10} \rightarrow \dfrac{x}{10}$

4 What's my number?

a I add 2 and multiply by 3. I get 42.
b I multiply by 4 and add 29. I get 129.

c I divide by 4 and add 6. I get 26.
d I subtract 14 and divide by 6. I get 5.

5 Work out the inverse functions for these functions.

a $\quad x \rightarrow \boxed{\times 5} \rightarrow \boxed{+9} \rightarrow 5x + 9$
b $\quad x \rightarrow \boxed{+6} \rightarrow \boxed{\times 4} \rightarrow 4(x + 6)$

c $\quad x \rightarrow \boxed{-2} \rightarrow \boxed{\times 11} \rightarrow 11(x - 2)$
d $\quad x \rightarrow \boxed{+3} \rightarrow \boxed{\div 2} \rightarrow \dfrac{x + 3}{2}$

e $\quad x \rightarrow \boxed{-7} \rightarrow \boxed{\div 10} \rightarrow \dfrac{x - 7}{10}$
f $\quad x \rightarrow \boxed{\div 8} \rightarrow \boxed{-3} \rightarrow \dfrac{x}{8} - 3$

6 Match the functions **A** to **D** to their inverses **E** to **H**.

A $x \to \boxed{\times 5} \to \boxed{+9} \to 5x + 9$

E $\dfrac{x}{9} - 5 \leftarrow \boxed{-5} \leftarrow \boxed{\div 9} \leftarrow x$

B $x \to \boxed{+5} \to \boxed{\times 9} \to 9(x + 5)$

F $9x - 5 \leftarrow \boxed{-5} \leftarrow \boxed{\times 9} \leftarrow x$

C $x \to \boxed{+5} \to \boxed{\div 9} \to \dfrac{x + 5}{9}$

G $\dfrac{x - 9}{5} \leftarrow \boxed{\div 5} \leftarrow \boxed{-9} \leftarrow x$

D $x \to \boxed{-5} \to \boxed{\div 9} \to \dfrac{x - 5}{9}$

H $9x + 5 \leftarrow \boxed{+5} \leftarrow \boxed{\times 9} \leftarrow x$

7 Sketch the graphs of the function and its inverse.
Use a different grid for each pair of graphs.
Label each line with its equation.

a $x \to \boxed{\times 2} \to \boxed{+1} \to 2x + 1$

b $x \to \boxed{\times 0.5} \to \boxed{+3} \to 0.5x + 3$

c $x \to \boxed{\times 5} \to \boxed{-2} \to 5x - 2$

d $x \to \boxed{+2} \to \boxed{\times 3} \to 3(x + 2)$

e $x \to \boxed{-3} \to \boxed{\times 5} \to 5(x - 3)$

f $x \to \boxed{\div 2} \to \boxed{+7} \to \dfrac{x}{2} + 7$

Extension problem

8 Write the equation of each line after a reflection in $y = x$.

a $y = 6x - 2$

b $y = 9x + 3$

c $y = 2(x - 7)$

d $y = 3(x + 10)$

e $y = \dfrac{x}{2} + 14$

f $y = \dfrac{x - 6}{5}$

⦿ Points to remember

⊙ An **inverse function** does the reverse of a function.

⊙ When you **reflect** the graph of a function in the line $y = x$ you get the graph of the inverse function.

3 Properties of linear graphs

This lesson will help you to sketch and draw graphs of parallel and perpendicular lines.

Exercise 3

When a linear equation is written in its normal form:

$$y = ax + b$$

then a, the coefficient of x, is the gradient of its graph.

Any line **parallel** to the line $y = ax + b$ has a gradient of a.
Any line **perpendicular** to the line $y = ax + b$ has a gradient of $-\dfrac{1}{a}$.

For example, all the lines parallel to the red line have a gradient of 2.

All the lines perpendicular to the red line have gradient $-\dfrac{1}{2}$.

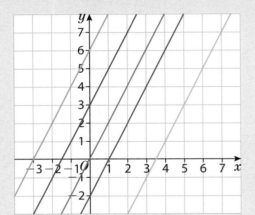
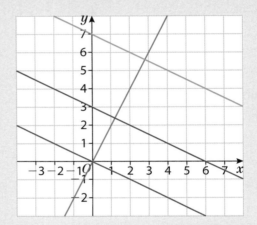

1. Work out the gradient of the line passing through the two given points.

   a (2, 3) and (4, 7)　　　　b (3, 1) and (4, 4)　　　　c (6, 4) and (8, 2)

   d (−4, 2) and (−2, 4)　　　e (1, −3) and (5, −2)　　　f (−3, 4) and (−2, −4)

2. a What is the gradient of the line $y = -5x + 2$?

   b A line is parallel to $y = 7x + 9$ and intersects the y-axis at (0, 21).
   What is its equation?

   c A line is parallel to $y = -3x + 5$ and intersects the y-axis at (0, 1).
   What is its equation?

   d A line is parallel to the line passing through (1, 2) and (3, 8) and
   intercepts the y-axis at (0, −2).
   What is its equation?

3 A line has equation $y = 4x - 3$.
What are the equations of the lines parallel to this line that pass through these points?

a (2, 10) b (1, 11) c (3, 7)

4 **a** What is the equation of the red line?

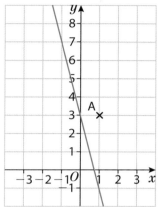

5 **a** What is the gradient of the blue line?

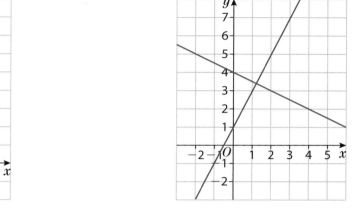

b What is the equation of the line parallel to the red line that passes through point A?

b What is the gradient of the green line?

c What is the angle between the blue and green lines?

6 For each question decide whether the lines AB and CD are parallel, perpendicular or neither.

a A (0, 3) B (1, 7) and C (1, 2) D (2, 6)

b A (−1, 5) B (2, 7) and C (1, 4) D (3, 7)

c A (−1, −2) B (1, 4) and C (0, 4) D (6, 2)

d A (0, −2) B (1, 3) and C (−5, 2) D (5, 0)

e A (0, 4) B (1, −2) and C (−1, 3) D (0, −3)

f A (0, 3) B (2, 7) and C (−4, 0) D (2, 3)

7 The points A (−3, −1), B (0, 8), C (3, 7) and D (0, −2) are the vertices of a quadrilateral.

a Prove that the quadrilateral is a parallelogram.

b Prove that the parallelogram is a rectangle.

Extension problems

8 The points W (0, 1), X (−2, 7), Y (4, 9) and Z (6, 3) are the vertices of a quadrilateral.

a Prove that the quadrilateral is a parallelogram.

b Prove that the quadrilateral is a rectangle.

c Prove that the quadrilateral is a square.

9 The points P (0, 4), Q (2, 8), R (4, 4) and S (2, 0) are the vertices of a quadrilateral.
Prove that the quadrilateral is a rhombus.

Points to remember

⊙ Graphs of **parallel** lines have the same gradient.

⊙ When the equation of a line is written in the form $y = ax + b$, the value
of a will be the same for any pair of parallel lines.

⊙ The gradient of a line **perpendicular** to $y = ax + b$ is $-\dfrac{1}{a}$.

⊙ The equation of any line perpendicular to $y = ax + b$ is $y = -\dfrac{1}{a}x + c$.

4 Solving simultaneous equations 1

This lesson will help you to solve pairs of equations graphically.

Exercise 4

Simultaneous means 'occurring at the same time'. To solve a pair of simultaneous
equations you need to find values of x and y that satisfy both equations at the same time.

You can do this be drawing the graphs of the equations and seeing where they intersect.

Example 1: one solution

Solve the simultaneous equations:

$2x + 3y = 13$ .... (1)

$3x + 2y = 12$ .... (2)

Draw graphs of the equations on the same grid.
The solution is where the two lines intersect, i.e. $x = 2$, $y = 3$.

Check the answer by substituting these values of x and y
back into the equations.

Example 2: no solution

Solve the simultaneous equations:

$2x + 3y = 2$ .... (1)

$2x + 3y = 6$ .... (2)

The graphs of these two equations are parallel.
They never intersect and so there is no solution.

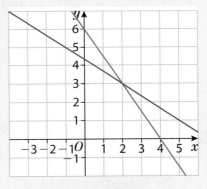

Example 3: infinite solutions

Solve the simultaneous equations:

$$x + 3y = 4 \dots\dots\dots\dots\dots (1)$$
$$4x + 12y = 16 \dots\dots\dots\dots (2)$$

The graphs of these two equations are identical.
There is an infinite number of solutions.

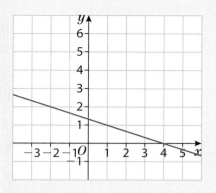

Example 4: using equations to solve problems

The sum of two numbers is 54 and their difference is 6.
What are the numbers?

Let one number be x and the other y.

$$x + y = 54$$
$$x - y = 6$$

From the graph, $x = 30$, $y = 24$.

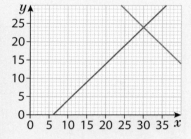

You will need a graph plotter or graphics calculator to draw graphs for this exercise.

1. Solve these pairs of simultaneous equations by drawing the graphs.
   Check your answers by substituting the values of x and y back into the equations.

   a $2x + 3y = 7 \dots\dots\dots (1)$
      $5x - 2y = 8 \dots\dots\dots (2)$

   b $5x - y = 1 \dots\dots\dots\dots (1)$
      $3x + y = 7 \dots\dots\dots\dots (2)$

   c $x + 4y = 15 \dots\dots\dots (1)$
      $5x + y = 18 \dots\dots\dots (2)$

   d $2x + 4y = 24 \dots\dots\dots (1)$
      $3x - 2y = 12 \dots\dots\dots (2)$

   e $2x + 5y = 24 \dots\dots\dots (1)$
      $3x - 8y = 5 \dots\dots\dots (2)$

   f $3x - 2y = 11 \dots\dots\dots (1)$
      $2x + y = 26 \dots\dots\dots (2)$

2. For each pair of equations say whether they have one solution, no solution or an infinite
   number of solutions. Check your answers by drawing the pairs of graphs.

   a $5x + 2y = 13 \dots\dots\dots (1)$
      $5x + 2y = 1 \dots\dots\dots (2)$

   b $4x + 3y = 10 \dots\dots\dots (1)$
      $3x + 6y = 15 \dots\dots\dots (2)$

   c $3x + 2y = 2 \dots\dots\dots (1)$
      $12x + 8y = 32 \dots\dots\dots (2)$

   d $2x - 3y = 2 \dots\dots\dots (1)$
      $10x - 15y = 10 \dots\dots\dots (2)$

   e $x + 3y = 2 \dots\dots\dots (1)$
      $2x + 6y = 6 \dots\dots\dots (2)$

   f $x - y = 3 \dots\dots\dots (1)$
      $5x - 5y = 17 \dots\dots\dots (2)$

   g $2x + 3y = 16 \dots\dots\dots (1)$
      $6x - 8y = 14 \dots\dots\dots (2)$

   h $4x + 6y = 24 \dots\dots\dots (1)$
      $6x + 9y = 36 \dots\dots\dots (2)$

③ For each problem set up two equations.
Draw their graphs and solve the problem.

a Bob and Hamish are buying tickets to take their families to a football match.

Bob buys 3 adult and 4 child tickets and pays £77.
Hamish buys 2 adult and 5 child tickets and pays £70.

Work out the price of:

i an adult's ticket

ii a child's ticket

b Shona and Pavla are taking their families to a fun park.

Shona buys 2 adult and 4 child tickets and pays £26.
Pavla buys 5 adult and 7 child tickets and pays £56.

Work out the cost of:

i an adult's ticket

ii a child's ticket

c Becky and Usha are buying drinks at a motorway café.

Becky buys 5 coffees and 3 teas for £17.
Usha buys 3 coffees and 5 teas for £15.

Work out the cost of:

i one tea

ii one coffee

d Karima and Fatima are at the market.

Karima buys 6 apples and 3 pears for £6.
Fatima buys 8 apples and 5 pears for £9.

Work out the cost of:

i one apple

ii one pear

e Tomasz and Nadia are buying CDs and DVDs.

Tomasz buys 4 CDs and 2 DVDs for £78.
Nadia buys 3 CDs and 5 DVDs for £111.

Work out the cost of:

  i   a DVD

  ii a CD

f Hussain and Nasir are buying vegetables.

Hussain buys 1 kg of carrots and 3 cabbages and pays £3.
Nasir buys 2 kg of carrots and 4 cabbages and pays £5.

Work out the cost of:

  i   1 kg of carrots

  ii one cabbage

Extension problem

 Solve these pairs of simultaneous equations by drawing the graphs.
Check your answers by substituting the values of x and y back into the equations.

a $4x + 2y = 2$ .... (1)
$3x + 4y = 9$ .... (2)

b $2x - 8y = 4$ .... (1)
$3x - 7y = 1$ .... (2)

c $5x + 9y = 7$ .... (1)
$4x - 3y = 26$ .... (2)

d $2x + 6y = 22$ .... (1)
$7x - 5y = 12$ .... (2)

e $4x - 5y = 5$ .... (1)
$6x - 7y = 6$ .... (2)

f $3x + 8y = 6$ .... (1)
$2x + 10y = 11$ .... (2)

◉ Points to remember

- ⊙ Two different non-parallel linear graphs intersect at one unique point.
- ⊙ Two linear equations are **simultaneously equal** at the point of intersection of their graphs.
- ⊙ Problems with two unknowns that are represented by two linear equations can be solved by finding the point of intersection of their graphs.
- ⊙ Two linear equations that are identical have an **infinite number of solutions**.
- ⊙ Two linear equations whose graphs are parallel have **no solutions**.

5 Solving simultaneous equations 2

This lesson will help you to solve simultaneous equations using the method of substitution or the method of elimination.

 Did you know that...?

Many practical problems can be solved using systems of linear equations.

Carl Friedrich Gauss (1777–1855) was a famous German mathematician who was a child prodigy. Gauss developed methods to solve simultaneous equations by a method of elimination. These methods are still used today, especially in economics.

Exercise 5

To solve a pair of simultaneous equations you need to find the values of the two variables that satisfy both equations.

You can solve the pair of equations by drawing graphs.
Two other methods are the **method of substitution** and the **method of elimination**.

To solve a pair of simultaneous equations using substitution:

- rearrange one equation to make one variable the subject;

- substitute for this variable in the other equation and solve it for the second variable;

- substitute this value in either equation to find the first variable.

Example 1: substitution

Solve the equations:

$$y - 2x = 2 \dots\dots\dots\dots\dots (1)$$
$$2y + 3x = 18 \dots\dots\dots\dots (2)$$

Rearrange equation (1)	$y = 2x + 2 \dots\dots\dots (3)$
Substitute y in equation (2)	$2(2x + 2) + 3x = 18$
Multiply out brackets	$4x + 4 + 3x = 18$
Simplify	$7x + 4 = 18$
Subtract 4	$7x = 14$
Divide by 7	$x = 2$
Substitute $x = 2$ in (3)	$y = 4 + 2 = 6$

Answer: $x = 2, y = 6$

To solve a pair of simultaneous equations using elimination, one of the variables needs to have the same coefficient in both equations. So:

- if the coefficients are not already the same, multiply every term in an equation by the same number to make the coefficients of one variable the same in both equations;

- subtract the equations and solve for the value of one variable;

- substitute this value in either equation to find the value of the other variable.

Example 2: elimination

Solve the equations:

$$2x + 7y = 29 \ldots\ldots\ldots (1)$$
$$2x + 5y = 23 \ldots\ldots\ldots (2)$$

Subtract (2) from (1) $\qquad 2y = 6$

Divide by 2 $\qquad y = 3$

Substitute $y = 3$ in (1) $\qquad 2x + 21 = 29$

Subtract 21 $\qquad 2x = 8$

Divide by 2 $\qquad x = 4$

Answer: $x = 4$, $y = 3$

Example 3: method of elimination

Solve the equations:

$$3x + 4y = 26 \ldots\ldots\ldots (1)$$
$$2x + 3y = 19 \ldots\ldots\ldots (2)$$

First multiply equations to get the coefficients of x the same.

Multiply (1) by 2 $\qquad 6x + 8y = 52 \ldots\ldots\ldots (3)$

Multiply (2) by 3 $\qquad 6x + 9y = 57 \ldots\ldots\ldots (4)$

Subtract (3) from (4) $\qquad y = 5$

Substitute $y = 5$ in (1) $\qquad 3x + 20 = 26$

Subtract 20 $\qquad 3x = 6$

Divide by 3 $\qquad x = 2$

Answer: $x = 2$, $y = 5$

---

1 Use **substitution** to solve these simultaneous linear equations.

a $y = 2x - 1 \ldots\ldots\ldots\ldots (1)$
$\quad 3x + 2y = 19 \ldots\ldots\ldots (2)$

b $x = 5y + 3 \ldots\ldots\ldots\ldots (1)$
$\quad 4x + 3y = 35 \ldots\ldots\ldots (2)$

c $y - x = 2 \ldots\ldots\ldots\ldots (1)$
$\quad 5x + 2y = 18 \ldots\ldots\ldots (2)$

d $x + 2y = 7 \ldots\ldots\ldots\ldots (1)$
$\quad 3x + 4y = 15 \ldots\ldots\ldots (2)$

e $2y = 4x - 4 \ldots\ldots\ldots (1)$
$\quad 5x - 2y = 7 \ldots\ldots\ldots (2)$

f $x - y = 1 \ldots\ldots\ldots\ldots (1)$
$\quad 3x + 2y = 8 \ldots\ldots\ldots (2)$

2 Use **elimination** to solve these simultaneous linear equations.

a $2x + 5y = 24$ .... (1)
   $2x + 3y = 16$ .... (2)

b $4x + 3y = 15$ .... (1)
   $x + 3y = 6$ .... (2)

c $4x + 5y = 13$ .... (1)
   $2x + 2y = 6$ .... (2)

d $3x + 9y = 21$ .... (1)
   $x + 2y = 4$ .... (2)

e $2x + y = 7$ .... (1)
   $4x + 3y = 18$ .... (2)

f $x + 2y = 11$ .... (1)
   $3x + y = 9$ .... (2)

3 For each problem set up two linear equations.
Solve them using substitution or elimination.
Use the solution to solve the problem.

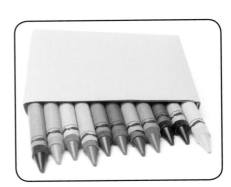

a 6 pencils and 4 crayons cost £4.
   5 pencils and 2 crayons cost £3.

   Work out the cost of:

   i   one pencil

   ii one crayon

b Ania and Jamal make up a puzzle to work out their ages in years.

   Three times Ania's age and twice Jamal's age is 40 years.
   Four times Ania's age and Jamal's age is 35 years.

   Work out their ages in years.

c 4 lemon fizz drinks and 2 orange juices cost £8.
   6 lemon fizz drinks and 8 orange juices cost £20.

   Work out the cost of:

   i   one lemon fizz

   ii one orange juice

d Rani collects £720 for 120 adult and 200 child tickets for the school fair.
   Mustafa collects £395 for 70 adult and 100 child tickets.

   Work out the cost of:

   i   one adult's ticket

   ii one child's ticket

e Safiya thinks of two numbers. She says:

'3 times the first number and 5 times the second number is 294.
6 times the first number and 7 times the second number is 453.'

What are Safiya's two numbers?

Extension problem

 4 Look at the pairs of simultaneous linear equations. Explain whether the method of substitution or elimination is most suitable for solving the equations. Give your reasons. Work out the solution.

a $9x + 5y = 108$ .... (1)
$9x + 3y = 90$ .... (2)

b $y = 7x - 13$ .... (1)
$x + 3y = 27$ .... (2)

c $2x + 3y = 27$ .... (1)
$12x + 7y = 107$ .... (2)

d $x - y = 7$ .... (1)
$17x + 11y = 203$ .... (2)

e $2x + 5y = 50$ .... (1)
$3x + 7y = 70$ .... (2)

f $x - 3y = 1$ .... (1)
$9x + 4y = 71$ .... (2)

⊙ Points to remember

- ⊙ You can use **substitution** to solve simultaneous equations in x and y:
  - rearrange one equation to make y the subject;
  - substitute for y in the second equation, which gives the value of x;
  - substitute the value for x into either equation to find the value for y.
- ⊙ You can use **elimination** to solve simultaneous equations in x and y:
  - when the coefficient of one variable is the same in both equations, subtract the equations, which will give the value of the other variable;
  - substitute this value into either equation to find the value of the first variable.
- ⊙ You can multiply every term in an equation by the same number to change the coefficients of the variables.

6 Solving linear inequalities

This lesson will help you to solve problems with a range of solutions.

Exercise 6

The statement $x = 3$ is an **equation**.
It tells you that the number x is exactly 3.

The statement $x < 3$ is an **inequality**.
The statement tells you that the number x is any number **less than** 3.
The statement can be shown using a number line.

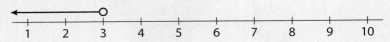

Here are some more inequalities:
$x > 3$: x is any number **greater than** 3.
$x \leqslant 3$: x is any number **less than or equal to** 3.
$x \geqslant 3$: x is any number **greater than or equal to** 3.

Example 1

List all the integers that satisfy the inequality $-4 < x \leqslant 2$.

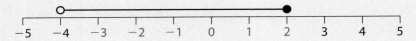

Integers are whole numbers. They can be positive or negative or zero.

So the integer values which satisfy the inequality $-4 < x \leqslant 2$ are $-3, -2, -1, 0, 1, 2$.

Example 2

Write this statement as an inequality.

'The speed limit for a vehicle driving at speed s through Little Brampton is 20 mph.'

Let a vehicle's speed be s. Then $0 \leqslant s \leqslant 20$.

Linear inequalities can be solved in a similar way to linear equations.
Remember that you need to do the same operation to each side of the inequality.

Example 3

Solve the linear inequality $3x - 5 \leqslant 7$.

Add 5 $3x \leqslant 12$
Divide by 3 $x \leqslant 4$

① Write the inequality shown on each number line:

a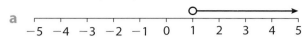

b

c
```
-5 -4 -3 -2 -1  0  1  2  3  4  5
```

d
```
-5 -4 -3 -2 -1  0  1  2  3  4  5
```

e
```
-5 -4 -3 -2 -1  0  1  2  3  4  5
```

f
```
-5 -4 -3 -2 -1  0  1  2  3  4  5
```

g
```
-5 -4 -3 -2 -1  0  1  2  3  4  5
```

h
```
-5 -4 -3 -2 -1  0  1  2  3  4  5
```

Answer questions 2, 3 and 4 on **A6.2 Resource sheet 6.1**.

② Show these inequalities on a number line.

a $x > 1$ b $x < 4$ c $x \geqslant 0$ d $x \leqslant -1$

③ Show on a number line the values of x which satisfy both:

a $x > 1$ and $x < 5$ b $x > -2$ and $x \leqslant 0$ c $x \geqslant -3$ and $x \leqslant -2$

④ Show these inequalities on a number line.

a $-2 < x \leqslant 4$ b $-3 \leqslant x < 0$ c $-5 < x \leqslant -2$

⑤ List all the integers that satisfy these inequalities.

a $0 \leqslant x < 7$ b $14 < x < 19$ c $72 \leqslant x \leqslant 76$

d $-2 \leqslant x \leqslant 2$ e $-1 < x \leqslant 4$ f $-10 < x < -5$

⑥ Write an inequality to describe the information in each statement.

a An apple's weight w is at least 60 g and less than 90 g.

b The speed s on a racing track is a maximum of 130 km per hour and a minimum of 60 km per hour.

c The amount A that Keri can spend on food each week is a maximum of £80.

d The weight w of a healthy baby at birth is usually between 2.5 kg and 4.5 kg.

e The amount P that Henry spends on his friends' presents is no more than £20 and no less than £5.

7 Solve these inequalities.

a $5x - 15 \leqslant 25$ b $4x + 3 < 43$ c $2x - 5 > 3$

d $3x + 9 \geqslant 15$ e $2(3x - 4) \leqslant 10$ f $5(2x + 3) > 25$

g $7(2x - 4) \geqslant 42$ h $3(8x - 30) \leqslant 390$ i $5(7x + 15) < 460$

Extension problems

8 A rectangular lawn has width $(x + 6)$ metres
and length $(2x - 1)$ metres.
The perimeter of the lawn is no more than 70 metres.

Find the greatest possible area of the lawn.

9 Solve these inequalities.

a $10x - 9 > 9x - 6$

b $7x - 3 \leqslant 5x + 11$

c $12x - 8 < 7x + 17$

d $8x + 9 \geqslant 6x + 17$

e $3(2x - 6) \leqslant 4x + 2$

f $5(3x - 7) > 2(3x + 5)$

⊙ Points to remember

⊙ A statement using one of the four symbols $<$, $>$, $\leqslant$ or $\geqslant$
  is an **inequality**.

⊙ $x < 3$ means that x is any number that is **less than** 3.
  $x > 5$ means that x is any number that is **greater than** 5.
  $x \leqslant 10$ means that x is any number that is **less than or equal to** 10.
  $x \geqslant 0$ means that x is any number that is **greater than or equal to** zero.

⊙ Solutions of linear inequalities can be shown on a number line, e.g.

$x < 3$

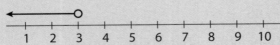

$x \geqslant 5$

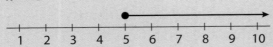

How well are you doing?

Can you:

- sketch and draw linear graphs and their inverses?
- use properties of linear graphs?
- solve simultaneous linear equations?
- solve linear inequalities?

(1) *2005 level 7*

Solve these simultaneous equations using an algebraic method.

$$4x + 3y = 21$$
$$2x + y = 8$$

You must show your working.

(2) *2003 Mental Test level 7*

Look at this inequality: $2 \leqslant x \leqslant 8$.
How many integer solutions are there?

(3) *2001 level 7*

Here are six different equations, labelled A to F.

A	$y = 3x - 4$		B	$y = 4$		C	$x = -5$

D	$x + y = 10$		E	$y = 2x + 1$		F	$y = x^2$

Think about the graphs of these equations.

a Which graph goes through the point (0, 0)?

b Which graph is parallel to the y-axis?

c Which graph is not a straight line?

d Which two graphs pass through the point (3, 7)?

4 *1999 level 7*

Look at this graph:

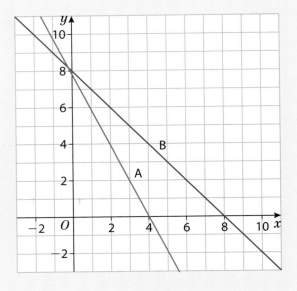

a Show that the equation of line A is $2x + y = 8$.

b Write the equation of line B.

c On graph paper, draw the line whose equation is $y = 2x + 1$.

d Solve these simultaneous equations.

$$y = 2x + 1$$
$$3y = 4x + 6$$

Show your working.

5 *2003 level 7*

Solve this inequality. Show your working.

$$\frac{4(7 - 2y)}{12} > 1$$

Trigonometry 1

This unit will help you to:

- ⊙ understand and use Pythagoras' theorem;
- ⊙ understand the ratios tangent, sine and cosine;
- ⊙ use these functions on a calculator;
- ⊙ use the ratios to calculate lengths in right-angled triangles.

1 Pythagoras' theorem

This lesson will help you to understand and use Pythagoras' theorem.

Exercise 1

The **hypotenuse** of a right-angled triangle is the side opposite the right angle. It is the longest side of the triangle.

In this diagram, c is the hypotenuse.

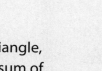

Pythagoras' theorem proves that, in any right-angled triangle, the area of the square on the hypotenuse is equal to the sum of the areas of the squares on the other two sides.

a^2 = area of pink square
b^2 = area of yellow square
c^2 = area of blue square

So $a^2 + b^2 = c^2$

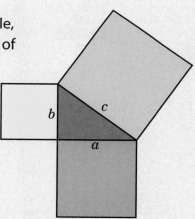

A **Pythagorean triple** is a set of three integers that satisfy Pythagoras' theorem, e.g.

 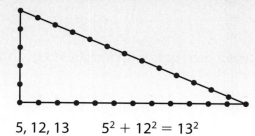

3, 4, 5 $3^2 + 4^2 = 5^2$ 5, 12, 13 $5^2 + 12^2 = 13^2$

Pythagoras' theorem can be used to check whether a triangle is right angled or not.

Example

Does a triangle with side lengths 12.5 cm, 30 cm and 32.5 cm have a right angle?

$a^2 = 12.5^2 = 156.25$ cm^2 and $b^2 = 30^2 = 900$ cm^2

$a^2 + b^2 = 156.25 + 900 = 1056.25$ cm^2

$c^2 = 32.5^2 = 1056.25$ cm^2

So $a^2 + b^2 = c^2$ and the triangle has a right angle.

(1) Work out the length of each side marked with a letter in these triangles.
Give your answers to one decimal place.

a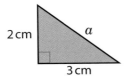

b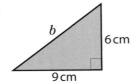

c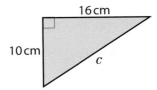

(2) Work out the length of each side marked with a letter in these triangles.
Give your answers to one decimal place.

a

b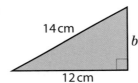

c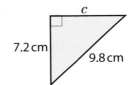

(3) a Calculate x in the right-angled triangle on the right.

Calculate the area of the triangle.

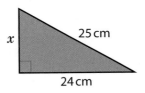

b Calculate y in the right-angled triangle on the right.

Calculate the area of the triangle.

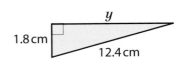

(4) The diagram shows a rectangle with length 12 cm and width 6 cm.

Show that the diagonal of the rectangle is $\sqrt{180}$ cm.

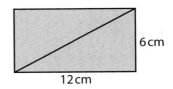

(5) Show that each of these triangles has a right angle at B.

a
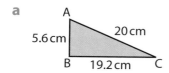

b
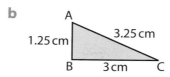

(6) Which of these triangles is the odd one out?
Explain why.

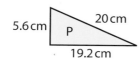
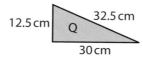
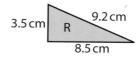

(7) How many of these triangles have a right angle?

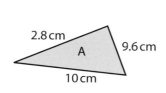
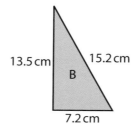
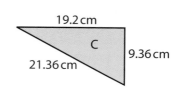

Extension problems

 Did you know that...?

Pythagoras of Samos lived in the 6th century BC. Little is known about him because none of his writing has survived. Many of the discoveries credited to Pythagoras may actually have been achievements of his colleagues and successors.

However, Pythagoras is regarded as a great mystic, mathematician and scientist. He is best known for his theorem but he was also known as 'the father of numbers'. He and his students believed that, through mathematics, everything could be predicted and measured in rhythmic patterns or cycles.

This statue in memory of Pythagoras and his theorem was built in Samos in 1989 by Nikolaos Ikaris.

8 Explain how these diagrams **prove** Pythagoras' theorem.

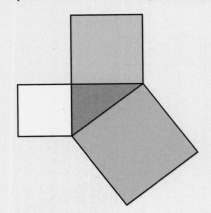 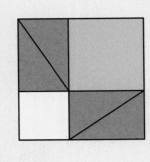 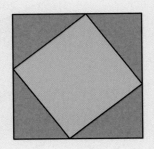

 9 A **Pythagorean triple** gives the sides a, b and c of a right-angled triangle, where a, b and c are integers. The table shows the basic Pythagorean triples with lengths less than 100.

3, 4, 5	5, 12, 13	7, 24, 25	8, 15, 17
9, 40, 41	11, 60, 61	12, 35, 37	13, 84, 85
16, 63, 65	20, 21, 29	28, 45, 53	33, 56, 65
36, 77, 85	39, 80, 89	48, 55, 73	65, 72, 97

Four triangles have been highlighted blue at random. For each of these triangles show that:

a the product of the two shorter sides is always a multiple of 12;

b the area of the triangle is always a multiple of 6;

c the product of all three sides is always a multiple of 60.

◉ Points to remember

⊙ In a right-angled triangle, the **hypotenuse** is opposite the right angle and is the longest side.

⊙ **Pythagoras' theorem** shows that in a right-angled triangle the area of the square on the hypotenuse is equal to the sum of the areas of the squares on the other two sides, or $a^2 + b^2 = c^2$.

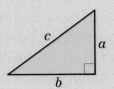

⊙ **Pythagorean triples** are sets of three integers that satisfy the relationship $a^2 + b^2 = c^2$: for example, 3, 4, 5 or 5, 12, 13.

⊙ You can use Pythagoras' theorem to check whether a triangle has a right angle or not.

2 Introducing trigonometry

This lesson will introduce you to a new branch of mathematics called trigonometry. This will help you to work out the lengths of sides and the sizes of angles in right-angled triangles.

Exercise 2

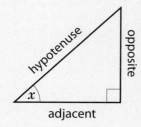

Trigonometry is a branch of mathematics that includes calculating the lengths of sides and sizes of angles in right-angled triangles.

In a right-angled triangle:

- the **hypotenuse** is the longest side and is opposite the right angle;
- the side opposite the angle marked is the **opposite** side;
- the side next to the angle marked is the **adjacent** side.

You will need a protractor, ruler and pencil and a calculator.

 a Choose one of these angles: 20°, 30°, 45°, 60° or 70°.
Pick a different angle from the people sitting next to you.

b Make a copy of this table in your book. Three of the columns are blank.

Triangle	Length (cm)					
	Hypotenuse	Opposite	Adjacent			
1						
2						
3						
4						
5						
6						

c Draw six right-angled triangles of different sizes, each with one angle of the size you picked in part **a**.

d Label the sides of each of your six triangles: hypotenuse, opposite and adjacent.

e Measure the lengths of the three sides in each of your six triangles. Enter the data in your table.

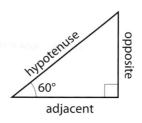

(2) Use the table that you started in question 1. Add these headings to the last three columns:

$$\frac{\text{opposite}}{\text{adjacent}} \qquad \frac{\text{opposite}}{\text{hypotenuse}} \qquad \frac{\text{adjacent}}{\text{hypotenuse}}$$

Use a calculator to work out the ratios of the sides.
Enter the answers to 2 decimal places in your table.

What do you notice?

 Points to remember

- The **hypotenuse** is the side opposite the right angle.
- The **opposite side** is opposite the marked angle.
- The **adjacent side** is between the marked angle and the right angle.

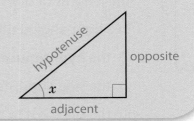

3 Using the tangent ratio

This lesson will help you to use the tangent ratio to find a missing length in a right-angled triangle.

(i) **Did you know that...?**

The word trigonometry means 'triangle measurement'. The Ancient Greeks are known to have studied trigonometry, which they used in astronomy.

Since early times, engineers, surveyors, navigators and astronomers have used triangles to work out distances that could not be measured directly.

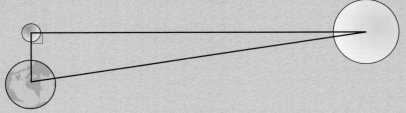

Aristarchus of Samos (c. 320–250 BC) was a Greek mathematician and astronomer. He concluded that the Sun was the centre of the universe and he used the properties of triangles to calculate the distance from the Earth to the Moon and to the Sun.

He calculated that the Sun was about 20 times as distant from the Earth as the Moon, and 20 times the Moon's size. Both these estimates were too small, but the fault was in Aristarchus's lack of accurate instruments to measure angles, not his method of reasoning.

The Aristarchus crater on the Moon was named in his honour.

Exercise 3

The **trigonometric ratios** depend only on the size of the angle.
The ratios are the same for all similar triangles.

$$\sin x = \frac{\text{opposite}}{\text{hypotenuse}} \qquad \cos x = \frac{\text{adjacent}}{\text{hypotenuse}} \qquad \tan x = \frac{\text{opposite}}{\text{adjacent}}$$

SOH   **CAH**   **TOA**

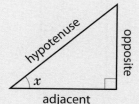

You can use a calculator to work out these ratios for a given angle.

Remember to check that your calculator is in degree mode first.
You should see D or DEG in the display.

To find the value of the tangent of an angle, use the (**tan**) key.

On some calculators, you press the tan key then key in the size of the angle: (**tan**)(**2**)(**5**)

On others, you key in the size of the angle before you press the tan key: (**2**)(**5**)(**tan**)

In either case the display should show   0.466307658 .
This is 0.466 to 3 decimal places.

You can find the sine or cosine of an angle in a similar way.

You can use the ratios to find the length of a missing side of a right-angled triangle.
These are the steps to take.

⊙ Sketch the triangle. Mark the right angle and any other angle that you know.

⊙ Label the sides hypotenuse, opposite and adjacent.

⊙ Write down the formula for the ratio you will use, e.g. $\tan = \dfrac{\text{opposite}}{\text{adjacent}}$

⊙ Substitute the values you know into the formula.

⊙ Use your calculator to solve the equation.

⊙ Remember to include the correct units for your answer.

Example 1

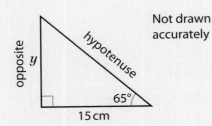

Not drawn accurately

15 cm

Work out the value of y.

$$\tan = \frac{\text{opposite}}{\text{adjacent}}$$

$$\tan 65° = \frac{y}{15}$$

$$2.144 = \frac{y}{15}$$

$$y = 32.2 \text{ cm (to 1 decimal place)}$$

Example 2

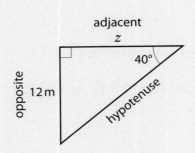

Work out the value of z.

$$\tan = \frac{\text{opposite}}{\text{adjacent}}$$

$$\tan 40° = \frac{12}{z}$$

$$0.839 = \frac{12}{z}$$

$$z = \frac{12}{0.839} = 14.3 \text{ m (to 1 decimal place)}$$

You will need a scientific calculator. Write all your answers to two decimal places.

1. Write the tangent of these angles.

   a 25°   b 37°   c 68°   d 81°   e 85°

2. Write the sine of these angles.

   a 63°   b 46°   c 8°   d 53°   e 30°

3. Write the cosine of these angles.

   a 54°   b 71°   c 33°   d 11°   e 60°

4. Use your calculator to work these out in one sequence.
   Write your answers to one decimal place.

   a 15 tan 24°   b 12.8 sin 71°   c 14.6 cos 43°

   d $\dfrac{7}{\tan 36°}$ e $\dfrac{12.5}{\sin 52°}$ f $\dfrac{22.8}{\cos 47°}$

5 Use the tangent ratio to work out the lengths of the sides marked with letters.
You will need to sketch the triangles. They are not drawn accurately.
Remember to show your working.

a
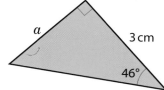

b
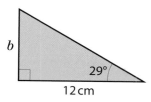

c
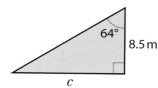

d
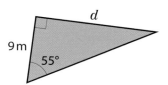

e
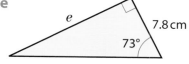

f
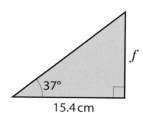

6 Use the tangent ratio to work out the lengths of the sides marked with letters.
You will need to sketch the triangles. They are not drawn accurately.
Remember to show your working.

a
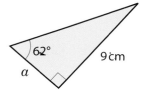

b
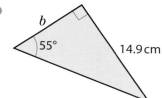

c
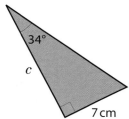

d
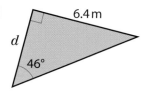

e
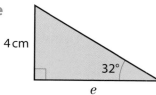

f
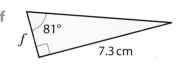

> **● Points to remember**
>
> ⊙ Use the **tangent** ratio to find unknown lengths of shorter sides in right-angled triangles.
>
> ⊙ $\tan x = \dfrac{\text{opposite}}{\text{adjacent}}$

4 Using sine and cosine ratios

This lesson will help you to use the sine and cosine ratios to find unknown lengths in right-angled triangles.

Exercise 4

$$\sin x = \frac{\text{opposite}}{\text{hypotenuse}} \qquad \cos x = \frac{\text{adjacent}}{\text{hypotenuse}} \qquad \tan x = \frac{\text{opposite}}{\text{adjacent}}$$

$$\textbf{SOH} \qquad\qquad\qquad \textbf{CAH} \qquad\qquad\qquad \textbf{TOA}$$

You can use the **cosine** and **sine** ratios to find lengths in triangles in a similar way as you did using the tangent ratio.

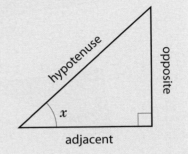

Example 1

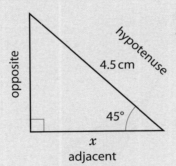

Not drawn accurately

Work out the value of x.

$$\cos = \frac{\text{adjacent}}{\text{hypotenuse}}$$

$$\cos 45° = \frac{x}{4.5}$$

$$0.707 = \frac{x}{4.5}$$

$$x = 3.2 \text{ cm (to 1 decimal place)}$$

Example 2

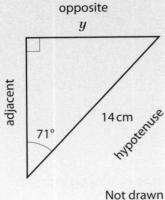

Not drawn accurately

Work out the value of y.

$$\sin = \frac{\text{opposite}}{\text{hypotenuse}}$$

$$\sin 71° = \frac{y}{14}$$

$$0.946 = \frac{y}{14}$$

$$y = 13.2 \text{ cm (to 1 decimal place)}$$

Example 3

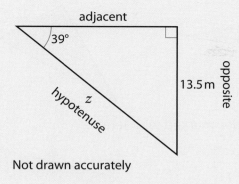

adjacent

39°

hypotenuse
z

13.5 m
opposite

Not drawn accurately

Work out the value of z.

$$\sin = \frac{\text{opposite}}{\text{hypotenuse}}$$

$$\sin 39° = \frac{13.5}{z}$$

$$z = \frac{13.5}{0.629} = 21.5 \text{ m (to 1 decimal place)}$$

You will need a scientific calculator. Write all your answers to two decimal places.

Sketch the triangles, which are not drawn accurately. Remember to show your working.

1 Use the cosine ratio to work out the lengths of the sides marked with letters.

a
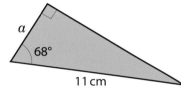
a
68°
11 cm

b
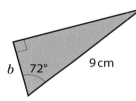
b 72°
9 cm

c
6 cm
31°
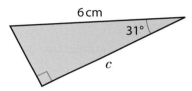
c

d
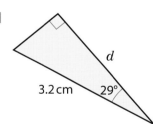
d
3.2 cm 29°

e
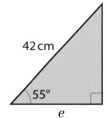
42 cm
55°
e

f
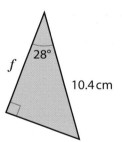
28°
f
10.4 cm

2 Use the sine ratio to work out the lengths of the sides marked with letters.

a
11 cm
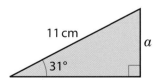
a
31°

b
b
4.8 cm
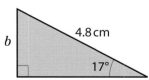
17°

c
c
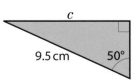
9.5 cm 50°

d
62°
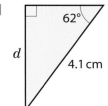
d
4.1 cm

e
20 cm
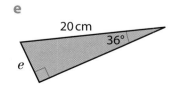
36°
e

f
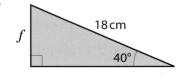
18 cm
f
40°

3 Use the cosine ratio to work out the lengths of the sides marked with letters.

a
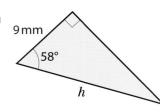
9 mm
58°
h

b
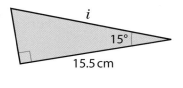
i
15°
15.5 cm

c
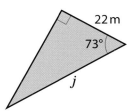
22 m
73°
j

4 Use the sine ratio to work out the lengths of the sides marked with letters.

a
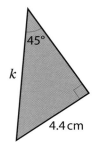
45°
k
4.4 cm

b
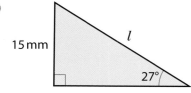
15 mm
l
27°

c
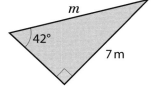
m
42°
7 m

Extension problems

5 In these problems you will need to decide which trigonometric ratio to use.

a Calculate the length of BC.

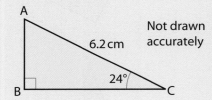
A
6.2 cm
Not drawn accurately
24°
B   C

b Calculate the length of AB.

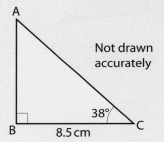
A
Not drawn accurately
38°
B   8.5 cm   C

6 A helicopter takes off from a heliport.
It flies for 82 km on a bearing of 075°.

a How far east has the helicopter flown?

b How far north has it flown?

Points to remember

⊙ Use the **sine**, **cosine** and **tangent** ratios to find unknown lengths in right-angled triangles.

⊙ Choose the right ratio to use to solve each problem.

$$\sin x = \frac{\text{opposite}}{\text{hypotenuse}} \qquad \cos x = \frac{\text{adjacent}}{\text{hypotenuse}} \qquad \tan x = \frac{\text{opposite}}{\text{adjacent}}$$

How well are you doing?

Can you:

- use Pythagoras' theorem and the trigonometric ratios to calculate lengths in right-angled triangles?
- use the sine, cosine and tangent functions on a calculator?

You will need a scientific calculator.
Write your answers to two decimal places. Remember to show your working.

The diagrams in these questions are not drawn accurately.
In each question, make a sketch of the diagram.

$$\sin x = \frac{\text{opposite}}{\text{hypotenuse}} \qquad \cos x = \frac{\text{adjacent}}{\text{hypotenuse}} \qquad \tan x = \frac{\text{opposite}}{\text{adjacent}}$$

1. Calculate the area of this triangle.

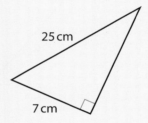

2. Use the sine ratio to find the length of side a.

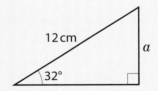

3. Use the cosine ratio to find the length of side b.

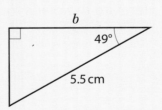

4. Use the tangent ratio to find the length of side c.

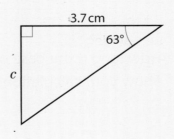

a In which triangle below does $a^2 + b^2 = c^2$?

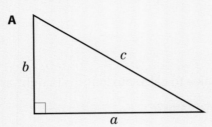

For the **other** triangle, write an equation linking a, b and c.

b In which triangle below does $a^2 + b^2 = c^2$?

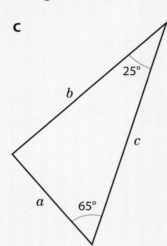 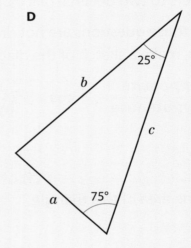

Not drawn accurately

For the **other** triangle, explain why $a^2 + b^2$ does not equal c^2.

⑥ *1997 level 7*

Here are the plans for a ramp:

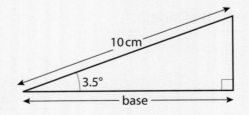

Not drawn accurately

How long is the base of this ramp?
Show your calculations.

Expressions, equations and graphs

This unit will help you to:

- solve pairs of simultaneous equations;
- expand brackets;
- factorise quadratic expressions;
- use identities;
- solve quadratic equations using graphs;
- investigate sequences.

1 Simultaneous equations 1

Did you know that...?

One of the earliest surviving mathematical texts is *The Nine Chapters on the Mathematical Art*, which was written by generations of Chinese scholars from the 10th to the 1st century BC. The book centres on general methods of solving problems. Chapter 8 is about the method of solving linear equations by elimination, illustrated in 18 different problems.

This lesson will remind you how to solve simultaneous equations using graphical, substitution and elimination methods.

Exercise 1

To solve a pair of simultaneous equations you need to find the values of the two variables that satisfy both equations.

The solution is at the point of intersection of their graphs.
For example:

$$2x + 3y = 13 \dots\dots\dots\dots (1)$$
$$3x + 2y = 12 \dots\dots\dots\dots (2)$$

Solution: $x = 2, y = 3$

If the graphs are **parallel**, there are **no solutions**.

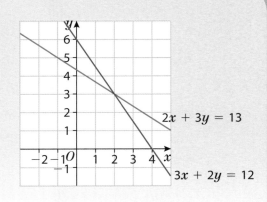

You can solve pairs of simultaneous equations using the **method of substitution**.

Example 1

Solve the equations:

$$y - 2x = 2 \dots\dots\dots\dots (1)$$
$$2y + 3x = 18 \dots\dots\dots\dots (2)$$

Rearrange equation (1)	$y = 2x + 2 \dots\dots\dots (3)$
Substitute y in equation (2)	$2(2x + 2) + 3x = 18$
Multiply out brackets	$4x + 4 + 3x = 18$
Simplify	$7x + 4 = 18$
Subtract 4	$7x = 14$
Divide by 7	$x = 2$
Substitute $x = 2$ in (3)	$y = 4 + 2 = 6$

Answer: $x = 2, y = 6$

You can solve pairs of simultaneous equations using the **method of elimination**.

Example 2

Solve the equations

$$3x + 4y = 26 \dots\dots\dots\dots (1)$$
$$2x + 3y = 19 \dots\dots\dots\dots (2)$$

First multiply equations to get the coefficients of x the same, then eliminate x.

Multiply (1) by 2	$6x + 8y = 52 \dots\dots\dots\dots (3)$
Multiply (2) by 3	$6x + 9y = 57 \dots\dots\dots\dots (4)$
Subtract (3) from (4)	$y = 5$
Substitute $y = 5$ in (1)	$3x + 20 = 26$
Subtract 20	$3x = 6$
Divide by 3	$x = 2$

Answer: $x = 2, y = 5$

You will need a graph plotter or graphics calculator for this exercise.

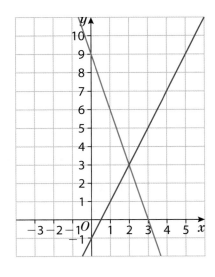

1 a What is the equation of the purple graph?

   b What is the equation of the red graph?

   c What is the value of (x, y) where the lines intersect?

   d Explain what you know about the values of x and y at the point of intersection.

2 For each pair of equations say whether they have one solution for x and y or no solution.
Check your answers by drawing the pairs of graphs on a computer or graphics calculator.

    a $11x + 6y = 20$ .... (1)
        $11x + 6y = -7$ .... (2)

    b $18x - 4y = 9$ .... (1)
        $9x - 2y = 7$ .... (2)

    c $8x + y = 15$ .... (1)
        $3x + 2y = 17$ .... (2)

    d $7x - y = 10$ .... (1)
        $8x - 3y = 4$ .... (2)

    e $6x + 7y = 5$ .... (1)
        $-12x - 14y = -10$ .... (2)

    f $2x + y = 13$ .... (1)
        $x - 2y = 4$ .... (2)

3 Use substitution to solve these pairs of simultaneous equations.
Check your answers by drawing the pairs of graphs on a computer or graphics calculator.

    a $3x + y = 4$ .... (1)
        $2x + 3y = 5$ .... (2)

    b $x + 5y = 20$ .... (1)
        $3x + 4y = 27$ .... (2)

4 Use elimination to solve these pairs of simultaneous equations.
Check your answers by drawing the pairs of graphs on a computer or graphics calculator.

    a $7x + 2y = 12$ .... (1)
        $5x + 2y = 16$ .... (2)

    b $4x + 5y = 22$ .... (1)
        $4x + 3y = 18$ .... (2)

    c $3x + 2y = 16$ .... (1)
        $9x + 5y = 43$ .... (2)

    d $5x + 2y = 11$ .... (1)
        $9x + 5y = 17$ .... (2)

5 For each problem set up two equations and solve the problem.

    a Darren and Jan go to the farm shop.

        Darren buys 3 turnips and 5 cabbages for £7.
        Jan buys 4 turnips and 2 cabbages for £7.

        Work out the price of:

        i one turnip   **ii** one cabbage

    b Basmina and Faruq meet their friends at a café.

        Basima buys 5 teas and 4 coffees for £8.80.
        Faruq buys 3 teas and 7 coffees for £10.80.

        Work out the cost of:

        i one tea   **ii** one coffee

Extension problem

 6 Solve these pairs of simultaneous equations.
Check your answers by drawing the pairs of graphs on a computer or graphics calculator.

a $5x = 16 - 2y$ .... (1)
$2x + y = 7$ .... (2)

b $8x + 3y = 10$ .... (1)
$10x = 7 - y$ .... (2)

c $6x = 9 - 5y$ .... (1)
$5x + 4y = 7$ .... (2)

d $6x + 5y = 26$ .... (1)
$2x = 8 - 1.5y$ .... (2)

Points to remember

- A pair of **simultaneous linear equations** has a solution at the point where their graphs intersect.
- A pair of equations whose graphs are parallel has no solution.
- When one variable is given in terms of the other you can use the **method of substitution** to solve the equations.
- When one variable is not given in terms of the other you can use the **method of elimination** to solve the equations.
- Multiply every term in an equation by the same number to change the coefficients of the variables.

2 Simultaneous equations 2

This lesson will help you to solve simultaneous equations using the method of elimination.

Exercise 2

You can solve pairs of simultaneous equations using the **method of elimination**.

Example 1: coefficients of y have different signs

Solve the equations

$$3x + 2y = 23 .... (1)$$
$$5x - 2y = 17 .... (2)$$

Eliminate y by addition.

Add (1) + (2)	$8x = 40$
Divide by 8	$x = 5$
Substitute $x = 5$ in (1)	$15 + 2y = 23$
Subtract 15	$2y = 8$
Divide by 2	$y = 4$

Answer: $x = 5, y = 4$

Example 2: coefficients of y have the same signs

Solve the equations

$$5x - 3y = 11 \ldots\ldots\ldots\ldots (1)$$
$$3x - 3y = 3 \ldots\ldots\ldots\ldots (2)$$

Eliminate y by subtraction.

Subtract (2) from (1)	$2x = 8$
Divide by 2	$x = 4$
Substitute $x = 4$ in (1)	$20 - 3y = 11$
Subtract 20	$-3y = -9$
Divide by -3	$y = 3$

Answer: $x = 4$, $y = 3$

You will need a graph plotter or graphics calculator for this exercise.

1 Solve these pairs of simultaneous linear equations using the method of elimination.
Check your answers by drawing the pairs of graphs on a computer or graphics calculator.

a $3x + 5y = 22 \ldots\ldots\ldots\ldots (1)$
$7x - 5y = 18 \ldots\ldots\ldots\ldots (2)$

b $4x - 3y = 9 \ldots\ldots\ldots\ldots (1)$
$5x + 3y = 18 \ldots\ldots\ldots\ldots (2)$

c $3x + 2y = 21 \ldots\ldots\ldots\ldots (1)$
$5x - 4y = 13 \ldots\ldots\ldots\ldots (2)$

d $8x + 3y = 50 \ldots\ldots\ldots\ldots (1)$
$-2x + 5y = -24 \ldots\ldots\ldots\ldots (2)$

2 Solve these pairs of simultaneous linear equations using the method of elimination.
Check your answers by drawing the pairs of graphs on a computer or graphics calculator.

a $7x - 2y = 20 \ldots\ldots\ldots\ldots (1)$
$5x - 2y = 8 \ldots\ldots\ldots\ldots (2)$

b $13x - 3y = 8 \ldots\ldots\ldots\ldots (1)$
$10x - 3y = 2 \ldots\ldots\ldots\ldots (2)$

c $7x - 4y = 44 \ldots\ldots\ldots\ldots (1)$
$3x - 2y = 20 \ldots\ldots\ldots\ldots (2)$

d $3x - 4y = 18 \ldots\ldots\ldots\ldots (1)$
$5x - 3y = 19 \ldots\ldots\ldots\ldots (2)$

3 Solve these pairs of simultaneous linear equations using the method of elimination.
Check your answers by drawing the pairs of graphs on a computer or graphics calculator.

a $2x + 6y = 10 \ldots\ldots\ldots\ldots (1)$
$3x + 5y = 13 \ldots\ldots\ldots\ldots (2)$

b $7x + 3y = 2 \ldots\ldots\ldots\ldots (1)$
$5x - 3y = 22 \ldots\ldots\ldots\ldots (2)$

c $8x - 3y = 18 \ldots\ldots\ldots\ldots (1)$
$10x - 3y = 24 \ldots\ldots\ldots\ldots (2)$

d $2x - 5y = 13 \ldots\ldots\ldots\ldots (1)$
$3x - 10y = 17 \ldots\ldots\ldots\ldots (2)$

e $9x + 5y = 34 \ldots\ldots\ldots\ldots (1)$
$3x - 4y = 34 \ldots\ldots\ldots\ldots (2)$

f $7x + 5y = 19 \ldots\ldots\ldots\ldots (1)$
$14x + 9y = 37 \ldots\ldots\ldots\ldots (2)$

g $4x + 2y = 23 \ldots\ldots\ldots\ldots (1)$
$3x - 5y = 1 \ldots\ldots\ldots\ldots (2)$

h $7x - 8y = 82 \ldots\ldots\ldots\ldots (1)$
$3x - 4y = 38 \ldots\ldots\ldots\ldots (2)$

4   For each problem set up two equations.
    Draw their graphs on a computer or graphics calculator and solve the problem.

    a   The sum of two numbers is 74.
        Their difference is 12.

        What are the two numbers?

    b   In 10 years' time, Amber's mum will be
        twice as old as Amber.
        In 20 years' time, the sum of their ages will be 86.

        How old is Amber now?

Extension problems

5   Solve these pairs of simultaneous linear equations.

    a $3x = 12 - 2y$ .... (1)   b $5x = 62 - 3y$ .... (1)
        $3y = 5x - 1$ .... (2) $5y = 7x - 4$ .... (2)

    c $4x = 5y + 10$ .... (1)   d $13 + 2y = 9x$ .... (1)
        $8y = 7x - 19$ .... (2) $5x + 27 = 6y$ .... (2)

    e $2x = 41 - 11y$ .... (1)   f $15x = 3 + 2y$ .... (1)
        $2y = 11x - 38$ .... (2) $3y = 17x + 1$ .... (2)

6   A hospital has a target of completing a certain number of
    operations in a given number of days.

    If the hospital does an average of 37 operations per day
    it will fall short of its target by 35 operations.
    If it does an average of 45 operations per day it will
    exceed its target by 21.

    a   What was the target number of operations given
        to the hospital?

    b   In how many days should that target be completed?

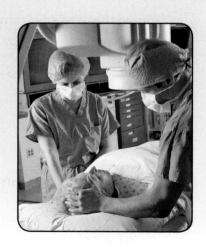

Points to remember

- Look carefully at pairs of simultaneous equations to decide which method to use.
- If one variable is given in terms of the other, use **substitution**.
- Otherwise, use **elimination**. Make the number part of the coefficients of one of the variables the same by multiplying each equation by a suitable scale factor.
  - If the signs of the coefficients are both the same, subtract the equations.
  - If the signs of the coefficients are different, add the equations.

3 Expanding brackets 1

This lesson will help you to multiply two linear expressions when all the signs are positive.

Exercise 3

When you expand two brackets, every term in the first bracket has to be multiplied by every term in the second bracket.

You can use a **multiplication grid** to help you.

Example

Expand the brackets in the expression
$(x + 3)(x + 7)$.

$\times$	x	$+$	7
x	x^2	$+$	$7x$
$+$			
3	$3x$	$+$	21

$$x^2 + 7x$$
$$+$$
$$3x + 21$$
$$x^2 + 10x + 21$$

You can use the mnemonic **FOIL** as a quick method of expanding two brackets.

$(x + 3)(x + 7)$

First: $x \times x = x^2$

Outside: $x \times 7 = 7x$

Inside: $3 \times x = 3x$

Last: $3 \times 7 = 21$

$x^2 + 10x + 21$

---

① Expand the brackets and then simplify the expressions.

a $7(a + 3) + 4$

b $3(x + 2) + 5x$

c $8(b + 4) - 4(b + 1)$

d $9p + 11(p + 8)$

e $3(2a + 1) + 9(a - 4)$

f $6(4x + 7) + 3x - 14$

2 Expand the brackets.

   a $(x + 6)(x + 3)$ **b** $(y + 7)(y + 11)$ **c** $(s + 4)(s + 9)$

   d $(x + 10)(x + 14)$ **e** $(a + 9)(a + 8)$ **f** $(x + 15)(x + 4)$

   g $(t + 20)(t + 30)$ **h** $(b + 18)(b + 6)$ **i** $(x + 9)^2$

3 Write, expand and simplify an expression for the area of the rectangle.

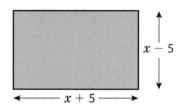

4 Write, expand and simplify an expression for the area of the trapezium.

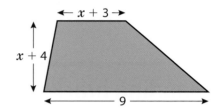

5 Look at the number grid. It has five columns.

   a Select any box of four numbers.

   Find the products of opposite corners, for example:

   $12 \times 8 = 96$
   $7 \times 13 = 91$

1	2	3	4	5
6	7	8	9	10
11	12	13	14	15
16	17	18	19	20
21	22	23	24	25

   b Find the difference in the products: $96 - 91 = 5$
   Is the answer always 5?

   c Explain why every 2×2 box in the grid can be represented like this using algebra.

x	$x + 1$
$x + 5$	$x + 6$

   d Find the products of opposite corners of this box.

   e Prove that the difference in the products is always 5.

   f Investigate for grids with different numbers of columns.

Extension problem

6 Expand the brackets.

   a $(2x + 1)(3x + 2)$ **b** $(4x + 3)(2x + 3)$

   c $(3x + 7)(5x + 9)$ **d** $(7x + 5)^2$

Points to remember

- To expand $2x(3x + 4)$ multiply every term inside the bracket by $2x$ to get $6x^2 + 8x$.
- To expand $(x + 3)(x + 5)$ multiply every term in the first bracket by every term in the second bracket to get $x^2 + 3x + 5x + 15 = x^2 + 8x + 15$.
- You can use a multiplication grid to help you expand brackets, e.g.

  $(a + 2)(a + 4) = a^2 + 2a + 4a + 8 = a^2 + 6a + 8$

$\times$	a + 4	
a	a^2 + $4a$	$a^2 + 4a$
+		+
2	$2a$ + 8	$2a + 8$
		$a^2 + 6a + 8$

- Use 'First Outside Inside Last' (FOIL) to remember how to expand brackets.

4 Expanding brackets 2

This lesson will help you to multiply two linear expressions with positive or negative signs.

Exercise 4

When you expand two brackets every term in the first bracket has to be multiplied by every term in the second bracket.

You can use a **multiplication grid** to help you.

Example 1: one sign positive and one sign negative

Expand the brackets in the expression $(x + 8)(x - 6)$.

$\times$	x − 6	
x	x^2 − $6x$	$x^2 - 6x$
+		+
8	$8x$ − 48	$8x - 48$
		$x^2 + 2x + 48$

You can use the mnemonic **FOIL** as a quick method of expanding two brackets.

$(x + 8)(x - 6)$

First: $x \times x = x^2$
Outside: $x \times -6 = -6x$
Inside: $8 \times x = 8x$
Last: $8 \times -6 = -48$

$x^2 + 2x - 48$

Example 2: both signs negative

Expand the brackets in the expression $(x - 4)(x - 3)$.

$\times$	x	$-$	3	
x	x^2	$-$	$3x$	$x^2 - 3x$
$-$				$-$
4	$4x$	$-$	12	$4x - 12$
				$x^2 - 7x + 12$

You can use the mnemonic **FOIL** as a quick method of expanding two brackets.

$(x - 4)(x - 3)$

First: $\quad x \times x = x^2$

Outside: $\quad x \times -3 = -3x$

Inside: $\quad -4 \times x = -4x$

Last: $\quad -4 \times -3 = 12$

$x^2 - 7x + 12$

---

1. Expand the brackets.

   a $(x + 2)(x - 3)$

   b $(y - 5)(y + 4)$

   c $(a - 2)(a + 7)$

   d $(p - 9)(p + 8)$

   e $(t + 9)(t - 11)$

   f $(b - 12)(b + 10)$

   g $(x - 7)(x + 7)$

   h $(y + 5)(y - 5)$

   i $(z - 3)(z + 5)$

2. Expand the brackets.

   a $(x - 2)(x - 6)$

   b $(a - 7)(a - 5)$

   c $(y - 8)(y - 6)$

   d $(p - 10)(p - 8)$

   e $(a - 30)(a - 40)$

   f $(b - 9)(b - 12)$

   g $(x - 8)^2$

   h $(y - 9)^2$

   i $(s - 10)(s - 15)$

3. Match the products **A** to **F** with the expressions **G** to **L**.

   A $(x - 6)(x + 8)$

   G $x^2 - 15x + 44$

   B $(x + 2)(x + 3)$

   H $x^2 + 14x + 48$

   C $(x + 6)(x + 8)$

   I $x^2 + 2x - 48$

   D $(x - 5)(x - 17)$

   J $x^2 - 22x + 85$

   E $(x + 4)(x - 10)$

   K $x^2 - 6x - 40$

   F $(x - 4)(x - 11)$

   L $x^2 + 5x + 6$

4 **a** Write an expression for the area of the rectangle.

b Work out the area of the rectangle if $x = 7$ cm.

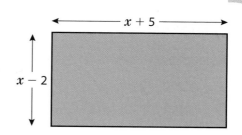

Extension problem

5 Expand the brackets.

a $(2x - 1)(3x + 2)$

b $(8a + 2)(8a - 2)$

c $(6x - 5)(2x - 3)$

d $(9x - 4)^2$

⊙ Points to remember

⊙ You can use a **multiplication grid** to help you expand brackets.
For example,
$(a + 2)(a - 4) = a^2 + 2a - 4a - 8 = a^2 - 2a - 8$

⊙ Use **FOIL** to remember how to expand brackets.

×	a	−	4	
a	a^2	−	$4a$	$a^2 - 4a$
+				**+**
2	$2a$	−	8	$2a - 8$
				$a^2 - 2a - 8$

---

5 Factorising quadratic expressions

ⓘ Did you know that...?

The word *factor* was first used in England in 1673 in *Elements of Algebra* by **John Kersey**, in which he said: 'The Quantities given to be multiplied one by the other are called Factors.'

The word *factorise* first appeared in 1886 in *Algebra* by **G. Chrystal**.

This lesson will help you to factorise quadratic expressions.

Exercise 5

The reverse of expanding brackets is called **factorisation**.

Some quadratic expressions can be factorised into the product of two simple linear expressions.

Example 1

Factorise $x^2 - 4x - 21$.

The coefficient of x^2 is 1 $(x \quad)(x \quad)$
The sign in front of 21 is $-$ $(x + \quad)(x - \quad)$

Using a grid

Search for a factor pair of -21 with a sum of -4 (-7 and 3).
Enter numbers in the grid and check the answer.

$\times$	$x \quad - \quad 7$	
x	$x^2 - 7x$	$x^2 - 7x$
$+$		$+$
3	$3x - 21$	$3x - 21$
		$x^2 - 4x - 21$

Example 2

Factorise $x^2 + 3x - 10$.

Working logically:

The coefficient of x^2 is 1 $(x \quad)(x \quad)$
The sign in front of 10 is $-$ $(x + \quad)(x - \quad)$
Factor pair of -10 with a sum of 3 $(x + 5)(x - 2)$

So $x^2 + 3x - 10 \equiv (x + 5)(x - 2)$

You will need a graph plotter or graphics calculator for question 6.

1. Write all the factors of these numbers.

   a   7   b   22   c   16   d   30

2. Write all the factors of these terms.

   a ab b $3x$ c $5mn$ d $2x^2$

3. Factorise these expressions.

   a $6x + 4$ b $5x - 15y$ c $2x - 10$ d $6x^2 - 3x$

4. Factorise these quadratic expressions.

   a $x^2 + 6x + 8$ b $x^2 - 2x - 8$ c $x^2 + 2x - 8$ d $x^2 - 6x + 8$

   e $x^2 + 9x + 8$ f $x^2 - 9x + 8$ g $x^2 - 7x - 8$ h $x^2 + 7x - 8$

(5) Factorise these quadratic expressions.

a $x^2 + 9x + 18$ b $x^2 + x - 12$ c $a^2 - 5a - 14$ d $x^2 + 2x - 48$

e $x^2 + 6x - 40$ f $s^2 - 11s + 30$ g $y^2 + 13y + 40$ h $b^2 - b - 56$

Extension problems

(6) Factorise these quadratic equations.
Draw a graph of the equation on a computer or graphics calculator.

a $y = x^2 + x - 6$ b $y = x^2 - 2x - 3$ c $y = x^2 - x - 12$

d $y = x^2 - 3x - 10$ e $y = x^2 + x - 42$ f $y = x^2 - x - 20$

(7) Look again at each graph in question 6.
Compare the graph with the equation in its factorised form.
What do you notice?

Points to remember

- The reverse of expanding brackets is called **factorisation**.
- To factorise a quadratic expression find two linear expressions that are factors, e.g.
  $x^2 + x - 6 = (x + 3)(x - 2)$
- To work out the factors of $x^2 + x - 6$:
  - as the coefficient of x^2 is 1 each bracket begins with x, i.e. $(x \quad)(x \quad)$;
  - as the sign in front of 6 is $-$, the brackets must be $(x + \quad)(x - \quad)$;
  - now find a factor pair of -6 with a sum of $+1$: $(x + 3)(x - 2)$.

6 Using identities

This lesson will help you to use identities to solve problems.

Exercise 6

Two expressions are **identical** when they have the same value when any numbers are substituted for the variables.

The symbol $\equiv$ is used to show that two expressions are identical. For example,

$3x(5x + 2y) \equiv 15x^2 + 6xy$

Three identities are so useful that they need to be memorised. These are:

$$x^2 - y^2 \equiv (x + y)(x - y)$$

$$(x + y)^2 \equiv x^2 + 2xy + y^2$$

$$(x - y)^2 \equiv x^2 - 2xy + y^2$$

1 Use the identity $(x - y)(x + y) \equiv x^2 - y^2$ to work out the answers.

a $68^2 - 32^2$ b $65^2 - 45^2$ c $33^2 - 17^2$

d $48^2 - 22^2$ e $19^2 - 15^2$ f $43^2 - 37^2$

2 Use the identity $(x + y)^2 \equiv x^2 + 2xy + y^2$ to work out the answers.

a 41^2 b 62^2 c 23^2 d 91^2

e 33^2 f 82^2 g 71^2 h 65^2

3 Use the identity $(x - y)^2 \equiv x^2 - 2xy + y^2$ to work out the answers.

a 79^2 b 18^2 c 27^2 d 56^2

e 98^2 f 95^2 g 59^2 h 37^2

4 a Use algebra to prove that this identity is true for any vale of x:

$$(x + 2)^2 - x^2 \equiv 4(x + 1)$$

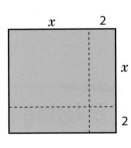

b Use the area of the whole square and each of the smaller areas to show that:

$(x + 2)^2 - x^2 \equiv 4(x + 1)$

c Use the identity $(x + 2)^2 - x^2 \equiv 4(x + 1)$ to work out:

i $23^2 - 21^2$ ii $101^2 - 99^2$ iii $6.5^2 - 4.5^2$

Show your working.

5 Let n be any whole number.

a Explain why $2n$ is always an even number.

b Explain why $2n + 1$ is always an odd number.

c Will the product of two odd numbers always be odd? Explain your answer.

6 Let a, b and c be any whole numbers.

The missing number in any cell is found by adding the two numbers beneath it.

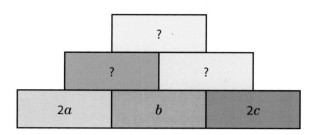

Prove that the number in the top cell will always be even.

Extension problems

 7 **a** Use algebra to prove that $(x + 2)^2 - (x - 2)^2 \equiv 8x$, for any value of x.

b Use the difference between the area of the large square and the area of the yellow square to show that:

$(x + 2)^2 - (x - 2)^2 \equiv 8x$

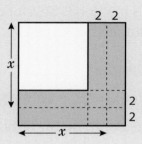

c Use the identity $(x + 2)^2 - (x - 2)^2 \equiv 8x$ to work out:

   i $52^2 - 48^2$ **ii** $102^2 - 98^2$ **iii** $27^2 - 23^2$

Show your working.

8 Let a, b and c be positive whole numbers.

Pythagorean triples are numbers such that $a^2 + b^2 = c^2$, for example $3^2 + 4^2 = 5^2$.

a Write another example of a Pythagorean triple.

b Rearrange $a^2 + b^2 = c^2$ to express a^2 as a difference of two squares.

Use this to help you find further examples of Pythagorean triples.

 Points to remember

- Two expressions are **identical** if their value is the same for any number.
  e.g. $x^2 - y^2 \equiv (x + y)(x - y)$, where $\equiv$ means 'is identically equal to'.

- You can often prove that two expressions are identical using properties of geometrical shapes.

7 Solving quadratic equations graphically

This lesson will help you to solve quadratic equations by using graphs.

Exercise 7

You can solve the equation $ax^2 + bx + c = 0$ by drawing the graph of $y = ax^2 + bx + c$ and looking at the points where the graph intersects with the x-axis.

The values of x at these points are called the **roots** of the equation.

If the graph does not cut the x-axis the equation does not have any real solutions.

This method is best for quadratic equations with integer solutions.

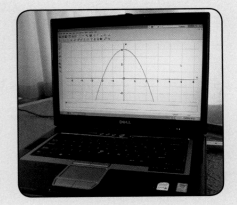

Example

Solve $y = x^2 + 2x + c$ for $c = -3$, 1 and 4.

The graphs on the right are of:

$y = x^2 + 2x - 3$
$y = x^2 + 2x + 1$
$y = x^2 + 2x + 4$

The solution of $x^2 + 2x - 3 = 0$ is $x = -3, x = 1$.
The solution of $x^2 + 2x + 1 = 0$ is $x = -1$.
There is no real solution for $x^2 + 2x + 4 = 0$.

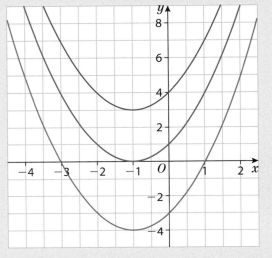

You will need a graph plotter or graphics calculator.

1. Solve these equations.

   a $x^2 = 81$
   b $x^2 = 64$
   c $x^2 = 1$
   d $x^2 = 169$

2. Use a calculator to solve these equations. Give your answers to 3 decimal places.

   a $x^2 = 40$
   b $x^2 = 26$
   c $x^2 = 53$
   d $x^2 = 69$
   e $x^2 = 203$

3. Write the equation of the graph you would draw to help you solve these equations.

   a $x^2 + 4x - 21 = 0$
   b $x^2 + 12x + 32 = 0$

   c $x^2 - x - 30 = 0$
   d $x^2 - 16x + 63 = 0$

④ Use a graph plotter or graphics calculator to draw graphs to solve these equations.
Check your answers by substituting each value for x back into the original equation.

a $x^2 + 3x - 10 = 0$ b $x^2 - x - 30 = 0$

c $x^2 + 3x - 18 = 0$ d $x^2 - 5x + 4 = 0$

e $x^2 + 8x + 15 = 0$ f $x^2 + 7x - 8 = 0$

⑤ Use a graph plotter or graphics calculator to draw graphs to solve these equations.
Say whether the equation has no real solution, two different solutions or two equal solutions.
Give the solutions to the equation if they exist.

a $x^2 + x - 6 = 0$ b $x^2 + x = 0$

c $x^2 + x + 8 = 0$ d $x^2 + x - 12 = 0$

e $x^2 + x + 0.25 = 0$ f $x^2 + x + 2 = 0$

Extension problems

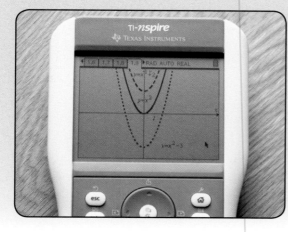

⑥ a Draw the graph of $y = (x + 4)^2$.

b Explain why the graph can be used to solve the equation $x^2 + 8x + 16 = 0$.

c Describe what you notice.

⑦ a Draw the graph of $y = (x - 6)^2$.

b Explain why the graph can be used to solve the equation $x^2 - 12x + 36 = 0$.

c Describe what you notice.

⊙ Points to remember

⊙ A **quadratic equation** is of the form $y = ax^2 + bx + c$.

⊙ The graph of a quadratic equation is a **U-shaped graph**.

⊙ A quadratic graph may intersect the x-axis at two points, just touch the x-axis at one point or not touch the x-axis at all.

⊙ Where a quadratic graph intersects or touches the x-axis, $y = 0$ and the values of x are the *solutions* or *roots* of $ax^2 + bx + c = 0$.

8 Sequences and patterns

This lesson will help you to find and use the nth terms of sequences.

Exercise 8

The **second difference** between consecutive terms of a **quadratic sequence** is **constant**.

The nth term T_n of a quadratic sequence is an expression of the form $T_n = an^2 + bn + c$.

If you know the nth term of a sequences, you can substitute $n = 1, n = 2, n = 3, \ldots$ into the nth term of a sequence to find the 1st, 2nd, 3rd, … terms.

If you know the first three terms of the sequence you can use substitution to create three simultaneous equations which you can solve. You can use the solutions to find the nth term.

Example

Find the nth term of the sequence 2, 5, 10, 17, …

Sequence		2		5		10		17
1st difference			3		5		7		9
2nd difference				2		2		2

The second difference is constant, so the sequence is quadratic:

$$T_n = an^2 + bn + c$$

When $n = 1$ $T_1 = a + b + c = 2$
When $n = 2$ $T_2 = 4a + 2b + c = 5$
When $n = 3$ $T_3 = 9a + 3b + c = 10$

$T_2 - T_1$	$3a + b = 3 \ldots\ldots\ldots\ldots (1)$
$T_3 - T_2$	$5a + b = 5 \ldots\ldots\ldots\ldots (2)$
Subtract (1) from (2)	$2a = 2$
Divide by 2	$a = 1$
Substitute $a = 1$ in (1)	$b = 0$
Substitute $a = 1$ and $b = 0$ in T_1	$c = 1$

So $T_n = n^2 + 1$

---

1   Write the next four terms of these quadratic sequences.

     a   1, 4, 9, 16, …   **b**   2, 6, 12, 20, …

     c   −1, 2, 7, 14, …   **d**   4, 13, 28, 49, …

2 Generate the first four terms of these quadratic sequences using their nth terms.

    a $T_n = n^2 + 3$ **b** $T_n = n^2 - 5$ **c** $T_n = n^2 + 2n$

    d $T_n = n^2 + n + 1$ **e** $T_n = 2n^2 + 3$ **f** $T_n = 3n^2 - 1$

3 Complete difference tables for these quadratic sequences and find their nth terms.

    a 3, 6, 11, 18, …   **b** −5, −2, 3, 10, …

    c 4, 10, 18, 28, …   **d** 3, 9, 19, 33, …

    e 7, 16, 31, 52, …   **f** −3, 3, 13, 27, …

    g 4, 9, 16, 25, …   **h** 1, 13, 33, 61, …

4 Pentagon numbers

    a How many dots are in the next three pentagon numbers?

    b Work out a formula for the number of dots in the nth pentagon.

1   5   12

  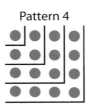

5 Here is a sequence of patterns made from dots.

    Pattern 1   Pattern 2   Pattern 3   Pattern 4

    a What is the value of:

       i 1 + 3   **ii** 1 + 3 + 5   **iii** 1 + 3 + 5 + 7

    b Draw a group of five rows of dots, with five dots in each row. Divide it up in the same way. What is the value of 1 + 3 + 5 + 7 + 9?

    c What is the sum of:

       i the first 20 odd numbers   **ii** the first n odd numbers?

    d Look at the sequence of patterns again. This time add up the dots along the diagonals. Use Pattern 4 to show that:

$$1 + 2 + 3 + 4 + 4 + 3 + 2 + 1 = 4^2 + 4$$

    e What is the sum of the first n numbers?

Extension problems

 6 Investigate this **Frogs puzzle**.

Rules

- ⊙ Blue 'frogs' can only move to the right and red 'frogs' to the left.
- ⊙ To move, a frog can slide into a blank space or it can jump over one frog of the other colour into a blank space.

a What is the least number of moves needed to get the blue frogs and red frogs to change places?

b A similar game has three frogs of each colour. What is the least number of moves needed for the blue and red frogs to change places?

c Find a formula for the least number of moves needed for frogs to change places when there are n frogs of each colour.

7 Any quadratic sequence has a formula for its nth term of $T_n = an^2 + bn + c$.

a Write the first four terms of the sequence.

b Find the first and second differences for this sequence.

c Find the second difference for the quadratic sequence: 2, 3, 10, 23, …
Use this to find the value of a.

d Find the formula for the nth term of the quadratic sequence: 2, 3, 10, 23, …

Points to remember

- ⊙ T_n is shorthand for the nth term of a sequence.

- ⊙ In a **linear sequence**, the difference between consecutive terms of a sequence is constant and T_n is a linear expression, e.g.

  1, 4, 7, 10, 13, 16, …. Difference is 3, and $T_n = 3n - 2$

- ⊙ In a **quadratic sequence**, the first difference is not constant but the second difference is *constant*, and T_n is a quadratic expression, e.g.

  1, 3, 6, 10, 15, 21, …. Second difference is 1, and $T_n = \dfrac{n(n + 1)}{2}$

- ⊙ Substitute $n = 1, n = 2, n = 3, …$ into the nth term of a sequence to find the 1st, 2nd, 3rd, … terms.

How well are you doing?

Can you:

- ⊙ solve pairs of simultaneous equations?
- ⊙ expand brackets?
- ⊙ factorise quadratic expressions?
- ⊙ solve quadratic equations using graphs?
- ⊙ investigate quadratic sequences?

Algebraic expressions and equations (no calculator)

1 *2003 level 7*

   a Write which statement is true.

      When x is even $(x-2)^2$ is even.   When x is even $(x-2)^2$ is odd.

   b Show how you know it is true for all even values of x.

   c Write which statement is true.

      When x is even $(x-1)(x+1)$ is even.   When x is even $(x-1)(x+1)$ is odd.

   d Show how you know it is true for all even values of x.

2 *1998 level 7*

   a Find the values of a and b when $p = 10$.

$$a = \frac{3p^3}{2} \qquad\qquad b = \frac{2p^2(p-3)}{7p}$$

   b Simplify this expression as fully as possible:

$$\frac{3cd^2}{5cd}$$

   c Multiply out and simplify these expressions:

      i $3(x-2) - 2(4-3x)$ **ii** $(x+2)(x+3)$

      iii $(x+4)(x-1)$ **iv** $(x-2)^2$

3 *2003 Mental Test level 7*

$18y^2 + 6y = 6y(\ldots\ldots + \ldots\ldots)$

4 *2001 level 7*

Each year a school has a concert of readings and songs.

In one year the concert had 3 readings and 9 songs. It lasted 120 minutes.
In another year the concert had 5 readings and 5 songs. It lasted 90 minutes.

Next year the school plans to have 5 readings and 7 songs.
Use simultaneous equations to estimate how long the concert will last.

Call the time estimated for a reading x minutes.
Call the time estimated for a song y minutes.

Show your working.

5 *2008 level 7*

Here are the nth term expressions for three different sequences.

$2^{(n-1)}$	$\dfrac{n^2 - n + 2}{2}$	$\dfrac{n(n^2 - 3n + 8)}{6}$
Sequence A	Sequence B	Sequence C

The first three terms of each sequence are 1, 2 and 4.

What is the 4th term of each sequence?
You must show your working.

6 *2006 level 8*

Factorise these expressions.

a $x^2 + 7x - 18$

b $x^2 - 49$

Transformations and loci

This unit will help you to:

- ⊙ given the coordinates of its endpoints, find the length of a line segment and the coordinates of a point that divides it in a given ratio;

- ⊙ enlarge shapes using positive, fraction and negative scale factors;

- ⊙ understand how enlargement affects the perimeter of a shape;

- ⊙ rotate a shape about any point and measure the angle of rotation;

- ⊙ transform shapes by combinations of transformations;

- ⊙ understand that lengths and angles stay the same after a translation, rotation or reflection;

- ⊙ explore loci.

1 How long is that line?

This lesson will help you to find the length of a line segment given the coordinates of its endpoints.

Exercise 1

If you know the coordinates of the endpoints of a line, you can use Pythagoras' theorem to find its length.

Example

AB is the line segment joining the points (1, 1) and (9, 5). Calculate its length.

Draw the right-angled triangle ABC so that AC = 8 and BC = 4.

$AB^2 = 8^2 + 4^2$

$AB^2 = 64 + 16 = 80$

$AB = \sqrt{80} = 8.94$ to 2 decimal places

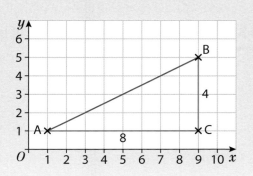

Where appropriate, give your answers to 2 decimal places.

1 Find the length of each line segment **a** to **e**.

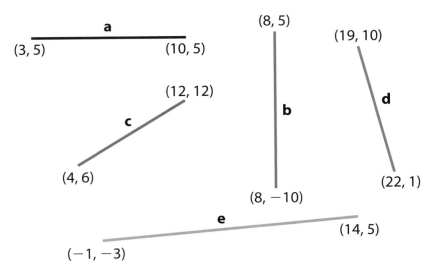

2 Find the lengths of the lines joining these pairs of points.

   a A (3, 5), B (6, 9)

   b C (6, 4), D (9, 12)

   c E (6, 12), F (9, 2)

   d G (7, 4), H (3, 15)

   e I (1, 1), J (7, 7)

   f K (−1, 5), L (3, 8)

   g M (−3, −5), N (−8, −8)

   h P (3, 6), Q (−3, 14)

3 The points A (1, 4), B (5, 7) and C (2, 3) form a triangle.
   Prove that triangle ABC is an isosceles triangle.

Extension problems

4 Line AB is 5 units long.
   Find the value of y.

   A (3, 9)   B (7, y)

5 The rhombus WXYZ has sides of length 5 units.
   Find the values of x and y.

   X (x, 7)
   Y (13, 4)
   W (6, 3)
   Z (10, y)

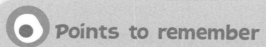
2 Divide that line

This lesson will help you to find the coordinates of a point that divides a line segment in a given ratio.

Exercise 2

To divide the line segment AB in a given ratio:

⊙ draw a right-angled triangle with AB as hypotenuse;

⊙ divide the shorter sides in the given ratio at points X and Y;

⊙ draw lines through X and Y parallel to the axes to meet AB at Z;

⊙ calculate the x- and y-coordinates of Z.

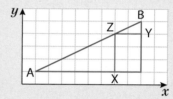

Example 1

Divide the line AB in the ratio 2:1.

Draw a right-angled triangle ABC with AB as hypotenuse.

Work out the lengths of the two shorter sides.

AB is 6 and CB is 9.

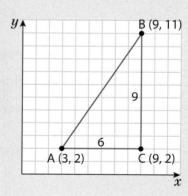

Divide the two shorter sides in the ratio 2:1.

$2 + 1 = 3$

$\frac{2}{3}$ of 6 = 4 and $\frac{2}{3}$ of 9 = 6.

So X is the point (7, 2) and Y is the point (9, 8).

Draw lines through X and Y parallel to the axes to meet AB at Z.

Work out the coordinates of Z (7, 8).

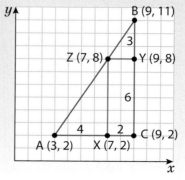

Example 2

Find the midpoint of the line joining A (3, 5) and B (13, 7).

For the x-coordinate of the midpoint, find the mean of the x-coordinates of A and B.

$3 + 13 = 16$ and $16 \div 2 = 8$

For the y-coordinate of the midpoint, find the mean of the y-coordinates of A and B.

$5 + 7 = 12$ and $12 \div 2 = 6$

So the midpoint of AB is the point (8, 6).

① Write the coordinates of the midpoint of AB.   A (3, 9) ———————— B (15, 9)

② Work out the coordinates of the point   C (−6, −9) ———————— D (12, 0)
that divides CD in the ratio 7 : 2.

③ Work out the coordinates of the point that divides EF in the ratio 3 : 1.

F (4, 8)

E (4, 0)

④ Work out the coordinates of the point that divides GH in the ratio 2 : 3.

H (7, 12)

G (7, −3)

⑤ Line JK has coordinates J (3, 9) and K (3, −5).

   a Write the coordinates of the midpoint of JK.

   b Work out the coordinates of the point that divides JK in the ratio 3 : 4.

⑥ a Write the coordinates of the midpoint of AB.

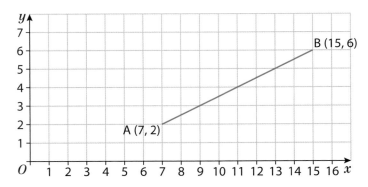

   b Work out the coordinates of the point that divides the line AB in the ratio 3 : 1.

(7) Line LM has coordinates L (3, 8) and M (7, 16).

    a Write the coordinates of the midpoint of LM.

    b Work out the coordinates of the point that divides LM in the ratio:

       i 1:1   ii 1:3

(8) The midpoint of line AB is (7, 9).
A has coordinates (2, 1).
What are the coordinates of B?

(9) Line PQ has coordinates P (−1, 3) and Q (13, 10).
Work out the coordinates of the point that divides PQ in the ratio 2:5.

(10) Line XY has coordinates X (14, −3) and Y (−2, 5).
Work out the coordinates of the point that divides XY in the ratio 3:5.

Extension problems

(11) Line CD has coordinates C (3, 4) and D (11, 8).
Work out the coordinates of the point that divides CD in the ratio 3:5.

(12) The line MN is divided in the ratio 3:4 by the point X (7, 8).
M has coordinates (1, 2).
What are the coordinates of N?

Points to remember

⊙ To divide the line segment AB in a given ratio:

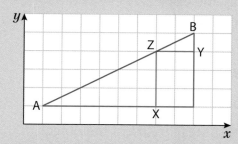

    – draw a right-angled triangle with AB as hypotenuse;

    – divide the base and height in the given ratio at points X and Y;

    – draw lines through X and Y parallel to the axes to meet AB at Z;

    – calculate the x- and y-coordinates of Z.

Did you know that...?

The principles of **enlargement** have many applications, including mapmaking, architecture, art and design as well as applications within mathematics.

This lesson will help you to enlarge a 2D shape using positive, fraction and negative scale factors.

Exercise 3

In an **enlargement**, the size of the object changes but the angles of the object stay the same.

To describe an enlargement, give the **centre of enlargement** and the **scale factor**.

Fraction scale factor

This object has been enlarged by scale factor $\frac{1}{2}$.

The image is smaller than the object but the transformation is still called an enlargement.

The image is closer to the centre of enlargement and is smaller than the object.

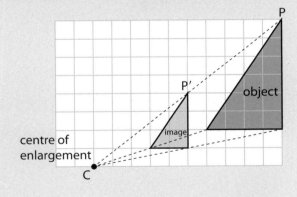

Negative scale factor

This object has been enlarged by scale factor -3.

The image is three times the size of the object but it has also been rotated through 180°.

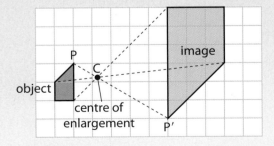

In both cases, to find the **centre of enlargement**, join each vertex of the object to the corresponding vertex of the image to find the point where the dotted lines cross.

You will need squared paper, a ruler and a sharp pencil.
You may need tracing paper for question 3.

① Draw the diagram on squared paper.

Mark the centre of enlargement.

Enlarge the object by scale factors $\frac{3}{4}$, $\frac{1}{2}$ and $\frac{1}{4}$ to form image A, image B and image C.

Label the images.

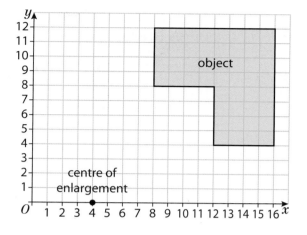

② Draw the diagram on squared paper.

Mark the centre of enlargement.

Enlarge the object by scale factors −1, −2 and −3 to form image X, image Y and image Z.

Label the images.

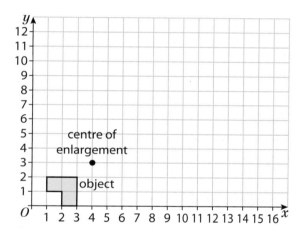

③ Find the scale factor and the coordinates of the centre of enlargement.
Use tracing paper if it helps you.

a
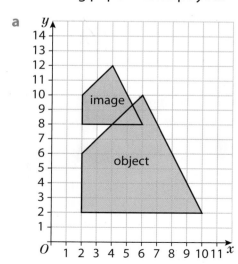

b
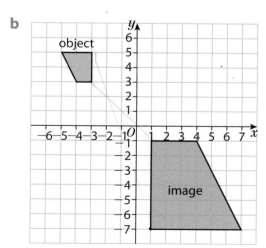

c
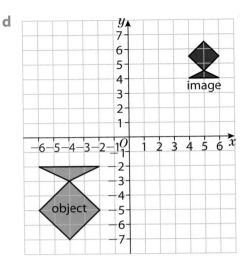

d

4 Draw a square with side length 2 cm.
Now draw enlargements of the square with scale factors 2, 3, 4 and 5.
Calculate the perimeter for each square.
What effect does enlargement have on perimeter?

5 A shape has perimeter 17 cm. It is enlarged by scale factor 0.3.
What is its new perimeter?

6 A model car, the image, is 15 cm long. The real car, the object, is 480 cm long.
What is the scale factor of the enlargement?

7 An aeroplane is 71 m long. A model of the plane is made with a scale factor of 0.007.
How long is the model?

Extension problems

8 A photocopier enlarges a photograph by a scale factor of 1.25.

The enlargement is 8 cm wide.

What is the width of the original photograph?

9 A photocopier enlarges a picture by a scale factor of 2.5.
What scale factor would reduce the enlarged picture back to the original size?

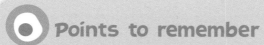

Points to remember

- When a shape is enlarged, its angles stay the same. The object and image are similar.
- **Scale factor** $= \dfrac{\text{length of side of image}}{\text{length of corresponding side of object}}$
- Lines joining corresponding points of the object and image meet at the **centre of enlargement**.

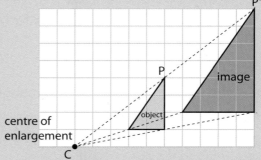

- When you enlarge a shape, measure distances of the vertices from the centre of enlargement. If C is the centre, for corresponding points P and P' on the object and image:

  $CP' = \text{scale factor} \times CP$

- For a scale factor between 0 and 1, the object is smaller than the image. It is still called an enlargement.
- For a negative scale factor, the object and the image are on opposite sides of the centre of enlargement.
- When a perimeter is enlarged it is multiplied by the scale factor.

4 Rotation

This lesson will help you to draw and describe rotations using the centre, direction and angle of rotation.

 Did you know that...?

Snowflakes have rotation symmetry of order 6. No two are alike.

The American **Wilson Alwyn Bentley** (1865–1931), also known as 'Snowflake' Bentley, was the first known photographer of snowflakes. He caught them on black velvet and photographed them under a microscope before they melted. He was also the first American to record raindrop sizes and was one of the first cloud physicists.

When a shape is rotated, the object and image are congruent.

To describe a rotation you need to give:

◉ the centre of rotation;

◉ the angle of rotation in degrees or as a fraction of a turn;

◉ the direction of the rotation, clockwise or anticlockwise.

Example

Describe the transformation from triangle A to triangle B.

Triangle A is mapped onto triangle B by a rotation of 180° (a half turn) about the point (5, 5).

Use tracing paper to check the transformation.

Trace the shape of the object. Fix the centre of rotation with a pencil or compass point so that it does not move.

Turn the tracing paper about the centre of rotation to check that it is a half turn of 180°.

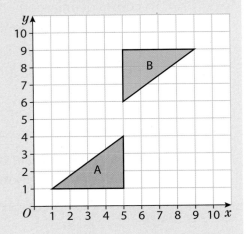

You will need squared paper, tracing paper, ruler, protractor and pencil.

① Copy each of the shapes below on squared paper. Draw the image after each one is rotated about the point marked X through the angle shown. You may use tracing paper to help.

a 90°
clockwise

b 90°
anticlockwise

c 180°
clockwise

d 270°
clockwise

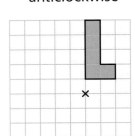
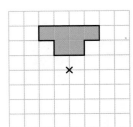
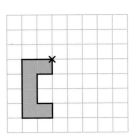

② P is an equilateral triangle.

A rotation about point C maps triangle P onto triangle Q.

What is the angle of rotation?

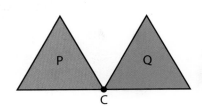

3 **a** Describe fully the rotation that maps shape A onto each of B, C and D.

b Describe fully the rotation that maps shape D onto shape C.

c Describe fully the rotation that maps shape C onto shape A.

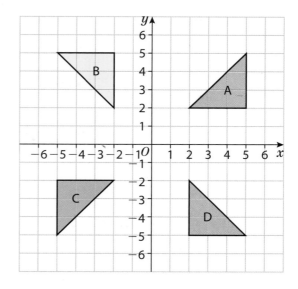

4 **a** Describe fully the rotation that maps shape A onto each of the other shapes.

b Describe fully the rotation that maps shape C onto shape F.

c Describe fully the rotation that maps shape E onto each of shapes B, D and F.

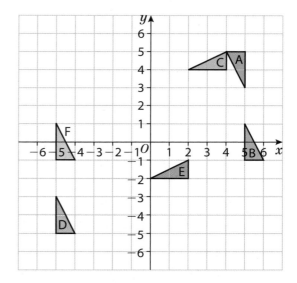

5 **a** Triangle A is rotated 90 degrees clockwise about the origin O. The image is triangle B. Write the coordinates of the vertices of triangle B.

b Triangle A is rotated 90 degrees anticlockwise about the origin O. The image is triangle C. Write the coordinates of the vertices of triangle C.

c Triangle A is rotated 180 degrees clockwise about the origin O. The image is triangle D. Write the coordinates of the vertices of triangle D.

You may use tracing paper.

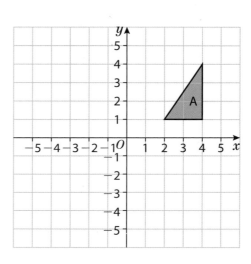

6 On squared paper, draw x- and y-axes from -6 to 6.

   a Draw the rectangle formed by joining the points (3, 1), (4, 1), (4, 5) and (3, 5).
      Rotate the rectangle through 90° anticlockwise about the centre (1, 1).
      Label the image A.

   b Draw the triangle formed by joining the points $(-6, -2)$, $(-5, 1)$ and $(-2, -1)$.
      Rotate the triangle through 180° about the centre $(-2, -2)$.
      Label the image B.

   You may use tracing paper.

Extension problem

7 Use these instructions to **tessellate** a quadrilateral.

   ⊙ Draw any quadrilateral in the middle of a page.

   ⊙ Rotate it 180° about the midpoint of each of its sides.

   ⊙ Repeat with the new quadrilaterals to extend the tessellation.

Points to remember

⊙ When a shape is rotated, the object and image are **congruent**.

⊙ Use tracing paper to rotate shapes and to find the centre of rotation.

⊙ A rotation is described by giving:

   – the **centre of rotation**;

   – the **angle of rotation** in degrees or as a fraction of a turn;

   – the **direction** of the rotation, clockwise or anticlockwise.

5 Combining transformations

This lesson will help you to transform shapes by combining transformations.

Exercise 5

To describe a **translation**, give the distance and direction of the movement.

To describe a **reflection**, give the mirror line.

To describe a **rotation**, give the centre of rotation, the angle of turn and its direction.

To describe an **enlargement**, give the centre of the enlargement and the scale factor.

Example

a Describe fully a combination of two transformations that move the object to the image.

Rotate the object 90° clockwise about centre of rotation B followed by a translation across 0 down 4.

b Describe fully a single transformation that moves the object to the image.

Rotate the object 90° clockwise about centre of rotation A.

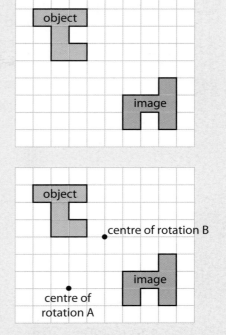

You will need squared paper, tracing paper, a ruler and pencil.

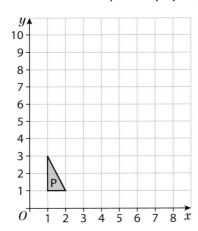

1 Copy the diagram on squared paper.

  a Reflect triangle P in the line $x = 3$.
     Label the new triangle Q.

  b Reflect triangle Q in the line $y = 5$.
     Label the new image R.

  c Describe fully the single transformation which maps triangle P onto triangle R.

2 A shape is rotated by 90° clockwise about centre (3, 3).
The image is then rotated by 60° anticlockwise about centre (3, 3).
What single transformation maps the original object onto the final image?

3 Copy the diagram on squared paper.

  a Rotate triangle P 90° anticlockwise about (3, 5).
     Label the new triangle Q.

  b Rotate triangle Q 90° clockwise about (6, 2).
     Label the new triangle R.

  c Describe fully the single transformation which maps triangle P onto triangle R.

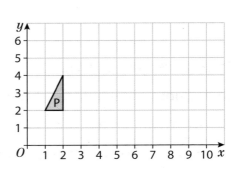

4 A shape is translated 4 units to the right and 3 units down to form image Q.
Image Q is then translated 6 units to the left and 2 units down to form image R.
What single transformation will take you directly from the object to the final image?

5 Describe fully three different combinations
of two transformations that will map shape A
onto shape B.

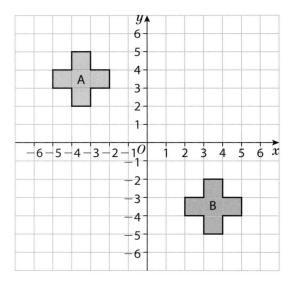

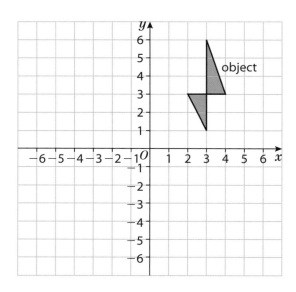

6 a The shape shown is rotated 180°
about the origin.
It is then reflected in the y-axis.

What single transformation would map
the object onto the final image?

b What happens if you do the two single
transformations in the reverse order?

7 a The shape shown is enlarged by scale
factor 2 with centre (0, 0).
It is then translated 2 units to the right
and 3 units up.

What single transformation would map
the object onto the final image?

b What happens if you do the two single
transformations in the reverse order?

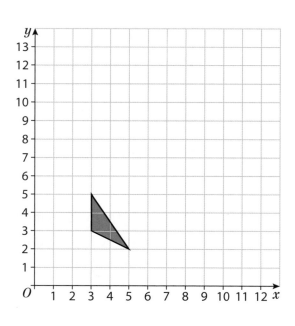

Extension problem

 Did you know that...?

Tiling and wallpaper patterns are based on **combinations of transformations**.

This pattern of traditional Portuguese tiles is based on a square tile which is rotated about one of its corners. A square of four tiles is then translated in two directions at right angles to each other to form a diagonal pattern.

8 Describe fully a combination of two transformations that will map:

a shape A to shape C

b shape B to shape C

c shape A to shape D

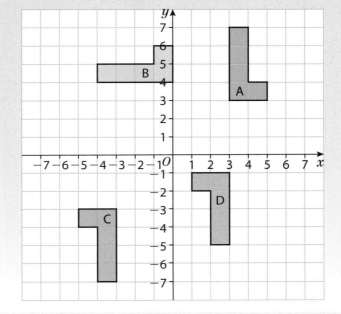

 Points to remember

- For **rotation**, **translation** and **reflection**, the image is congruent to the object; for **enlargement**, the image is similar to the object.
- Repeated rotations about the same centre of rotation can be replaced by a single rotation.
- Repeated translations can be replaced by a single translation.
- Rotation, translation, reflection and enlargement can be combined in any order to transform an object.
- It is sometimes possible to find a single transformation which has the same effect as a combination of transformations.
- Different combinations of transformations can have the same effect.
- In any combination of transformations, the angles and symmetries of the object are unchanged.

6 Loci 1

This lesson will help you to draw the locus of all the points that satisfy given conditions.

Exercise 6

A **locus** is defined as 'the set of points that satisfy given conditions'. The plural is **loci**.

Example 1

A point moves so that it is always 5 cm from a fixed point A. Draw its locus.

The locus is the set of points that lie on a circle of radius 5 cm, centre A.

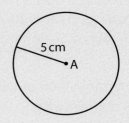

Example 2

A point moves so that it is always 1 cm from a fixed line AB. Draw its locus.

Here are some points that are 1 cm from the line AB. They make lines parallel to AB and 1 cm away from it.

Here are some points 1 cm from point A or 1 cm from point B. They make semicircles, centres A and B, with radius 1 cm.

Combining the two parallel lines and the two semicircles gives the complete locus.

You will need a pair of compasses, a ruler and a pencil.

1. A point moves so that it is always 3 cm away from a fixed point P. Draw its locus.

2. A fixed line segment AB is 6 cm long. A point moves so that it is always 2 cm away from AB. Draw its locus.

3. Draw a rectangle 5 cm wide by 7 cm long. Leave space around the rectangle. Draw the locus of all the points that are 1 cm from its perimeter. Hint: Some points will be inside the rectangle and some will be outside the rectangle.

4. Make an accurate drawing of this L-shaped line. Draw the locus of all the points that are 2 cm from the L-shape.

4 cm

2 cm

5 Draw an angle ABC of 60°.

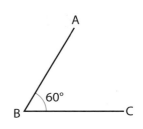

    a Construct the locus of the points that are equidistant from AB and BC.

    b Measure the angle between the locus and each arm of the angle. What do you notice?

6 Mark two points A and B 8 cm apart.

    a Construct the locus of all the points that are an equal distance from each point.

    b Join the two points A and B.
Measure the angle between AB and the locus. What do you notice?

For questions 7 and 8, you will need some squared paper.

7 A point P moves so that it is 2 cm from A and 3 cm from B.

Find the two possible positions of P. Mark them with a cross.

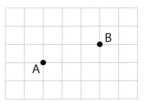

8 A point P moves so that it is equidistant from A and B and 2 cm from C.

Find the two possible positions of P. Mark them with a cross.

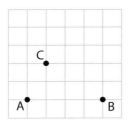

⊙ Points to remember

- A **locus** is the set of points that satisfy given conditions.
- In 2D, the locus of all points that are:
  - a given distance from a fixed point is a circle;
  - equidistant from a line segment is a shape formed by two parallel lines joined at each end by a semicircle;

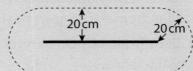

  - equidistant from the arms of an angle is the bisector of the angle;
  - equidistant from two points is the perpendicular bisector of the line segment joining the two points.
- Construction lines and arcs should be visible and not be rubbed out.

7 Loci 2

This lesson will help you to identify a region defined by a locus.

Exercise 7

Example

A goat is tethered 1 m from the edge of a barn by a rope of length 6 m.

Draw and shade the area of grass that the goat can eat.

When the rope is stretched along the side of a wall, the amount of available rope is reduced, so the radius of the arc alters.

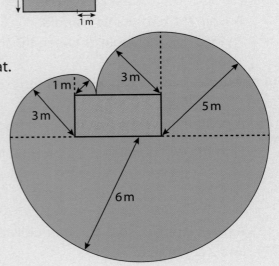

You will need squared paper, a pair of compasses, ruler and pencil.

1. A farmer has a large rectangular field with a circular pond in the middle of it.
    The pond has a radius of 5 m.
    The farmer wants to keep her cows from falling in the pond so puts a fence round the pond, exactly 2 m from its edge.

    Draw an accurate diagram of the pond and the position of the fence.
    Use a scale of 1 cm to represent 1 m.

2. Jan and Gerry are gardeners.
    They have a semicircular flower bed of radius 5 m.
    There is a low fence 1 m from the edge of the flowerbed.

    Copy the diagram. Use a scale of 1 cm to represent 1 m.
    Draw the position of the fence.

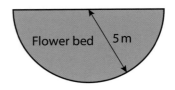

3. A goat is tethered to a wall 3 m from the corner of a rectangular field by a piece of rope 6 m long.

    Draw accurately the area of grass that the goat can eat.
    Use a scale of 1 cm to represent 1 m.

Extension problems

 4 Here is a plan of Jan and Gerry's garden.

They want to plant an apple tree more than 3 m from the house, more than 2 m from the fence and more than 1 m from the flower bed.

Draw the plan on squared paper using a scale of 1 cm to represent 1 m.

Shade all the possible areas in which the apple tree could be planted.

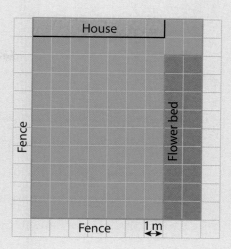

5 A town needs a mobile phone mast. The mast must be more than 300 m from the school and more than 200 m from the power lines.

Draw the plan on squared paper using a scale of 1 cm to represent 50 m.

Shade all the possible areas in which the mast could be placed.

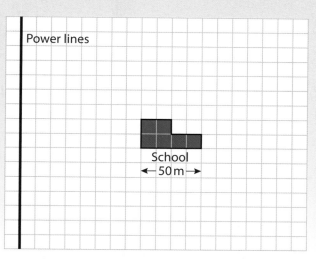

⊙ Points to remember

⊙ A locus can define a region, e.g. the set of points that are less than 20 cm from a line segment is the region inside the dashed line below.

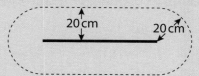

⊙ More than one locus can define a region that complies with all the conditions.

How well are you doing?

Transformations and loci

You will need squared paper, a pair of compasses, a ruler and a pencil.

1. Calculate the lengths of these lines.
   Where appropriate, write your answer to 1 decimal place.

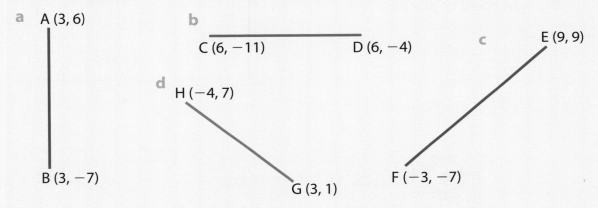

a   A (3, 6)

b

C (6, −11)   D (6, −4)

c   E (9, 9)

d   H (−4, 7)

B (3, −7)

G (3, 1)

F (−3, −7)

2. Work out the coordinates of the point that divides the line JL in the ratio 3 : 2.

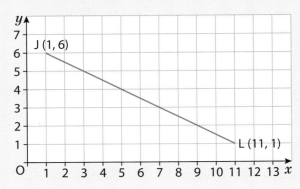

J (1, 6)

L (11, 1)

3 *1996 level 7*

Jill has drawn an original picture of a giraffe
for an animal charity.
It measures 6.5 cm high by 4 cm wide.

ORIGINAL
PICTURE

Different-sized copies of the original picture
can be made to just fit into various shapes.

a Jill wants to enlarge the original picture so
that it just fits entirely inside a rectangle on a
carrier bag. The rectangle measures
24 cm high by 12 cm wide.

By what scale factor should she multiply the original picture?
Show your working.

b Jill wants to multiply the original picture by a
scale factor so that it just fits entirely inside
the square shown on the right for a badge.

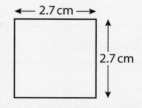

By what scale factor should she multiply the
original picture? Show your working.

4 A quadrilateral has vertices at (4, 1), (4, 5), (2, 6) and (2, 3).
It is reflected in the x-axis and the image is then rotated 180° about (0, 0).
Describe fully the single transformation that maps the original quadrilateral
to the final image.

5 *2006 level 7*

In a wildlife park in Africa, wardens want to
know the position of an elephant in a certain
area.

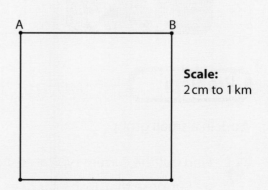

Scale:
2 cm to 1 km

a They place one microphone at each corner
of a 4 km by 4 km square.
Draw accurately a diagram of a 4 km by 4 km
square. Use a scale of 2 cm to represent 1 km.

b Each microphone has a range of 3.5 km.
The elephant is out of range of microphones A and B.
Where in the square could the elephant be?

Show the region accurately on your diagram, and label the region R.

How far can you go for £100?

This group activity will help you to:

⊙ decide on the methods, operations and tools to use, including ICT;

⊙ examine patterns and relationships;

⊙ change values and assumptions to see the effect on answers in the model;

⊙ choose appropriate language to communicate results and solutions.

Background

Different forms of transport cost different amounts of money. Walking, for example, or riding in a horse and cart, cost very little money but travelling by space rocket is very expensive!

Problem

Work in a small group.

1. Find out the current typical cost of petrol and diesel per litre. Agree an average cost to use.

   a Suppose that Josh's car does an average of 8 miles per litre.
   How far could you go in Josh's car for £100?

   b Do you think this is a reasonable estimate for the cost of travelling by car?
   Explain your answer.

   c Discuss your answer with another group. Refine it if you wish.

The table shows some information about different forms of transport.

Transport	Cost per mile	Average speed (mph)
Car	20p	50
Train	12p	80
Ferry	£2.30	30
Jumbo jet	£1	1330
Cruise liner	42p	24

2 For each form of transport in the table, work out how far you can go for £100.

3 Find some other forms of transport, e.g. bicycle, taxi, motor bike, hot air balloon, …
Use the Internet to find out the approximate cost per mile and average speed.
Then work out how far you could go for £100.

4 The map shows the distances between some world cities.

a Choose a journey and a form of transport.
Work out how much the journey would cost and how long it would take.

b How would you decide which form of transport to use for a particular journey?
What factors should you take into account besides cost and time?

c If you have time, choose another two cities in the world.
Use the Internet to find out how far apart they are.
Plan a journey between the two cities.
Use the Internet to find out what the journey would cost you.

Be prepared to discuss your decisions with other groups.

Decimals and accuracy

This unit will help you to:

- change a recurring decimal to a fraction;
- multiply and divide by numbers between 0 and 1;
- round numbers to a given number of significant figures and estimate results of calculations;
- work out the greatest and least possible values of a measurement;
- use a calculator efficiently.

1 Recurring decimals

This lesson will help you to change a recurring decimal to a fraction.

Exercise 1

Here are three decimals:

$$\frac{5}{8} = 0.625 \qquad \frac{1}{3} = 0.333\,333\ldots \qquad \pi = 3.141\,59\ldots$$

From left to right they are examples of a **terminating decimal**, a **recurring decimal**, and a decimal that neither terminates nor recurs, called an **irrational number**.

To show a recurring decimal a small dot is placed over the first and last of the group of recurring digits, for example:

$$\frac{7}{18} = 0.3\dot{8} = 0.388\,88\ldots \quad \frac{9}{11} = 0.\dot{8}\dot{1} = 0.818\,181\ldots \quad \frac{2}{7} = 0.\dot{2}85\,71\dot{4} = 0.285\,714\,285\,714\,28\ldots$$

You can change **fractions to decimals** by writing them as the equivalent number of tenths, hundredths or thousands, or by using division.

Example 1

a Write $\frac{11}{25}$ as a terminating decimal.

Change $\frac{11}{25}$ to hundredths.

$$\frac{11}{25} = \frac{11 \times 4}{25 \times 4} = \frac{44}{100} = 0.44$$

b Write $\frac{5}{11}$ as a recurring decimal.

Use a calculator.

$\frac{5}{11}$ means $5 \div 11 = 0.454\,545\ldots = 0.\dot{4}\dot{5}$

You can change **terminating decimals to fractions** by expressing them in tenths, hundredths or thousandths.

Example 2

Write 0.375 as a fraction.

Write 0.375 as a number of thousandths.

$0.375 = \frac{375}{1000} = \frac{3}{8}$ (cancelling by 125)

You can change **recurring decimals** to fractions by using algebra and forming an equation.

Example 3

Write $0.\dot{1}\dot{8}$ as a fraction in its simplest form.

Let	$f = 0.181\ 181\ldots$ (1)
Since there are two recurring digits, multiply (1) by $10^2 = 100$	
Then	$100f = 18.181\ 181\ldots$ (2)
Subtract (1) from (2):	$99f = 18$
Divide by 99:	$f = \frac{18}{99} = \frac{2}{11}$ (cancelling by 9)

① Write each fraction as a recurring decimal.

     a $\frac{2}{3}$ **b** $\frac{25}{33}$ **c** $\frac{4}{7}$ **d** $\frac{5}{9}$ **e** $\frac{5}{6}$ **f** $\frac{30}{101}$

② Write each terminating decimal as a fraction in its simplest form.

     a 0.675   **b** 0.875   **c** 0.735   **d** 0.9375   **e** 0.203 125

③ Write each recurring decimal as a fraction in its simplest form. Show your working.

     a $0.\dot{4}$ **b** $0.\dot{1}\dot{2}$ **c** $0.\dot{6}$ **d** $0.\dot{3}2\dot{1}$

     e $0.\dot{4}\dot{5}$ **f** $0.8\dot{0}\dot{1}$ **g** $0.\dot{8}\dot{1}$ **h** $0.\dot{7}\dot{8}$

④ Write a list of the fractions $\frac{1}{9}$ to $\frac{8}{9}$ as recurring decimals, e.g. $\frac{1}{9} = 0.\dot{1}$.
     Describe the patterns that you see.

⑤ Write a list of the fractions $\frac{1}{11}$ to $\frac{10}{11}$ as recurring decimals, e.g. $\frac{1}{11} = 0.\dot{0}\dot{9}$.
     Describe the patterns that you see.

⑥ Write a list of the fractions $\frac{1}{7}$ to $\frac{6}{7}$ as recurring decimals, e.g. $\frac{1}{7} = 0.\dot{1}42\ 85\dot{7}$.
     Describe the patterns that you see.

Extension problems

 7 Write each recurring decimal as a fraction in its simplest form. Show your working.

 a $0.9\dot{1}\dot{5}$ b $0.1\dot{1}8\dot{8}$ c $0.0\dot{3}$ d $0.05\dot{6}$

 8 Write the value of each of the fractions $\frac{1}{13}$ to $\frac{9}{13}$ as a recurring decimal. What do you notice?

Points to remember

- Fractions whose denominators have only 2s or 5s as prime factors convert to **terminating decimals**.
- Other fractions convert to **recurring decimals**.
- Convert terminating decimals to fractions by expressing them as tenths, hundredths or thousandths.
- Use algebra to convert recurring decimals to fractions.
- Some decimals cannot be converted to an exact fraction, e.g. π. These are called **irrational numbers**.

2 Significant figures

This lesson will help you to round numbers to one significant figure and estimate results of calculations.

Did you know that...?

Estimates are an important part of maths and science.

When a car is damaged, a **loss adjuster** who works for the insurance company estimates what it will cost to repair using a series of approximate calculations.

Harlow Shapley (1885–1972), an American astronomer, was the first to estimate the size of our galaxy, the Milky Way. Its diameter is about 100 000 light years.

To find the most significant digit in a number, find the first non-zero digit counting from the left.

The **first significant digit** is the **red** digit.

37.8   950   3.961   0.0583   0.002 004

To round a number **correct to 1 significant figure**, look at the **second** significant figure in the number.

- If it is 5 or more, increase the first significant figure by 1.

- If it is less than 5, leave the first significant figure unchanged.

For example:

48.76 rounded correct to 1 significant figure is **50** as it is nearer to 50 than it is to 40.

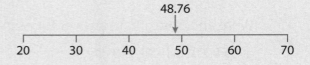

0.042 68 rounded correct to 1 significant figure is **0.04** as it is nearer to 0.04 than it is to 0.05.

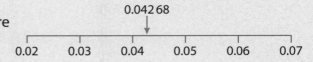

You can round numbers to any number of significant figures.

- Look at the first unwanted digit.

- Use the normal rules of rounding to adjust the digit to the left of it if necessary.

> **353.84** ≈ **353.8** (to 4 s.f.) ≈ **354** (to 3 s.f.) ≈ **350** (to 2 s.f.) ≈ **400** (to 1 s.f.)
>
> **0.087 54** ≈ **0.0875** (to 3 s.f.) ≈ **0.088** (to 2 s.f.) ≈ **0.09** (to 1 s.f.)

You can find approximate answers to calculations by writing each number correct to 1 significant figure and then doing the calculation.

Example

Write an approximate answer for $(6.4 \times 179.8) \div 0.52$.

Round each number to 1 significant figure.

$(6.4 \times 179.8) \div 0.52 \approx (6 \times 200) \div 0.5$
$= 1200 \div 0.5$
$= 2400$

① Round each number to one significant figure.

a 16.3   b 4.7   c 324.9   d 5327   e 19 045

2 Round each number to one significant figure.

a 0.71   b 0.88   c 0.043   d 0.056   e 0.0079

3 Write an approximate answer for each calculation.

a 4.9×3.4 b 3.8×5.4 c 9.4×9.9

d 13.4×3.7 e 24.4×4.7 f 275×42

4 Write an approximate answer for each calculation.

a $211 \div 12$ b $377 \div 48$ c $985 \div 478$

d $346 \div 48$ e $2334 \div 12.9$ f $275 \div 42$

5 Write an approximate answer for each calculation.

a $(29.2 \times 0.019) \div 0.37$ b $(0.042 + 0.059) \times 0.081$

c $5.62 \times (0.91 - 0.67)$ d $0.475 \times (29.66 \div 0.64)$

e $(0.057 + 0.038) \times (0.069 - 0.041)$ f $5.2^2 \times 7.6 \div 1.68^2$

6 Write an approximate answer for each calculation.

a $\dfrac{217 \times 0.582}{0.041}$ b $\dfrac{341 + 388}{0.072}$ c $\dfrac{1.93^2}{0.44^2}$ d $\dfrac{725 \times 0.725}{349 \times 0.069}$

7 Play this **Estimation** game with a partner.
Each of you should copy this grid in your book.

0.014	0.15	0.597	0.69
3.48	4.83	8.75	11.35

Rules

◉ In turn, choose two numbers from your own list of numbers.

◉ Write down the product of the two numbers.

◉ Work out the approximate value of the product by rounding each number to 1 s.f.
This is your score for this turn, so write it down.

◉ Cross out the two numbers that you chose in your own list.
They cannot be used again.

◉ Repeat three more times until all the numbers have been used up.

◉ The winner is the player with the score nearest to 50.

8 A rectangular playing field measures by 183.5 m by 94.6 m.

   a Weed killer costs 3.4p per square metre.
     What is the approximate cost of spraying weed killer on the whole field?

   b The cost of white paint for outlining the perimeter of the field is £27.80.
     What is the approximate cost per metre for the white paint?

9 Round each number to the given number of significant figures.

   a 548 to 2 s.f.   **b** 597 to 2 s.f.   **c** 6319 to 2 s.f.

   d 6319 to 3 s.f.   **e** 0.7378 to 2 s.f.   **f** 0.7378 to 3 s.f.

   g 0.0695 to 2 s.f.   **h** 968.43 to 4 s.f.   **i** 968.43 to 2 s.f.

Extension problem

 Did you know that...?

The 400 m sprint is a track running event. It is the longest sprint distance and is one lap around the track. Runners start in staggered positions and race in separate lanes all the way round.

In the UK and other countries, athletes previously competed in the 440 yard dash (402.336 m) instead of the 400 m. This ended in the UK in 1976, when metric measures were introduced.

The current world record for the men's 400 m race is held by **Michael Johnson**, with a time of 43.18 seconds.

10 **a** Michael Johnson ran 400 m in 43.18 seconds.
     Approximately, what was his average speed in kilometres per hour?

   b At the same average speed, about how much longer would it take
     Michael Johnson to run 440 yards?

 Points to remember

⊙ The first **significant figure** of a number is its first non-zero digit.

⊙ A number rounded to one significant figure has only one non-zero digit.

⊙ In general, estimates of calculations are made by rounding numbers to one significant figure. Sometimes other approximations of the numbers in a calculation are more sensible.

3 Using a calculator

This lesson will help you to use a calculator efficiently.

Exercise 3

You can use a calculator to work out complex calculations. Not all calculators are the same, so make sure you know how to use your own calculator efficiently.

Check that you know how to use the:

bracket keys	square root and square keys
fraction key	power and root keys
π key	memory

and that you can enter numbers in standard form.

Example

Work out $\dfrac{21.13 + \sqrt{46.24}}{3.5^2}$.

You could work out the numerator and denominator separately and write them down. Then divide the numerator of 27.93 by the denominator of 12.25 to get the answer 2.28.

This is not as efficient as entering the whole calculation in one key sequence. This involves using brackets, the square and the square root keys.

(2 1 . 1 3 + √ 4 6 . 2 4) ÷ 3 . 5 x^2 =

You will need a scientific calculator.

1. Work out:

a $4.6^2 + (3.2 - 1.73)^2$

b $\dfrac{28.4 \times 5.65}{1.52 \times (3.4 - 1.9)}$

c $\sqrt{16.5^2 - 4.7^2}$

d $3.2^4 \div 2.0^6$

e $\sqrt[3]{1152 \times 1.5}$

f $\dfrac{2.5 \times 10^4}{0.5 \times 10^3}$

2. Use the fraction key to work out these.

a $1\frac{9}{14} + 3\frac{16}{21}$

b $\left(\frac{7}{8} - \frac{5}{6}\right) \times \left(\frac{5}{7} - \frac{3}{5}\right)$

c $\left(\frac{2}{3} + \frac{5}{8}\right) \div \left(\frac{4}{9} - \frac{1}{6}\right)$

d $\dfrac{1\frac{5}{6} + 4\frac{5}{9}}{2\frac{11}{12}}$

(3) Seven friends won £1 million in the National Lottery.
They shared out the money as fairly as possible and left the change in the bank.
How much money was left in the bank?

(4) Play **Target 1000** with a partner.
You need one calculator between you.

Take turns to go first.
The aim is to get a number in the display
as close as possible to 1000.

Rules

- The first player clears the display and enters a starting number between 0 and 100. The player then passes the calculator to the second player.

- The second player chooses a number to multiply the number in the display, then presses $\boxed{=}$.

- An answer between 975 and 1025, including decimals, scores 1 point.

- The winner is the first to get 5 points.

For example:

Ruth clears the display and enters 14.

Aziz multiplies by 72 to get 1008.

Aziz scores one point.

$$14 \times 72 = 1008$$

Aziz clears the display and enters 46.

Ruth multiplies by 21.1 to get 970.6.

$$46 \times 21.1 = 970.6$$

Ruth gets no score.

(5) Arun is trying to get as close as he can to 1 million.
He must use each digit 1 to 9 once and only once.
He can use any of the operations $+$, $-$, $\times$ and $\div$, and brackets.

Arun has started recording his answers and how far they are from 1 million.

Calculation	Answer	How far from 1 million?
$(953 + 721) \times 864$	1 446 336	446 336
$12\,345 \times 678 \div 9$	929 990	70 010

How close can you get to one million?

(6) What is the smallest whole number that you can subtract from a million to make the answer exactly divisible by 7924?

Extension problem

 7 Enter 6 in your calculator display. Square it using the x^2 key and write down the answer. Keep on squaring and writing down the answer.

   a What is the largest power of 6 that your calculator will accept?

   b What happens when the numbers get too big for the display?

   c What is the biggest number that you can show in your calculator display?

⦿ Points to remember

- ⦿ Make sure you can use your calculator efficiently, including keys for fractions, brackets, π, square root, square, powers, negative numbers and the memory.

- ⦿ A string of multiplications and divisions can be entered into a calculator in one go; there is no need to work out each step separately.

- ⦿ When you do an **exact calculation**, round the final answer, not the intermediate steps.

- ⦿ Don't give too many figures in answers. In general, the answer should not have more significant figures (s.f.) than those in the problem. 2 or 3 s.f. are usually enough.

4 Back of an envelope calculations

This lesson will help you to estimate results of calculations.

Exercise 4

If an exact answer isn't needed, we often round numbers to form a calculation that is easy to work out, maybe on the back of an envelope. We also make assumptions based on likely averages.

Example

About how many litres of milk are drunk each day in the UK?

Assume that one person drinks about 0.5 litre of milk each day or 3.5 litres per week.

Assume that there are about 50 weeks in a year.
So one person drinks about $3.5 \times 50 = 175$ litres of milk each year.

Assume that the population of the UK is about 60 million $= 6 \times 10^6$.
So in the UK we drink about $175 \times 6 \times 10^6 = 1050 \times 10^6 = 1.05 \times 10^9$ litres per year, or just over 1 billion litres per year.

Work on these problems with a partner.

For question 3, you will need **N6.3 Resource sheet 4.1** and two pens or counters in two colours.

1 If you had to move 1 000 000 cubic millimetres of sand, which of these would be the right size for the job?

    A a bucket   **B** a wheelbarrow

    C a van   **D** a lorry

    Explain your answer.

2 Explain your answers and the assumptions you made.

    a Could you walk 1 million miles in your lifetime?

    b What year was it 1 billion minutes ago?

    c How much water is flushed away in toilets in the UK in a single day?

    d How long would it take you to drink enough water to fill a small swimming pool?

3 Play this game with a partner.
You need 18 counters in two colours, or two coloured pens, a calculator and
a copy of **Resource sheet 4.1**.

Rules

◉ Take turns to choose two of these containers.

egg cup	cup	jug	milk carton	bottle	pan	bucket
0.05 ml	0.2 litres	0.4 litres	0.5 litres	1 litre	2.8 litres	5 litres

◉ Make up a division question about them, such as: 'How many egg cups will fill the jug?' or 'What fraction of the pan will the cup hold?'

◉ Work out the answer, if necessary correct to two decimal places.
You can use a calculator if you wish but you can't change your mind about your question.

◉ If the answer is on the grid on the resource sheet, ring the number with your coloured pen or cover it with one of your counters.

◉ The winner is the first player to get four counters in a line in any direction.

4 The plug hole of a wash-basin is blocked.
A tap is dripping at the rate of 1 drop per second.
Each drop has a volume of 10 mm³.
The wash-basin holds 10 litres when it is full.

The plumber says he cannot get there to fix it for 2 weeks.
Will he get there before the wash-basin overflows?

Explain your answer.

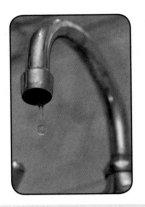

Extension problem

5 About how many chips are eaten each day at lunchtime in UK schools?
There are roughly 12 million pupils in UK schools.
Explain how you worked out your answer and the assumptions that you made.

Points to remember

- **Approximate calculations** can provide good estimates.
- Approximate calculations are often called 'back of an envelope' calculations because they are easy enough to work out on the back of an envelope.
- When you do approximate calculations, you can round the numbers at any stage of the calculation.
- To estimate measurements, it helps to know some 'benchmarks', e.g. the approximate height of a door (2 m) or the capacity of a tea cup (200 ml).

5 Measurement errors

This lesson will help you to work out the greatest and least possible values of a measurement.

Did you know that...?

The degree of accuracy of a measurement depends on the equipment used. For example, using a stop-watch with a seconds hand, it is possible to time an event to the nearest second.

Using electronic equipment, as used in the Olympic Games, a measurement to the nearest thousandth of a second is possible.

Michael Phelps, USA, Athens 2004

Exercise 5A

Lower and upper limits or bounds

The width of a laptop is measured with a tape measure as 32 cm to the nearest centimetre. Its exact width can be any value between 31.5 cm and 32.5 cm.

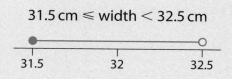

$31.5\,\text{cm} \leqslant \text{width} < 32.5\,\text{cm}$

32 cm is halfway between 31.5 cm and 32.5 cm.

31.5 is the smallest value that rounds to 32.

31.5 cm is called the **lower limit or bound**.

The length cannot be exactly 32.5 cm, since this would round to 33 cm, but this is used as the **upper limit or bound**.

1. The length of a pencil is 12 cm to the nearest cm.
   Write down the greatest length it could be.

2. The weight of an envelope is 45 grams to the nearest gram.
   Write down the minimum weight it could be.

3. The capacity of a jug is 4 litres to the nearest litre.
   What is the maximum capacity of the jug?

4. The time it took to travel on a journey was 36 minutes to the nearest minute.
   What is the shortest length of time that the journey could have taken?

5. The number of matchsticks in a box is 120 to the nearest 10.
   What is the greatest possible number of matchsticks in the box?

6. A pair of shoes costs £26 to the nearest pound.
   What is the greatest possible cost of the shoes?

7. Find the upper and lower bounds for these quantities.

   a To the nearest 100, there are 1600 bees in a beehive.

   b The amount of honey in a jar is 300 ml to the nearest 10 ml.

   c Each pot of honey costs £1.60 to the nearest 10p.

8 Harriet's height is 1.59 m to the nearest centimetre. Write in metres:

    a her minimum possible height;

    b her maximum possible height.

9 The length of a pen is 12 cm to the nearest cm.
The length of a pencil case is 122 mm to the nearest mm.
Explain why the pen might not fit in the case.

10 A TV set is 82 cm wide to the nearest centimetre.
It must fit on a shelf that is 818 mm long.
Explain how the TV might fit on the shelf.

Exercise 5B

You can find the upper and lower limits of **combined measurements**.

Example

A primary school playground measures 64 m by 47 m, both to the nearest metre.

a What are the minimum and maximum possible areas of the playground?

To find the **minimum** area, take the lowest possible values of the length and width.

Minimum area = 63.5 × 46.5
            = 2952.75 m²

To find the **maximum** area, take the highest possible values of the length and width.

Maximum area = 64.5 × 47.5
            = 3063.75 m²

b What are the minimum and maximum possible perimeters of the playground?

Minimum perimeter = 63.5 + 46.5 + 63.5 + 46.5 = 220 m
Maximum perimeter = 64.5 + 47.5 + 64.5 + 47.5 = 224 m

1 A bottle of water holds 1 litre to the nearest 10 ml.

    a What is the smallest possible amount in the bottle?

    b What is the greatest possible amount that 10 bottles could hold?

2 Joe weighs 88 kg and Anna weighs 65 kg, both to the nearest kg.
Explain why their minimum combined weight could be 152 kg.

3 A rectangular postage stamp is 4.2 cm long by 3.5 cm wide.
Each measurement is accurate to the nearest mm.

   a What are the upper and lower bounds for the length of the stamp?

   b What are the upper and lower bounds for the width of the stamp?

   c What are the upper and lower bounds for the perimeter of the stamp?

4 The pitch of a table football game is 2.5 m by 1.5 m.
Each measurement is accurate to the nearest 10 cm.

   What are the upper and lower bounds for:

   a the length of the pitch;

   b the width of the pitch;

   c the perimeter of the pitch;

   d the area of the pitch?

5 A square airfield has sides of length 1.52 km to the nearest 10 metres. Calculate:

   a the upper bound of the perimeter of the airfield;

   b the lower bound of the area of the airfield.

Extension problems

6 A circular pond has a radius of 5.23 m and a depth of 0.92 m, both accurate to the nearest centimetre.
Calculate, in litres, the maximum and minimum amount of water needed to fill the pond.

7 A builder pays £15.26 per tonne for gravel. Each tonne is accurate to the nearest 10 kg.
How much money could the builder lose in an order of 10 tonnes?

⦿ Points to remember

⊙ Measurements may be inaccurate by up to half a unit in either direction, e.g. '4 kg to the nearest kilogram' has a least possible weight of 3.5 kg and a greatest possible weight of 4.5 kg.

⊙ The **lower bound** is the least possible value of the measurement and the **upper bound** is the greatest possible value of the measurement.

⊙ For **continuous quantities**, such as heights, the value of the measurement can equal the lower bound but not the upper bound.

⊙ For **discrete quantities**, such as numbers of objects, the value of the number can equal the lower bound or the upper bound.

How well are you doing?

Can you:

- change a recurring decimal to a fraction?
- multiply and divide by numbers between 0 and 1?
- round numbers to a given number of significant figures and estimate results of calculations?
- work out the greatest and least possible values of a measurement?
- use a calculator efficiently?

Decimals and accuracy (no calculator)

1 *Year 7 Optional Test level 6*

A teacher asked pupils to divide 28 by 3.

> Gail wrote: $28 \div 3 = 9.33$
>
> Ahmed wrote: $28 \div 3 = 9\frac{1}{3}$

The teacher marked both correct, but said Ahmed's answer was better than Gail's answer.

Explain why $9\frac{1}{3}$ is not the same as 9.33.

2 *2000 level 7*

Look at these numbers on cards.

| 0.2 | 2 | 10 | 0.1 | 0.05 | 1 |

a Choose two of the numbers which, when multiplied, give the lowest possible answer.
Write the numbers and work out the answer.

b Choose two of the cards which, when one number is divided by the other, give the answer 100. Write the numbers.

3 *2000 level 7*

  a Which of the blue numbers below is the best estimate of the answer to:

$$32.7 \times 0.48$$

       1.2   1.6   12   16   120   160

  b Estimate the answer to:

$$\frac{28.6 \times 24.4}{5.67 \times 4.02}$$

  Give your answer to 1 significant figure.

Decimals and accuracy (calculator allowed)

4 *2000 level 7*

A groundsman marks out a football pitch.

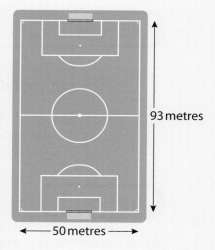

  a He makes the pitch 93 metres long, to the nearest metre. What is the shortest possible length of the pitch?

  b He makes the pitch 50 metres wide, to the nearest metre. What is the shortest possible width of the pitch?

  c Des wants to know how many times he should run around the outside of this pitch to be sure of running at least 3 km.

    Use your answer to parts **a** and **b** to find how many times Des should run around the pitch.
Show your working.

5 *1999 level 7*

The ship 'Queen Mary' used to sail across the Atlantic Ocean.

The ship's usual speed was 33 miles per hour.
On average, the ship used fuel at the rate of 1 gallon for every 13 feet sailed.

Calculate how many gallons of fuel the ship used in one hour of travelling at the usual speed. (5280 feet = 1 mile.)

Show your working and write down the full calculator display.

Now write your answer correct to 2 significant figures.

Functional skills 4

Where is the mathematics?

This group activity will help you to:

- identify the mathematics in a situation;
- identify mathematical questions to ask;
- choose appropriate language and forms of presentation to communicate conclusions.

Background

Maths is all around us.

Looking for the maths in a situation or in information will help you to appreciate how widely maths is used.

Problem 1

What mathematical questions could you ask about this picture?

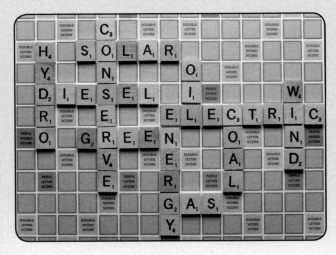

What answers to your questions would you give?

Problem 2

What mathematical questions could you ask about this picture?

What answers to your questions would you give?

Problem 3

What mathematical questions could you ask about this picture?

What answers to your questions would you give?

Be prepared to discuss your questions and answers with other groups.

Probability 1

This unit will help you to:

- ◉ use relative frequency to estimate probability;
- ◉ recognise when events are independent;
- ◉ use tree diagrams to represent outcomes of two independent events.

1 Relative frequency

This lesson will help you to calculate and use frequencies based on the total number of events.

Exercise 1

This table shows how long customers waited at two different tills in a supermarket over the same 1 hour period on a busy Saturday morning.

Till	Total number of customers	Frequency of customers waiting t minutes			
		$0 \leqslant t < 3$	$3 \leqslant t < 6$	$6 \leqslant t < 9$	$t \geqslant 9$
1	75	25	33	14	3
2	62	18	28	13	3

As the total number of customers differs for each till, it is not possible to use the frequencies in the table to compare the waiting times. Instead, the **relative frequency** is used.

The relative frequency of an event occurring is: $\dfrac{\text{the frequency of the event}}{\text{total frequency of all events}}$

Relative frequency can be written as a fraction, a decimal or a percentage.

This table shows the waiting time information expressed as relative frequencies to 2 d.p.

Till	Total number of customers	Frequency of customers waiting t minutes			
		$0 \leqslant t < 3$	$3 \leqslant t < 6$	$6 \leqslant t < 9$	$t \geqslant 9$
1	75	$\frac{25}{75} = 0.33$	$\frac{33}{75} = 0.44$	$\frac{14}{75} = 0.19$	$\frac{3}{75} = 0.04$
2	62	$\frac{18}{62} = 0.29$	$\frac{28}{62} = 0.45$	$\frac{13}{62} = 0.21$	$\frac{3}{62} = 0.05$

The relative frequencies make it possible to see that in general people waited longer at Till 2.

If the number of trials is large enough, the **relative frequency** of an event is used as a measure of the **probability** of that event occurring.

The relative frequency of an event occurring is: $\dfrac{\text{number of times the event occurs}}{\text{total number of trials}}$

This is similar to the definition of experimental probability.

Example

Terri picks a counter at random from a bag of red and blue counters.
She records the colour obtained and replaces the counter in the bag.

She repeats this 200 times.

Her results are shown in this table.

What is the probability that Terri picks a red counter?

Colour	Frequency
Red	138
Blue	62

There are 200 trials so the relative frequency of picking a red counter is $\frac{138}{200} = 0.69$.

The relative frequency of picking a blue counter is $\frac{62}{200} = 0.31$.

You will need a pack of digit cards from 1 to 10 for question 5.
Alternatively, use the Ace to 10 of one suit of a pack of ordinary playing cards.

Where appropriate, give your answers correct to two decimal places.

1 A biased coin is tossed 200 times.
It lands heads up 120 times and tails up 80 times.

   a Write the relative frequency of the coin landing tails up.

   b The coin is to be tossed again. Estimate the probability that it will land:

      i tails up   ii heads up.

2 A bag contains a red counter, a blue counter, a pink counter and a grey counter.
Iqbal picks a counter at random, then puts it back. He does this 400 times.
The table shows the number of times each of the coloured counters is picked.

Red	Blue	Pink	Grey
81	110	136	73

   a Write the relative frequency of Iqbal picking the red counter.

   b Write down the relative frequency of Iqbal picking the pink counter.

   c Iqbal takes a counter one more time. Estimate the probability that this counter will be:

      i blue   ii grey.

3 **a** 120 cars pass the school gate. 36 of the cars are silver.
What is the relative frequency of a silver car passing the school gate?

b There are 70 cars in the school car park. 14 of these cars are silver.
What is the relative frequency of a silver car in the school car park?

c Compare the numbers of silver cars passing the school gate and in the school car park.

4 Kylie carries out a survey about the length of words in a magazine.
She chooses an article at random.
She counts the number of letters in each of the first 300 words of the article.
The table shows Kylie's results.

Number of letters in a word	1	2	3	4	5	6	7	8	9	10
Frequency	14	28	84	62	41	26	21	12	8	4

A word is chosen at random from the 300 words.

a What is the most likely number of letters in the word?

b Estimate the probability that the word will have:

  i 1 letter   **ii** 7 letters   **iii** more than 5 letters.

c The whole article has 1000 words.
Estimate the total number of 3-letter words in this article.

5 **a** Spread out some cards from 1 to 10 face down and shuffle them.
Pick a card and record the number in a copy of the table below.

Number	Tally	Frequency
Square		
Not square		

Put the card back face down.
Repeat this trial 20 times, then complete the table.

b Calculate the relative frequency of obtaining a square number.

c Repeat the experiment, this time for 30 trials.
Is the relative frequency of obtaining a square number the same?

d Work out the relative frequency for the combined results of the two experiments.

e Work out the theoretical probability of picking a square number from your pack
of cards.

f Are your results what you expected? Explain your answer.

Extension problem

 6 The tables give information about the numbers of voters in different parts of the United
Kingdom in general elections that took place in the years 1950 and 2001.

1950	Number of eligible voters	Number of actual voters
England	28 372 970	23 954 509
Northern Ireland	865 085	561 428
Scotland	3 370 028	2 726 235
Wales	1 802 182	1 528 672

2001	Number of eligible voters	Number of actual voters
England	36 990 780	21 870 488
Northern Ireland	1 191 009	810 381
Scotland	3 983 306	2 313 581
Wales	2 236 143	1 372 542

a Compare the relative frequencies of the actual voters in the two elections in the
different parts of the United Kingdom.

b Explain why relative frequency is used to make this comparison.

c A person was picked at random from the eligible voters in England in 1950.
Estimate the probability that the person voted.

d A person was picked at random from the eligible voters in the United Kingdom in 2001.
Estimate the probability that the person voted.

 Points to remember

⊙ If an event occurs N times in T trials, its **relative frequency** is $\frac{N}{T}$, or:
$$\text{relative frequency} = \frac{\text{number of times the event occurs}}{\text{total number of trials}}$$

⊙ Relative frequency can be written as a fraction, a decimal or a percentage.

⊙ The probability of an event can be estimated by doing an experiment.

⊙ Experimental probability can be equated to relative frequency.

⊙ If the probability of an event is p, and there are to be T trials of an
experiment, the event is likely to occur an estimated $p \times T$ times.

2 Exploring relative frequency

This lesson will help you to appreciate what happens to relative frequency as the number of trials (or observations) increases and how this relates to probability.

Exercise 2

As the number of trials in a probability experiment increases, the relative frequency of an event gets closer and closer to a fixed value. This fixed value is called a **limit**.

You can see what happens by drawing a **relative frequency graph**.

Example 1

John picked a number from 1 to 10 at random.
After every 20 trials, he recorded how frequently he had picked a square number.
The table below shows his results.

a   Complete the row for relative frequency. Give your answers to 2 decimal places.

Number of trials	20	40	60	80	100	150	200	250	300	400
Frequency of square	8	15	20	25	27	42	58	76	93	121
Relative frequency	0.4	0.38	0.33	0.31	0.27	0.28	0.29	0.30	0.31	0.30

b   Represent the data on a relative frequency graph.

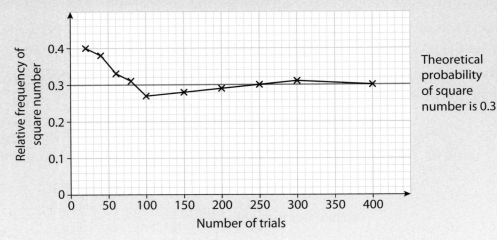

Theoretical probability of square number is 0.3

c   Describe what the relative frequency graph shows.

The graph shows that the relative frequency changes during the first few trials. It gradually settles down to approximately 0.3.

This corresponds to the theoretical probability of picking a square number.

This connection between relative frequency and theoretical probability for a large number of trials can be used to estimate probabilities in situations where outcomes are not equally likely.

Example 2

The graph shows the results of a survey of a sample of people in which they were asked whether or not they were left-handed.

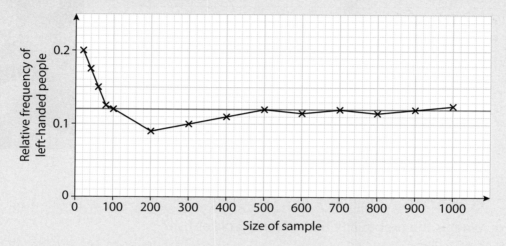

a What is the limit of the relative frequency of a person being left-handed?

As the number of people in the sample increases the relative frequency of being left-handed settles down to approximately 0.12.

b If a person is selected at random, what is the probability that they are left-handed?

The probability that a person selected at random is left-handed is approximately 0.12.

You can work out frequency values from relative frequency if you know the number of trials.

Example 3

Look at the relative frequency graph in Example 2.

In the survey, how many of the sample of 300 people were left-handed?

When the sample size is 300, the relative frequency of left-handed people is 0.1.

The frequency of left-handed people = 0.1 × 300 = 30

So 30 of the sample of 300 people are left-handed.

You will need graph paper and, for question 4, two drawing pins and a plastic cup.

1 600 teenagers were chosen at random.
They were asked if they liked to eat fish.
The table shows how frequently they said yes.

Number of teenagers	100	200	300	400	500	600
Frequency of liking fish	41	107	144	204	248	251
Relative frequency of liking fish	0.41					

a Copy and complete the table.

b Draw a relative frequency graph to show the data.

c What is the limit of the relative frequency of a teenager from the sample liking fish?

d What is the probability that a teenager likes fish?

2 A counter is taken at random from a bag of 10 counters of different colours.
The colour of the counter is recorded and the counter is then put back in the bag.

This trial is repeated 200 times.

The table shows the frequency of picking a red counter for different numbers of trials.

Number of trials	10	20	30	40	50	60	70	80	90	100
Frequency	2	5	8	12	14	18	21	25	28	30
Relative frequency										

a Copy and complete the table to show the relative frequency of picking a red counter.

b On graph paper, draw a relative frequency graph to show the data.

c What is the limit of the relative frequency of picking a red counter?

d What is the probability of picking a red counter from the bag?

e How many red counters do you think there are in the bag? Explain why.

3 David stands at the school gate in the middle of the morning to observe 400 passing cars.
He records whether or not each car is carrying passengers.
After each 20 cars, he works out the relative frequency of cars with a single occupant.
The table shows his results.

Total number of cars	20	40	60	80	100	150	200	250	300	400
Frequency of single occupant	11	23	35	49	63	99	134	160	198	260

  a Draw a relative frequency graph to show this information.

  b What is the limit of the relative frequency of cars with a single occupant?

  c What is the probability that the next car that passes the school gate has a single occupant? Explain your answer.

Extension problem

  Work with a partner. You need two drawing pins and a plastic cup.

  a Repeat this trial 100 times.

  One of you should put the drawing pins in a plastic cup.
  Shake the plastic cup and empty the drawing pins onto the desk.
  The second person should record the outcome in a copy of this table.

Outcome	Tally	Frequency
Both points down		
One point up, one point down		
Both points up		

  b The second person should copy this table and complete it after each 10 trials.

Number of trials	10	20	30	40	50	60	70	80	90	100
Relative frequency of both points down										

  c Each of you should draw a relative frequency graph to represent the data.

  d What is the limiting value of the relative frequency of both points down?

  e Estimate the probability of both drawing pins landing points down.

  f Combine your results with at least one other pair.
  Work out another estimate of the probability of the drawing pins landing both points down.
  Explain why this estimate is a more accurate measure of the probability.

◉ **Points to remember**

⊙ With repeated trials or observations, relative frequency tends to a limit, which can be shown in a **relative frequency graph**.

⊙ For equally likely outcomes, the values of relative frequencies (experimental probabilities) approach theoretical probabilities as the number of trials becomes large.

⊙ When outcomes are not equally likely, relative frequency is used to estimate probability.

3 Combined events

This lesson will help you to find and use all the possible outcomes of two or more events.

Exercise 3

To work out probabilities of the outcomes of two events that occur at the same time or one after the other, identify all the possible outcomes. There are three ways to do this:

⊙ making a systematic list;

⊙ drawing a two-way tables;

⊙ drawing a tree diagram.

Example 1

Zak has a bowl of red and green apples.
He picks an apple at random from the bowl.
He records its colour and replaces the apple.
He then picks another apple at random and
records its colour.

List all the possible outcomes of picking two apples.

Method 1: Systematic listing

Outcomes for the first pick are Red (**R**) or Green (**G**).

If the first pick is **R** the second pick can be **R** or **G**.
If the first pick is **G** the second pick can be **R** or **G**.

This gives four outcomes:

R and **R**   **R** and **G**   **G** and **R**   **G** and **G**

Method 2: two-way table

	First apple	
	R	**G**
R	R and R	G and R
G	R and G	G and G

Second apple (row label)

Method 3: tree diagram

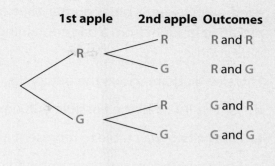

1st apple	2nd apple	Outcomes
R	R	R and R
R	G	R and G
G	R	G and R
G	G	G and G

In Example 1, the outcomes for each pick of an apple are **equally likely**.
For this reason the four outcomes when two apples are picked are also **equally likely**.

In many situations, the outcomes of combined events are **not equally likely**.

Example 2

There are some red socks, blue socks and green socks in a drawer.

Natalie picks two socks from the drawer.

Draw a tree diagram to show all the possible outcomes.

1st sock	2nd sock	Outcomes
R	R	R and R
R	B	R and B
R	G	R and G
B	R	B and R
B	B	B and B
B	G	B and G
G	R	G and R
G	B	G and B
G	G	G and G

---

1. A bag contains two balls. One ball is red and one ball is blue.

   A ball is taken out of the bag at random and then put back.
   Another ball is then taken out of the bag at random.

   a Draw a tree diagram to show all the possible the outcomes.

   b Explain why each of the possible outcomes is equally likely.

2. Tom rolls two fair dice.
   He records whether or not he rolls a six.
   The tree diagram shows the outcomes.

   a Write a list of all the possible outcomes.

   b Draw a two-way table to show all
      the outcomes.

   c State whether or not the outcomes
      are equally likely.

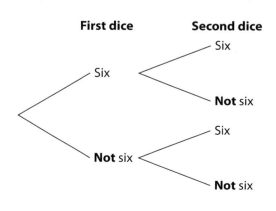

3 A counter is picked at random from a bag containing a red, a white and a blue counter, then a counter is picked at random from a bag containing a red and a blue counter.

This tree diagram shows the outcomes.

a Write a list of all the possible outcomes.

b Draw a two-way table to represent all the outcomes.

c State whether or not the combined outcomes are equally likely.

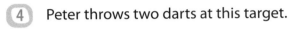

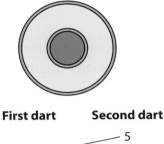

4 Peter throws two darts at this target.

If he hits the blue centre he scores 5 points.
If he hits the yellow ring he scores 1 point.
If he misses the target he scores 0 points.

a Copy and complete this tree diagram to find all the possible total scores that Peter could get.

b Explain why the total scores are not equally likely.

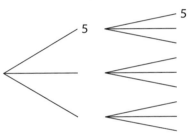

5 For breakfast Lilin drinks juice or tea. She eats cornflakes, croissants or toast.

Show all the possible outcomes for her choice of breakfast:

a in a two-way table;

b in a tree diagram.

6 The arrow on this fair spinner is spun twice.
The numbers the arrow lands on are added to give a total score.

a Draw a two-way table to show all the possible total scores.

b Draw a tree diagram to show all the possible total scores.

c What is the most likely score?

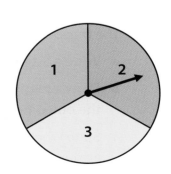

Points to remember

⊙ Two or more events can occur at the same time or one after the other.

⊙ The outcomes of a trial involving two combined events can be shown by using **systematic listing**, a **two-way table** or a **tree diagram**.

4 Tree diagrams and independent events

This lesson will help you to find the probabilities of the outcomes of two or more independent events.

Exercise 4

Two events are **independent** if one event happening does not affect the probability that the other event happens. For example:

Jim and Kim are brother and sister.
Event **A**: Jim catches chickenpox.
Event **B**: Kim catches chickenpox.

Events **A** and **B** are **not independent** since chickenpox is contagious and it is likely that if one sibling catches it then so will the other.

Jim rolls a dice and Kim rolls a dice.
Event **C**: Jim rolls a 6.
Event **D**: Kim rolls a 6.

Events **C** and **D** are **independent** since the outcome from the roll of one dice does not affect the outcome of the roll of the other.

When events are independent, you can use a two-way table or a tree diagram to work out the probabilities of the **combined outcomes**.

Example

A fair dice is rolled and a coin is tossed. What is the probability of getting a head and a six?

Method 1

The events are independent. This two-way table shows all the outcomes.

		Dice					
		1	2	3	4	5	6
Coin	Head	H1	H2	H3	H4	H5	H6
	Tail	T1	T2	T3	T4	T5	T6

There are 12 different mutually exclusive outcomes, so the probability of a head and a 6 is $\frac{1}{12}$.

Method 2

The events are independent. This tree diagram shows all the outcomes.

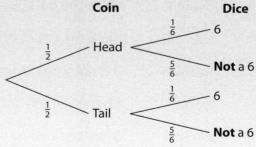

Working across the branches, the probability of getting a head and a 6 is $\frac{1}{2} \times \frac{1}{6} = \frac{1}{12}$.

1. For each pair of events decide whether or not it is likely that the events are independent. Give a reason for each of your answers.

   a. Event **A** It rains on Monday morning.
      Event **B** It rains on Monday afternoon.

   b. Event **C** It rains on a Monday in April.
      Event **D** It rains on a Monday in November.

   c. Two dice are rolled.
      Event **E** One dice shows 6.
      Event **F** The other dice shows 6.

   d. Li gets the bus to school.
      Event **G** The bus is late.
      Event **H** Li is late for school.

   e. Event **I** A cat meows.
      Event **J** The cat is hungry.

2. From this list of events, pick:

   a. three pairs of events that are likely to be independent;

   b. three pairs of events that are unlikely to be independent.

   Give reasons for your answers.

Event **A**	A baby boy is born.
Event **B**	A baby girl is born.
Event **C**	The baby has blue eyes.
Event **D**	The baby has blonde hair.
Event **E**	When the baby is a teenager its favourite colour is pink.
Event **F**	When the baby is a teenager its favourite colour is blue.
Event **G**	The baby grows up to be a professional footballer.
Event **H**	The baby grows up to be a teacher.
Event **I**	When the baby grows up it buys a Premium Bond.
Event **J**	When the baby grows up it wins a Premium Bond prize.

3 John has these two cards.

| 1 | | 2 |

Una has these two cards.

| 2 | | 3 |

John picks one of his cards at random.
Una picks one of her cards at random.

a Explain why John picking a card and Una picking a card are independent events.

b John and Una add the numbers on the cards to obtain a score.
Draw a tree diagram to show all the possible total scores.

c Work out the probability of a total score of 4.

4 A fair spinner has three sectors of equal size.
The sectors are coloured red (**R**), blue (**B**) and green (**G**).

Arbi spins the arrow.
Mary spins the arrow.

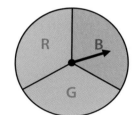

a Explain why events Arbi spinning the arrow and Mary
spinning the arrow are independent events.

b Draw a tree diagram to show all the possible outcomes.

c Find the probabilities of each of these outcomes.

 i **R** and **R**

 ii **R** and **B** in any order

 iii The arrow lands on **R** or **G** at least once

5 A gardener is putting up a garden shed.
The probability that the weather is fine is 0.6.
The probability that he has all the parts for the shed is 0.9.
To complete the job in a day, he needs the weather to be fine and to have all the parts.

a Draw a tree diagram to show all the possible outcomes.

b Calculate the probability that the gardener completes the job in a day.

c Calculate the probability that it is not fine and he does not have all the parts.

6 A game is played three times. The probability of winning each time is $\frac{1}{2}$.

a Show that the probability of winning all three games is $\frac{1}{8}$.

b What is the probability of winning exactly one game?

7 Nicola and Debbie each try to swim two lengths
   in 1 minute or less.
   They each have one attempt.
   The probability that Nicola will do it 0.75.
   The probability that Debbie will do it is 0.64.

   Work out the probability that:

   a they will both succeed;

   b only one of them will succeed.

8 A bag contains 2 red balls (**R**) and 1 blue ball (**B**).

   A ball is taken at random from the bag.
   Its colour is recorded and the ball is replaced.
   A second ball is taken at random from the bag and its colour is recorded.

   a Copy and complete this tree diagram to show all the possible outcomes.

First ball	**Second ball**	**Outcomes**

   R — R   R and R

   b Explain why the probability of each of the combined outcomes is $\frac{1}{9}$.

   c Work out the probability of each of these combined outcomes.

   i P(**R** and **R**)   ii P(**R** and **B**)   iii P(**B** and **R**)   iv P(**B** and **B**)

⊙ **Points to remember**

⊙ Two events are **independent** if one event happening does not affect the
   probability that the other event happens.

⊙ The probability that a spinner will land on 5 and a tossed coin will show
   a head is written as P(5, head).

⊙ A **probability tree diagram** shows all the possible outcomes of more
   than one event.

⊙ When you follow a path along the branches of a tree diagram, multiply
   the probabilities.

5 Probability experiments

Did you know that...?

Criminal law is about maintaining safe and orderly living for everyone. Those who break the law can be prosecuted. If they are found guilty, they can be fined or sent to prison, or both.

In criminal law, the evidence has to establish the person's guilt **'beyond reasonable doubt'**.

Civil law is different. It is mostly about disputes between individuals or organisations. The evidence has to show on **'the balance of probabilities'** that there is more than a 50% chance of the person being liable.

Which do you think would be harder to prove: whether something is the case 'beyond reasonable doubt' or 'on the balance of probabilities'?

This lesson will help you to compare theoretical probability with relative frequency for trials involving two independent events.

Exercise 5

Work in a group of two or three.

1 **Experiment 1**

In this experiment, an integer between 1 and 100 is selected at random.
A second integer between 1 and 100 is selected at random.
The 1st integer is **added** to the 2nd integer to give a 3rd integer.
Whether each integer is odd (**O**) or even (**E**) is recorded in a table.

Trial	1st integer O or E	2nd integer O or E	3rd integer O or E
1	O	E	O

One line of the table has been completed for you as an example.

To do Experiment 1, you will need to select pairs of integers between 1 and 100 by using the random number button on a scientific calculator, or a table of random numbers.

a First draw a tree diagram to show all the possible outcomes for the 3rd integer.

b Explain why the probability that the 3rd integer is odd is $\frac{1}{2}$.

c Complete a table like the one n page 211 for 20 trials.

One team member should pick the 1st integer.
One team member should pick the 2nd integer.
One team member should work out the 3rd integer and complete the table.

d After 20 trials, work out the relative frequency of the 3rd integer being odd.
Repeat for as many sets of 20 trials that you can in the time allowed.
Represent these relative frequencies on a relative frequency graph.

e Write a brief report on the experiment.
Are the theoretical probability of the 3rd integer being odd and the limit of the relative frequency approximately the same?

2 **Experiment 2**
Experiment 2 is similar to Experiment 1, except that the 3rd integer is obtained by **multiplying** integer 1 by integer 2.

In part **b**, explain why the probability that the 3rd integer is odd is $\frac{1}{4}$.

Points to remember

⊙ If A and B are independent events, the probability of A and B occurring is P(A) × P(B).

⊙ The connection between probability and relative frequency after a large number of trials is also valid for trials involving two independent events.

How well are you doing?

Can you:

- use relative frequency to estimate probability?
- draw and interpret relative frequency graphs?
- recognise when events are independent?
- use tree diagrams to represent all the outcomes of combined events?

Probability 1 (calculator allowed)

1 *2005 level 7*

Meg and Ravi buy sweet pea seeds and grow them in identical conditions.

Meg's results:

Number of packets	Number of seeds in each packet	Number of seeds that germinate from each packet
5	20	18, 17, 17, 18, 19

Ravi's results:

Number of packets	Number of seeds in each packet	TOTAL number of seeds that germinate
10	20	170

a Use Meg's results to work out the relative frequency of a sweet pea seed germinating.

b Use Meg's results and Ravi's results to work out two different estimates of the probability that a sweet pea seed germinates.

c Whose results are likely to give a better estimate of the probability? Explain your answer.

d Use Meg's results and Ravi's results to work out a more accurate estimate of the probability that a sweet pea seed germinates.

2 The Labour Party won the General Elections of February 1950 and May 2001.
The table shows the number of votes for the Labour Party in these elections
together with the number of people eligible to vote.

	Number of people eligible to vote	Number of votes for the Labour Party
February 1950	28 770 844	13 263 359
May 2001	34 410 265	10 731 366

Use relative frequency to compare the votes obtained by the Labour Party in the
General Elections of February 1950 and May 2001.

3 *2006 level 7*

Field voles are small animals that do not live for very long.
A scientist recorded data on 1000 of these voles that were born on the same day.
The graph shows how many voles were still alive after a number of weeks.

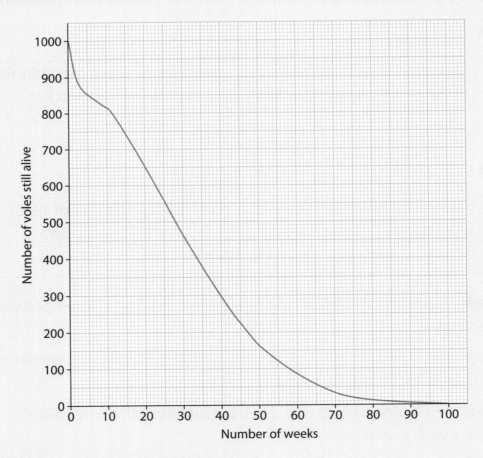

Use the graph to answer this question.
Estimate the probability that a field vole will live to be at least 20 weeks old.

(4) *2001 level 7*

A fair coin is thrown.
When it lands it shows heads or tails.

a Use a tree diagram to show all the possible outcomes when two coins
are thrown.

In a game a coin is thrown two times.

☺ Player A wins one point each time the coin shows a head.

☺ Player B wins one point each time the coin shows a tail.

b Show that the probability that player A scores two points is $\frac{1}{4}$.

c What is the probability that player B scores exactly one point?
Show your working.

(5) *2003 level 7*

A girl plays the same computer game lots of times.
The computer scores each game using 1 for win, 0 for lose.

After each game, the computer calculates her overall mean score.

The graph shows the results for the first 100 games.

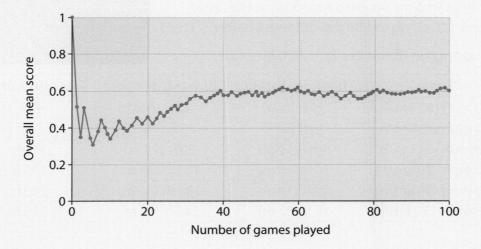

She is going to play the game again.
Estimate the probability that she will win.

Functional skills 5

Stopping distances

This group activity will help you to:

◉ decide on the information, methods and tools to use, including ICT;

◉ examine patterns and relationships;

◉ consider how appropriate and accurate your results are.

Background

The total distance needed for a car to slow down and stop is called the stopping distance. Two of the factors this depends on are the '**thinking distance**' and the '**braking distance**'.

Both depend on the car's speed since the faster a car is travelling the further it travels before it stops.

The **stopping distances** for a family car are:

Speed	Thinking distance	Braking distance	Total stopping distance
20 mph (32 km/h)	20 ft (6 m)	20 ft (6 m)	40 ft (12 m)
30 mph (48 km/h)	30 ft (9 m)	45 ft (14 m)	75 ft (23 m)
40 mph (64 km/h)	40 ft (12 m)	80 ft (24 m)	120 ft (36 m)
50 mph (80 km/h)	50 ft (15 m)	125 ft (38 m)	175 ft (53 m)
60 mph (96 km/h)	60 ft (18 m)	180 m (35 m)	240 ft (73 m)
70 mph (112 km/h)	70 ft (21 m)	245 ft (75 m)	315 ft (96 m)

Problem

Work in a small group. You may need a computer and the Excel file **Stopping distances**.

① Is there a formula connecting the speed of a car to the distance it needs to stop?
Can you find a simple way to express the relationship?
Would it help to use a spreadsheet or draw a graph?

To be safe, you need to be at least the overall stopping distance for your speed behind the car in front. This is hard to judge when you are moving.

There are two main ways you can check if you are a safe distance from the car in front.

1 Sometimes you see **chevrons** painted on the motorway. To be safe, you need to be at least two chevrons behind the car in front.

2 Another way to work out if you are a safe distance from the car in front is to use the **'two-second rule'**. You pick a stationary object like a road sign at the side of the road, watch the car in front pass it and then count how many seconds it takes until you pass it. If it is longer than 2 seconds then you are a safe distance behind.

More problems

Work in a small group.

2 **a** How far apart do the chevrons need to be painted if cars are travelling at 50 mph?

b How far apart do the chevrons need to be painted if cars are travelling at 70 mph?

3 Does the 'two-second rule' work at all speeds? Can you improve on the rule?

You may need to use this relationship: 1 mile = 5280 feet.

Be prepared to discuss your findings and their accuracy with other groups.

Measures and mensuration

This unit will help you to:

- calculate the length of arcs and the areas of sectors of circles;
- work out the areas and volumes of prisms and cylinders;
- convert between units of area and between units of volume;
- draw and interpret plans and elevations.

1 Arcs of circles

This lesson will help you to calculate the length of an arc of a circle.

Exercise 1

An **arc** is part of the circumference of a circle.

The small arc is the **minor arc** and the big one is the **major arc**.

For a **sector** with an angle of $x°$ at the centre of a circle of radius r:

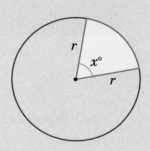

$$\text{arc length} = \frac{\text{angle of arc}}{360°} \times \text{circumference}$$

$$= \frac{x}{360°} \times 2 \times \pi \times \text{radius}$$

Example 1

Find the arc length for an angle of 30° at the centre
of a circle with radius 4 cm.

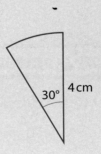

Circumference $= 2 \times \pi \times \text{radius} = 2 \times \pi \times 4 = 25.1327\ldots$

Arc length $= (\text{angle} \div 360°) \times \text{circumference}$

$\qquad = (30° \div 360°) \times 25.1327\ldots = 2.09 \text{ cm (to 2 d.p.)}$

When you **use a calculator** to calculate arc length, either use brackets, or:

- work out the circumference first;
- multiply the answer by the angle at the centre;
- divide by 360°.

Remember that you should only round up or down at the end of the calculation.

Example 2

Calculate the perimeter of this sector.

Arc length = (80° ÷ 360°) × 2 × π × 3 = 4.2 m (to 1 d.p.)

Perimeter = radius + radius + arc length

= 3 + 3 + 4.2 = 10.2 m (to 1 d.p.)

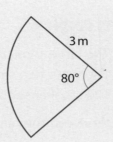

Give all your answers to 1 decimal place.

1. Calculate the arc length of each of these sectors.

a 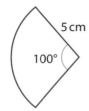 5 cm 100°

b 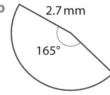 2.7 mm 165°

c 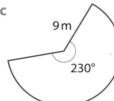 9 m 230°

d 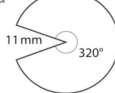 11 mm 320°

2. Calculate the perimeter of each of these sectors.

a 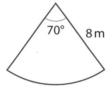 70° 8 m

b 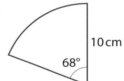 10 cm 68°

c 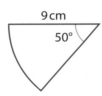 9 cm 50°

d 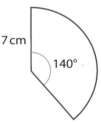 7 cm 140°

3. A shot put throwing area has a radius of 25 m and an angle at the centre of 40°.

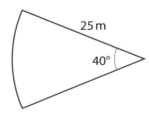

25 m 40°

Calculate the perimeter of the throwing area.

4. The throwing area for the javelin has a radius of 95 m and an angle at the centre of 29°. Calculate the perimeter of the throwing area.

Extension problem

 a The large semicircle has a radius of 3 cm.
   There are two small semicircles across its diameter.
   The smaller semicircles both have a radius of 1.5 cm.

   Work out the perimeter of the shaded shape.

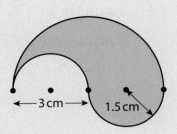

b This time the large semicircle still has a radius of 3 cm.
   There are three semicircles across the diameter.
   The smaller semicircles each have a radius of 1 cm.

   Work out the perimeter of the shaded shape now.

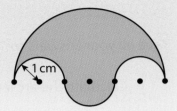

c What would the perimeter be if there were four semicircles across the diameter?

d Investigate other numbers of semicircles.

◉ Points to remember

- ⊙ **Circumference** of a circle $= \pi \times$ diameter $= 2 \times \pi \times$ radius
- ⊙ **Length of arc** $=$ (angle of arc $\div$ 360°) $\times$ circumference of circle
   $=$ (angle of arc $\div$ 360°) $\times \pi \times$ diameter
   $=$ (angle of arc $\div$ 360°) $\times 2 \times \pi \times$ radius

2 Sectors of circles

This lesson will help you to solve problems involving the area of a sector of a circle.

Exercise 2

The **sector** of a circle is the region in a circle bounded by two radii and an arc.
The small sector is the **minor sector** and the big one is the **major sector**.

For a **sector** with an angle of $x°$ at the centre of a circle of radius r:

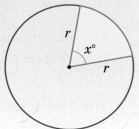

$$\text{sector area} = \frac{\text{angle of sector}}{360°} \times \text{area of circle}$$

$$= \frac{x}{360°} \times \pi \times \text{radius}^2$$

Example

Find the area of a sector of a circle of radius 3 m with an angle at the centre of 80°. Give your answer to 2 decimal places.

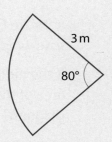

Area of sector = (angle ÷ 360°) × π × radius × radius

= (80° ÷ 360°) × π × 3 × 3 = 6.28 m² (2 d.p.)

When you **use a calculator** to calculate sector area, either use brackets, or:

- work out the area first;
- multiply the answer by the angle at the centre;
- divide by 360°.

Remember that you should only round up or down at the end of the calculation.

In this exercise give your answers to 1 decimal place.

1 Two concentric circles have radii 4 cm and 7 cm.

Calculate the shaded area.

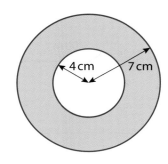

2 Calculate the area of each of these sectors.

a
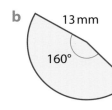
4 cm
105°

b
13 mm
160°

c
4.2 m
240°

d
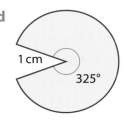
1 cm
325°

3 Da Vinci Pizzas make two sizes of pizza.

a A small pizza has a diameter of 20 cm.
What is the surface area of the top of the pizza?

b A large pizza has twice the surface area of the small one.
What is the diameter of the large pizza?

c A small boy says he can eat a 130° slice (sector) of the large pizza.
What is the area covered by the topping on this slice?

4 In Notre Dame Cathedral, Paris there is a large rose window.

If the radius of the rose window is 2 m, what is the area of the top part of the window shown in the diagram?

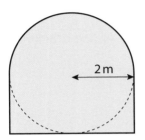

5 The inside of a running track is exactly 400 m. It is made up from two straights that are each 100 m long and two semicircles each of which is 100 m.

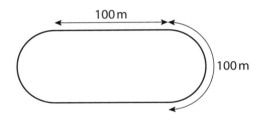

What is the area inside the running track?

Extension problem

 a The large semicircle has a radius of 3 cm.
There are two small semicircles across its diameter.
The smaller semicircles both have a radius of 1.5 cm.

Work out the area of the shaded shape.

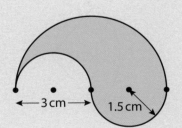

b This time the large semicircle still has a radius of 3 cm.
There are three semicircles across the diameter.
The smaller semicircles each have a radius of 1 cm.

Work out the area of the shaded shape now.

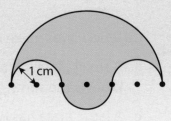

c What would the area be if there were four semicircles across the diameter?

d Investigate other numbers of semicircles.

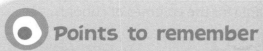

Points to remember

- Area of a **circle** = $\pi \times$ radius $\times$ radius = πr^2
- Area of a **sector** = (angle of sector $\div$ 360°) $\times$ area of circle
  = (angle of sector $\div$ 360°) $\times \pi \times$ radius $\times$ radius
  = (angle of sector $\div$ 360°) $\times \pi r^2$

3 Prisms and cylinders

This lesson will help you to solve problems involving the volume of prisms and cylinders.

Exercise 3

Example 1

Calculate the volume of this cuboid.

Volume of a cuboid = width $\times$ height $\times$ length

Volume = 8.1 $\times$ 16.4 $\times$ 12.7
= 1687.1 mm³ (to 1 d.p.)

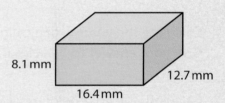

8.1 mm
12.7 mm
16.4 mm

Example 2

Calculate the volume of this cylinder.

Volume = area of cross-section $\times$ length

Volume = $\pi \times$ radius² $\times$ length
= $\pi \times 3^2 \times 15$
= 424.1 mm³ (to 1 d.p.)

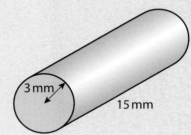

3 mm
15 mm

Example 3

The volume of a hexagonal prism is 63 cm³.
The area of its cross-section is 12 cm².

How long is the hexagonal prism?

Volume = cross-sectional area $\times$ length

63 = 12 $\times$ length

Length = 63 $\div$ 12 = 5.25 cm

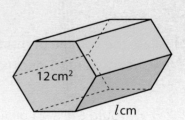

12 cm²
l cm

① Copy and complete this table for the volumes of cuboids.

	Length	Width	Height	Volume
a		2.5 m	4.3 m	53.75 m³
b	5.6 mm		1.2 mm	15.456 mm³
c	45 cm	18 cm		2025 cm³

② Calculate the volume of each prism.

a
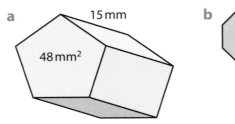
15 mm
48 mm²

b
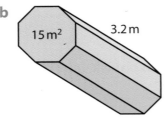
15 m²
3.2 m

c
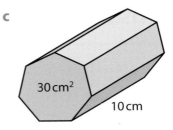
30 cm²
10 cm

③ Calculate the volume of a cylinder with a radius of 1 cm and length of 5 cm.
Give your answer to 1 decimal place.

④ Calculate the volume of a cylinder with a diameter of 6 cm and length of 8 cm.
Give your answer to 1 decimal place.

⑤ Calculate the volume of this prism.

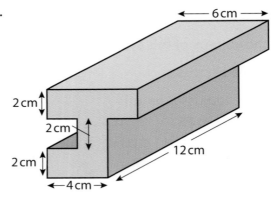
6 cm
2 cm
2 cm
12 cm
2 cm
4 cm

⑥ Calculate the volume of this triangular prism.
Give your answer to 1 decimal place.

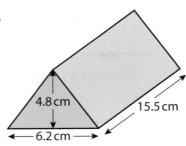
4.8 cm
15.5 cm
6.2 cm

(7) An octagonal prism has a volume of 225 mm³ and a length of 9 mm.
Calculate the area of the octagonal cross-section.

(8) A triangular prism has a volume of 180 cm³ and a length of 15 cm long.
The base of the triangular cross-section is 6 cm wide.
Calculate the perpendicular height of the triangle.

(9) The volume of a 5000 m piece of cylindrical pipe is 4000 m³.
What is the radius of the pipe?
Give your answer to 1 decimal place.

Extension problems

(10) Calculate the surface area of each prism.

a

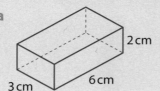

3 cm   6 cm   2 cm

b

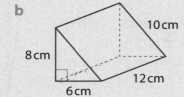

10 cm   8 cm   6 cm   12 cm

c

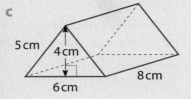

5 cm   4 cm   6 cm   8 cm

(11) Tammy pours acid from one measuring cylinder to another measuring cylinder.

The first cylinder has a radius of 1.5 cm.
The height of the acid is 3.5 cm.

The second cylinder has a radius of 0.5 cm.
What is the height of the acid when it is poured into this cylinder?

Points to remember

⊙ A **prism** is a solid with two parallel bases that are congruent polygons.
Cross-sections parallel to a base are identical to the base.

⊙ A **cylinder** is a solid with two parallel bases that are identical circles.
Cross-sections parallel to a base are circles identical to the base.

⊙ Volume of a prism = area of cross-section × length

⊙ Volume of a cylinder = area of cross-section × length
= π × radius × radius × length

⊙ The **surface area of a solid** is the sum of the areas of all the faces.

4 Units of area and volume

Did you know that...?

John Wilkins was an English clergyman who was the Warden of Wadham Hall at Oxford University and the chief founder of the Royal Society. He was married to Robina, the sister of Oliver Cromwell.

In 1668, Wilkins made the very first proposal for a **metric measurement system**. The idea did not catch on, and England continued with its existing system of various weights and measures.

However, the idea spread slowly in Europe. In 1791, the metre was officially defined by the French Academy of Sciences as one ten millionth of the line of longitude that runs from the equator to the North Pole through Paris.

Today, the definition of a metre is the distance travelled by light in an absolute vacuum in $\frac{1}{299\,792\,458}$ of a second.

John Wilkins (1614–1672)

This lesson will help you to convert between units of area and between units of volume.

Exercise 4

You can convert between units of area or units of volume using these facts.

Area

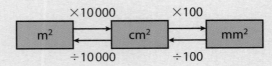

☉ $1\,cm^2 = (10\,mm)^2 = 100\,mm^2$

☉ $1\,m^2 = (100\,cm)^2 = 10\,000\,cm^2$

☉ $1\,m^2 = (1000\,mm)^2 = 1\,000\,000\,mm^2$

Volume

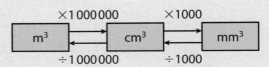

☉ $1\,cm^3 = (10\,mm)^3 = 1000\,mm^3$

☉ $1\,m^3 = (100\,cm)^3 = 1\,000\,000\,cm^3$

☉ $1\,m^3 = (1000\,mm)^3 = 1\,000\,000\,000\,mm^3$

Example 1

Convert 5.9 m³ to cm³.

$1\,m^3 = 1\,000\,000\,cm^3$

$5.9\,m^3 = 5.9 \times 1\,000\,000 = 5\,900\,000\,cm^3$

Example 2

Convert 5600 mm² to cm².

$1\,cm^2 = 100\,mm^2$

$5600\,mm^2 = 5600 \div 100 = 56\,cm^2$

1. Convert these areas to square centimetres.

   a 4 m²   b 2.3 m²   c 0.6 m²   d 820 mm²   e 30 mm²

2. Convert these areas to square millimetres.

   a 8 cm²   b 10.7 cm²   c 8 m²   d 0.9 m²   e 30 cm²

3. Convert these areas to square metres.

   a 7000 km²   b 3 km²   c 4.9 km²

   d 2 300 000 mm²   e 6 000 000 000 cm²   f 3.5×10^{10} mm²

4. The surface area of a cuboid is 120 cm².
   What is the surface area in square millimetres?

5. Coniston Water has a surface area of 4 900 000 m².
   Convert this area to square kilometres.

6. Convert these volumes to cm³.

   a 9 m³   b 4.1 m³   c 0.12 m³

   d 700 000 mm³   e 2 km³   f 4.6×10^{8} mm³

7. Convert these volumes to mm³.

   a 12 cm³   b 0.3 cm³   c 1.6 m³   d 0.09 m³

8. The boot of a large car holds 496 000 cm³. Write this capacity in:

   i   cubic metres   ii   cubic millimetres.

9. A litre bottle of water holds 1000 cm³ of water.
   How many 1 litre bottles would be needed to fill a 1 m³ container with water?

10. A petrol tank in the shape of a cuboid holds 70 litres of petrol when it is full.
    Its width is 35 cm and its length is 40 cm. Calculate its height.

Extension problem

11. A 1 cm³ cube is enlarged by an unknown scale factor.
    After it is enlarged, the surface area and volume of
    the enlarged cube are numerically the same.

    Find the scale factor of the enlargement.

Points to remember

- In area or volume problems, make sure that the sides or edges of shapes are in the same unit.
- $1\,cm^2 = (10\,mm)^2 = 100\,mm^2 = 1 \times 10^2\,mm^2$
- $1\,m^2 = (100\,cm)^2 = 10\,000\,cm^2 = 1 \times 10^4\,cm^2$
- $1\,m^2 = (1000\,mm)^2 = 1\,000\,000\,mm^2 = 1 \times 10^6\,mm^2$
- $1\,cm^3 = (10\,mm)^3 = 1000\,mm^3 = 1 \times 10^3\,mm^3$
- $1\,m^3 = (100\,cm)^3 = 1\,000\,000\,cm^3 = 1 \times 10^6\,cm^3$
- $1\,m^3 = (1000\,mm)^3 = 1\,000\,000\,000\,mm^3 = 1 \times 10^9\,mm^3$
- **1 litre** $= 1000\,ml = 1000\,cm^3$

5 Plans and elevations

This lesson will help you to draw and interpret plans and elevations of 3D shapes.

Exercise 5

You can draw different views of a 3D shape.

Example

Here is a shape made from cubes.

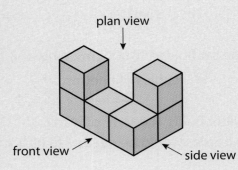

Draw a sketch of the plan, front elevation and side elevation.

Plan

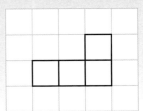

Front elevation

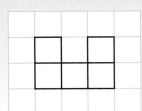

Side elevation

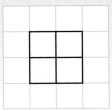

You will need squared paper, isometric paper and some interlocking cubes.

1 This shape is made from 6 cubes.
The front and side are labelled.

On squared paper, draw a plan and side and front elevations of the shape.

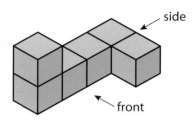

2 This shape is made from 9 cubes.
The front and side are labelled.

On squared paper, draw a plan and side and front elevations of the shape.

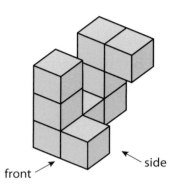

3 This shape is made from 8 cubes.
The front and side are labelled.

On squared paper, draw a plan and side and front elevations of the shape.

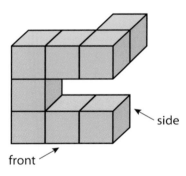

4 The diagrams show the plan and front and side elevations of a shape.

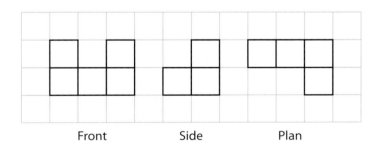

Front   Side   Plan

a Construct the shape using cubes.

b Draw the shape on isometric dotty paper.

c How many cubes are used to create the shape?

5 The diagrams show the plan and front and side elevations of a shape.

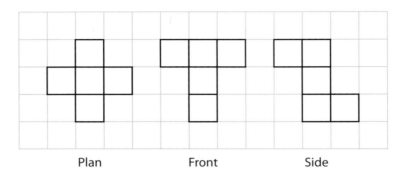

Plan   Front   Side

   a Construct the shape using cubes.

   b Draw the shape on isometric dotty paper.

   c How many cubes are used to create the shape?

6 Which 3D shape is represented by this plan and front and side elevations?

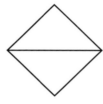 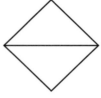 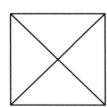

Front elevation   Side elevation   Plan

Extension problems

 ### Did you know that...?

Plans and elevations have been used for many years to illustrate the design of buildings.

This page from an old book shows plans and elevations of a church in Old Alexandria.

This page from an old book shows a side elevation and plan of Cluny Abbey, France.

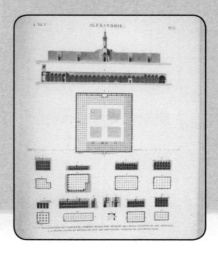 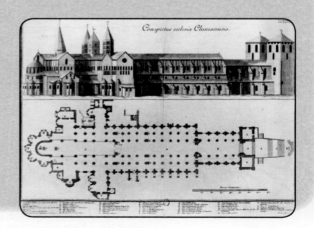

7 These buildings are in Sacramento, California.

The frustum of a pyramid is the section between the base and a plane parallel to the base. The building on the left is in the shape of the frustum of a square-based pyramid.

a Make sketches of the plan and side and front elevations of the building.

b Use your drawings to help you work out the number of planes of symmetry of the frustum of a square-based pyramid.

8 These diagrams show the shadows of four solids.

Describe the possible solids for each shadow.
There may be more than one answer for each shadow.

a    b   c    d

Points to remember

- The **plan** is a view of the object from directly above.
- An **elevation** is a view of the object from the side or the front.
- A sphere and a cube each have the same plan view, front elevation and side elevation.

How well are you doing?

Can you:

- calculate the lengths arcs and the areas of sectors?
- work out the areas and volumes of prisms and cylinders?
- convert between units of area and between units of volume?
- draw and interpret plans and elevations?

You need some squared paper.

Measures and mensuration (calculator allowed)

1. This shape is made from 10 centimetre cubes.

    On squared paper, draw its plan and front and side elevations.

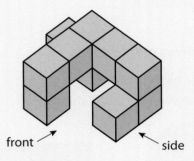

front   side

2. *2007 level 7*

    This shaded shape is made using two semicircles.

    One semicircle has a diameter of 20 cm.
    The other has a diameter of 30 cm.

    Calculate the perimeter of the shaded shape.

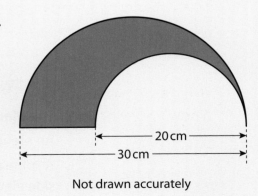

20 cm

30 cm

Not drawn accurately

③ Ravi buys a slice of a circular pizza.

The radius of the pizza is 9 cm.
The angle at the centre of the slice is 40 degrees.

a   What is the area of the slice of pizza?

b   What is the total perimeter of the slice of pizza?

Give your answers correct to 1 decimal place.

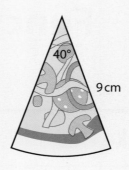

④ *2007 level 7*

a   Look at the triangular prism.

Work out the volume of the prism.

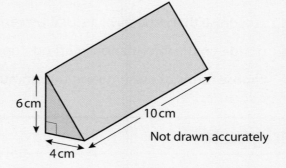

6 cm

10 cm

4 cm

Not drawn accurately

b   One face of another prism is made from 5 squares.

Each square has side length 3 cm.

Work out the volume of the prism.

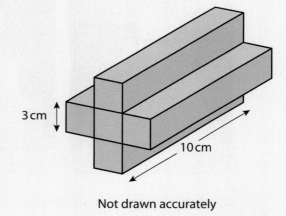

3 cm

10 cm

Not drawn accurately

⑤ *2003 level 8*

The cylinder has a radius of 2.5 cm.

The volume of the cylinder, in cm³,
is 4.5π cm³.

What is the height of the cylinder?
Show your working.

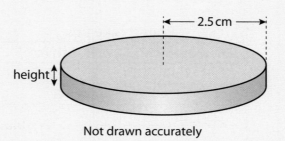

2.5 cm

height

Not drawn accurately

Functional skills 6

Cake tins

This group activity will help you to:

- recognise that aspects of a situation can be represented using mathematics;
- decide on the information, methods, operations and tools to use;
- choose forms of presentation to communicate results and solutions.

Background

Celebration cakes are usually round or square.

The tins they are baked in come in different sizes. The size of a round tin is given by its diameter and of a square one by the length of the side of the square.

Round cake tins	
Diameter (cm)	Depth (cm)
15	7.5
18	8
20	9
23	9
26	10.5

Square cake tins	
Side length (cm)	Depth (cm)
15	7.5
18	8
20	9
23	9
25	9
28	10
30	11

Problems

Work in a small group.

(1) Choose two round and two square tins from the tables on the previous page. Calculate their volumes.

(2) Pick a round tin and a square tin with matching measurements (i.e. the same diameter and side length, and the same depth).

    a How much more cake mixture do you need to fill the square tin than the round tin?

    b Is this the same for all pairs of square and round tins with matching measurements?

(3) What size of square tin corresponds to a round tin with a diameter of 18 cm?

More problems

A cake maker has to adjust a cake recipe for different cake sizes.

Here are the ingredients for a round celebration cake, 9 cm deep, with a 23 cm diameter.

225 g butter
225 g soft brown sugar
4 eggs
225 g plain flour
50 g ground almonds
800 g mixed fruit
Grated rind of an orange
$\frac{3}{4}$ teaspoon mixed spice
3 tablespoons orange juice
1 dessertspoon black treacle

(4) Gary makes a square cake using the recipe above.
His cake has the same depth as the 23 cm round cake.
What size is Gary's square cake?

(5) Write a list of ingredients you need to make a 26 cm round cake.

(6) Design your own celebration cake, with tiers.
Choose the sizes and shapes of the cakes you will make.
Write a list of the quantities of ingredients you will need for each part of your cake.

Be prepared to justify your decisions, assumptions and conclusions to other groups.

Enquiry 2

This unit will help you to:

- know how to select a sample so that bias is minimised;

- draw a frequency polygon to represent grouped data;

- estimate measures of average and spread for grouped data;

- draw a scatter graph and a line of best fit, and identify correlation;

- carry out a statistical investigation.

1 Biased data

This lesson will help you to understand the meaning of the terms population, sample, representative sample and biased sample.

Exercise 1

TV and radio shows and Internet sites often run opinion polls. Viewers or listeners are invited to phone in or send a text message giving their opinion. These polls nearly always give invalid results. There are two possible reasons for this:

- The questions themselves are often leading, i.e. the way they are written suggests that a particular answer is correct.

- Respondents have to choose to reply and only those with strong views will bother.

The purpose of a statistical enquiry is to find out information from or about a complete **population** of individual people or items.

In order to do this, information is collected from a **sample** from the population. This sample must represent the population fairly or the results of the enquiry will not be valid.

- A sample that does **not** represent a population fairly and favours one section of the population more than another is called a **biased sample**.

- A sample that represents a population fairly and is not biased towards any particular group or category in the population is called a **representative sample**.

Example

An investigation is being carried out on the size of leaves of oak trees in a wood
Describe the population and give examples of possible biased and representative samples.

Population	Biased sample	Possible groups in a representative sample
All the leaves on all the oak trees in the wood	The leaves on the lowest branch of an oak tree on the edge of the wood	Trees in different parts of the wood Branches on different parts of the tree Leaves on different parts of the branch

1. Some pupils did a survey to test this hypothesis.

> Most pupils in our school get more than £5 pocket money a week.

They asked pupils in their tutor group how much pocket money they get.

a What is the population for the survey?

b What is the sample?

c Why is this sample biased?

d Write down the groups of pupils that should be included in the sample to make it representative of the population.

2. Residents of a village were asked for their opinions about the plans for a new bus service.

Some people waiting at the village bus stop were asked to complete a questionnaire.

a What is the population for this survey?

b What is the sample?

c Why is the sample likely to be biased?

d Write down the groups in the population that should be included in the sample to make it representative.

3. David is investigating whether pupils at his school use an instant messaging service on their computers.

a What is the population in David's investigation?

b David decides to ask a sample of pupils.
   How should he choose a representative sample of size 30?

4 The PE department in a school plans to survey a sample of students in the school about their attitudes to PE.

a What is the population in this survey?

b Write down the groups of pupils that should be included in the sample to make it representative of the population.

5 A radio sports programme asked listeners to phone in with their views about who should be the new manager of a Premier League football team.

a What is the population for this survey?

b What is the sample?

c Why is the sample likely to be biased?

d Why are the conclusions from this enquiry likely to be invalid?

6 A questionnaire asks people what they think about increasing Value Added Tax on computers and spending the money raised on computers in schools.

The survey is carried out by sending random e-mails.

Explain why this is likely to produce a biased sample.

● Points to remember

⊙ A **population** is the whole set of individuals or items studied in a statistical investigation.

⊙ A **sample** is a selection from a population used to find out about the population without studying all of it.

⊙ A **representative sample** is not biased towards any group in the population.

⊙ A **biased sample** favours one section of the population more than another.

⊙ In a **random sample** each item has an equal chance of being chosen. It may not be representative.

2 Minimising bias

This lesson will help you to carry out a statistical enquiry in a way that minimises bias.

Exercise 2

When you carry out a statistical enquiry:

- avoid asking leading questions that suggest that a particular answer is correct;
- make sure that any sample is representative of the population you are investigating.

Example 1

A school receives a donation of £10 000.
The headteacher decides to ask pupils what the money should be spent on.
Explain whether these methods are likely to produce biased results.

a The headteacher asks boys in Year 9 this question.

> Do you think that the money should be spent on either computers or sports equipment?

This question doesn't suggest that a particular answer is correct but it only gives pupils two options to choose between, so is biased.

The sample is biased as it does not represent the whole school population. It includes only boys and only Year 9 pupils.

b The headteacher asks **all** boys and girls in Year 9 this question.

> Tick the item below that you think the money should be spent on.
>
> Computers
> Sports equipment
> New seats and tables in the school dining room
> Equipment for the Fitness Room
> Equipment for the Drama Studio

This question has several choices and minimises bias. It would be better still if respondents could give ideas of their own.

Instead of asking just for one choice an alternative would be to ask respondents to rank choices in order of preference.

The sample is biased because pupils in other year groups cannot give their opinion. The result would be more valid if a representative sample of boys and girls from each year group in the school were asked the question.

To choose a **representative sample** of the population being investigated:

◉ identify the different groups in the population;

◉ work out the proportion of each group in the population;

◉ identify a method of selecting members of these groups to take part in the survey.

In a **random sample** each member of the population has an equal chance of being chosen. Random selection needs to be applied to **each group** in the population, rather than to the population as a whole.

Example 2

There are 408 boys and 312 girls in a school. The school is planning to ask a representative sample of 60 pupils about their reading preferences.

a How many boys and how many girls should be included in the sample?

The number of pupils in the population is:

$408 + 312 = 720$

The proportion of the population sampled is:

$\frac{60}{720} = \frac{1}{12} = 8.3\%$

For a **representative** sample, the proportions of boys and girls sampled should be 8.3%.

The number of boys in the sample is:

$\frac{1}{12} \times 408 = 34$ (or 8.3% of 408 = 34)

The number of girls in the sample is:

$\frac{1}{12} \times 312 = 26$ (or 8.3% of 312 = 26)

b What else would you need to consider for the sample to be representative?

To work out the numbers in a truly representative sample other groups in the population might need to be considered, for example, year groups.

For example, the numbers of boys and girls in the sample could be worked out from $\frac{1}{12}$ of the boys and girls in each year group, rounded to the nearest whole number.

c Describe how you might choose which boys and which girls are in the sample so that bias is minimised.

When the numbers of pupils required from each group have been worked out the actual pupils in the sample can be selected at random.

This can be done by using a method that makes sure that each pupil in the population has an equal chance of being chosen.

1 Darren is a fan of R&B music.

In a questionnaire on the sorts of music that pupils in his school like he asks this question.

> I think R&B music is great. What do you think?

Darren asks his friends to complete the questionnaire.

According to Darren the result of his survey shows that R&B is the most popular sort of music.

a Explain why Darren's conclusion is not likely to be valid.

b Rewrite Darren's question to make it less biased.

c What is the population in Darren's enquiry?

d Write some advice for Darren about how he should sample this population.

2 Della is investigating whether pupils in her school give money to charity.

a She is thinking about using these questions in her questionnaire.

> **Question A** Tick the response below that best describes how often you give money to charity.
>
> About once a week ☐
>
> About once a month ☐
>
> About once a year ☐
>
> Never ☐
>
> **Question B** Everyone gives money to charity, don't they?
>
> Yes ☐   No ☐
>
> **Question C** Do you give money to charity?
>
> Yes ☐   No ☐

Which question should Della definitely **not** use in her investigation?
Give a reason for your answer.

b i What is the population in Della's investigation?

ii Della plans to ask a sample of 10% of this population to complete her questionnaire.
How should Della choose this sample?

3 The manager of a cinema has made some changes. She uses these questions as part of a questionnaire to find out what the public think of these changes.

Write down what is wrong with each of these questions.

a What do you think of the improvements to the cinema?

    Excellent   Very good   Good

     ☐   ☐   ☐

b How much money do you normally pay for a cinema seat?

    A lot   Average

    ☐   ☐

c How often do you come to the cinema?

   Not very often   Often

    ☐   ☐

4 In a school pupils are taught maths in sets.
The school is planning a survey to find out about pupils' attitudes to maths.

They decide to ask a sample of 10% of the school population.
Here are three ways they could choose the sample.

A 10% of the boys and 10% of the girls chosen at random from the whole school.

B 10% of the boys and 10% of the girls chosen at random from each tutor group.

C 10% of the boys and 10% of the girls chosen at random from each maths set.

Comment on each of these ways.

Which way is most likely to give a sample that is representative of attitudes to maths?

5 A school decides to carry out a survey to find out pupils' opinions on its plans to change the school uniform.

In the school there are 540 boys and 460 girls.

The school plans to ask a sample of 50 pupils to complete a questionnaire.

a What proportion of the population is the planned sample?

b Explain why there should be 27 boys and 23 girls in a representative sample.

c The school choose 27 boys and 23 girls at random from the whole school.
Explain why this might not accurately represent the school population.

6 The table shows the numbers in different age groups of a sports club.

Age group	15 to 19	20 to 25	26 to 30	30 to 40	40 to 50	Over 50
Number of males	23	36	24	35	16	9
Number of females	14	19	26	31	11	6

They decide to ask a representative sample of 20% of club members to complete a questionnaire to find out their views about a new development.

a What is the number of people in the population for this survey?

b What is the number of people in the sample for this survey?

c Find the number of males and females in each age group in the sample.

   i Round each of the numbers in the table above to the nearest 5.
     Work out 20% of each of these rounded values.

   ii Complete another table with the numbers of male and female members in each age group in the sample.

d Explain why the membership numbers were rounded in part c.

e How should the actual members in the sample be selected?

Extension problem

 7 a Write down five questions for a questionnaire on the types of holiday people prefer.

b Describe how this information might be collected and recorded.

 Points to remember

To **minimise bias** in a statistical investigation:

⊙ avoid questions that suggest that a particular answer is correct;

⊙ choose a representative sample by including groups in the same proportions as in the population;

⊙ choose the items for each group in the representative sample at random.

3 Frequency polygons

This lesson will help you to draw and interpret frequency polygons for discrete and continuous data.

Exercise 3

A large set of data is often grouped to make the data more manageable. The data can be represented in a **grouped frequency table** and a **frequency polygon**.

To draw a frequency polygon. plot the midpoint of each class interval against its frequency, then join the set of points with straight lines.

Example

The distribution of marks in a test are shown in this grouped frequency table.

Mark (%)	1 to 20	21 to 40	41 to 60	61 to 80	81 to 100
Frequency	9	16	46	35	8

Draw a frequency polygon for this data.

The data is **discrete** data grouped into **class intervals** of 1 to 20, 21 to 40 and so on.

In the interval 1 to 20, the lowest possible value is 1 and the highest possible value is 20. So the midpoint is $(1 + 20) \div 2 = 10.5$.

Mark (%)	Midpoint	Frequency
1 to 20	$(1 + 20) \div 2 = 10.5$	9
21 to 40	$(21 + 40) \div 2 = 30.5$	16
41 to 60	$(41 + 60) \div 2 = 50.5$	46
61 to 80	$(61 + 80) \div 2 = 70.5$	35
81 to 100	$(81 + 100) \div 2 = 90.5$	8

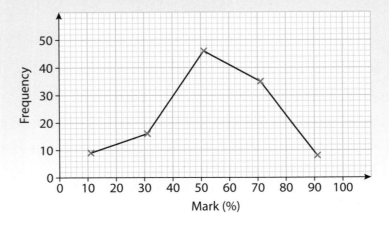

You will need graph paper.

1 A psychologist tested a representative sample of 100 ten-year-olds.
The results are represented in this grouped frequency table.

Test score	60 to 79	80 to 99	100 to 119	120 to 139	140 to 159	160 to 179
Frequency	4	21	47	17	9	2

Represent this data in a frequency polygon.

2 The table shows the number of lengths that some teenagers swam in a sponsored swim.

No. of lengths, l	$0 \leqslant l < 20$	$20 \leqslant l < 40$	$40 \leqslant l < 60$	$60 \leqslant l < 80$	$80 \leqslant l < 100$
Frequency	3	9	18	14	6

Represent this data in a frequency polygon.

3 This frequency polygon shows the number of ice creams sold by a kiosk on days in June.

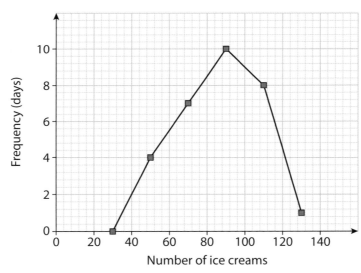

a On how many days were from 80 to 100 ice creams sold?

b On how many days were more than 100 ice creams sold?

4 The speed of 100 cars as they passed a 40 mph speed limit sign after they left a motorway
is shown in this grouped frequency table.

Speed, s (mph)	$30 \leqslant s < 35$	$35 \leqslant s < 40$	$40 \leqslant s < 45$	$45 \leqslant s < 50$	$50 \leqslant s < 55$	$55 \leqslant s < 60$
Frequency	3	9	25	28	4	1

Draw a frequency polygon to represent the data.

5   This frequency polygon represents the heights of a sample of plants.

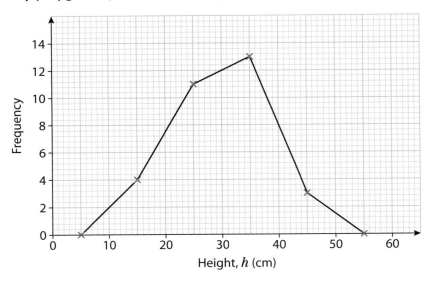

a   How many plants are there altogether in the sample?

b   How many plants are less than 10 cm high? Explain your answer.

c   How many plants are more than 50 cm high? Explain your answer.

d   How many plants are 20 cm or more and less than 40 cm high? Explain your answer.

Extension problem

6   This frequency polygon represents the waist measurement of a sample of adults.

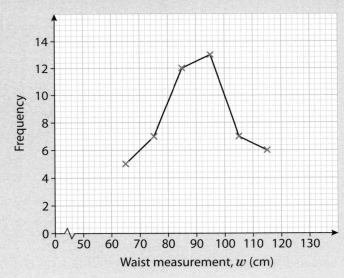

a   How many adults are in the sample?

b   Explain why lines joining (65, 5) to (55, 0) and (115, 6) to (125, 0) can be added to this frequency polygon.

c   What percentage of adults in the sample has a waist measurement of:

   i   between 60 cm and 70 cm   ii   100 cm or more   iii   less than 90 cm?

4 Estimating the mean of grouped data

This lesson will help you to calculate an estimate of the mean of a set of grouped data, either discrete or continuous.

Exercise 4

Large sets of data are organised in groups to make the data more manageable.

The disadvantage is that individual pieces of data are not shown. It is not possible to calculate an accurate measure of average or spread from grouped data.

However, it is possible to **estimate** measures of average and spread.

To estimate the mean:

◉ For each class interval, work out the midpoint, x, of the interval.

◉ For each class interval, work out $f \times x$, where f is the frequency of the class and x is the midpoint of the interval. This is an estimate of the sum of all the data items in that interval.

◉ Find the sum of all the values of $f \times x$.

  You can write this using the symbol Σ, which stands for 'the sum of'.

  $\Sigma(f \times x)$ means the estimated sum of all the items in the data set.

◉ Work out the sum of the frequencies, Σf.

◉ Calculate an estimate of the mean from $\Sigma(f \times x) \div \Sigma f$.

Example 1

The table represents the heights in centimetres of some boys.

Estimate the mean height of the boys.

Class interval Height, h (cm)	Frequency (f)
$120 \leqslant h < 130$	3
$130 \leqslant h < 140$	7
$140 \leqslant h < 150$	8
$150 \leqslant h < 160$	12

Extend the grouped frequency table:

Class interval Height, h (cm)	Frequency (f)	Midpoint (x)	$f \times x$
$120 \leqslant h < 130$	3	$(120 + 130) \div 2 = 125$	$3 \times 125 = 375$
$130 \leqslant h < 140$	7	$(130 + 140) \div 2 = 135$	$7 \times 135 = 945$
$140 \leqslant h < 150$	8	$(140 + 150) \div 2 = 145$	$8 \times 145 = 1160$
$150 \leqslant h < 160$	12	$(150 + 160) \div 2 = 155$	$12 \times 155 = 1860$
	$\Sigma f = 30$		$\Sigma(f \times h) = 4340$

Estimated mean height $= \Sigma(f \times x) \div \Sigma f = 4340 \div 30 = 145$ cm (to the nearest cm)

So the mean height of the boys is approximately 145 cm.

You can also estimate the mean for discrete data.

Example 2

This table shows the number of passengers on the 06.30 bus from Newcastle to Sunderland during June. Estimate the mean.

The calculations of the midpoints of the intervals are different for discrete data.

Number of passengers, n	Frequency (f)	Midpoint (x)	$f \times x$
10 to 19	2	$(10 + 19) \div 2 = 14.5$	$2 \times 14.5 = 29$
20 to 29	7	$(20 + 29) \div 2 = 24.5$	$7 \times 24.5 = 171.5$
30 to 39	12	$(30 + 39) \div 2 = 34.5$	$12 \times 34.5 = 414$
40 to 49	9	$(40 + 49) \div 2 = 44.5$	$9 \times 44.5 = 400.5$
	$\Sigma f = 30$		$\Sigma(f \times n) = 1015$

Estimated mean number of passengers $= \Sigma(f \times x) \div \Sigma f = 1015 \div 30 = 33.8\ldots$

So the mean number of passengers is approximately 34.

1. Calculate an estimate of the mean of each set of discrete data.

   a. The number of letters in 20 words of a book

Number of letters	Frequency
1 to 5	15
6 to 10	4
11 to 15	1

   b. The number of words in 20 sentences of a book

Number of words	Frequency
1 to 5	1
6 to 10	4
11 to 15	9
16 to 20	5
21 to 25	1

   c. The number of pages in 21 books

Number of pages	Frequency
126 to 150	1
151 to 175	1
176 to 200	5
201 to 250	7
251 to 275	6
276 to 300	1

2. Calculate an estimate of the mean for each set of continuous data.

   a. 50 estimates of a time of 30 seconds

Time, t (seconds)	Frequency
$0 \leqslant t < 10$	2
$10 \leqslant t < 20$	8
$20 \leqslant t < 30$	20
$30 \leqslant t < 40$	17
$40 \leqslant t < 50$	3

   b. 100 estimates of a length of 50 metres

Length, l (metres)	Frequency
$20 \leqslant l < 40$	18
$40 \leqslant l < 60$	34
$60 \leqslant l < 80$	32
$80 \leqslant l < 100$	16

   c. 20 estimates of the number of dots on a page

Estimated number of dots, d	Frequency
$1 \leqslant d < 25$	1
$26 \leqslant d < 50$	3
$51 \leqslant d < 75$	14
$76 \leqslant d < 100$	2

Extension problem

 3 A group of 50 male smokers and 50 female smokers recorded the number of cigarettes they smoked each day for a period of 20 days.

a The mean number of cigarettes smoked per day by the men is shown in this grouped frequency table.

Mean number of cigarettes smoked per day	1 to 10	11 to 20	21 to 30	31 to 40	41 to 50
Frequency	10	19	14	5	2

Calculate an estimate of the mean number of cigarettes smoked per day by men.

b The mean number of cigarettes smoked per day by the women is shown in this frequency polygon.

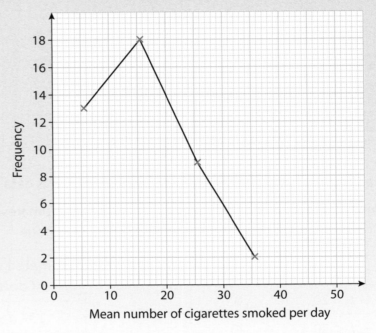

Calculate an estimate of the mean number of cigarettes smoked per day by women.

 Points to remember

⊙ Accurate values of average and spread cannot be calculated for grouped data but estimates can be made.

⊙ An **estimate of the mean** can be calculated from:

$$\Sigma(f \times x) \div \Sigma f$$

where: Σ is a symbol meaning 'the sum of'

x represents the midpoint of each class interval

f represents the frequency

5 Average and range of grouped data

This lesson will help you to find the modal class and estimate the median and range of grouped data.

Exercise 5

When data is grouped it is not possible to tell what the actual data items are but you can **calculate an estimate of the median**.

Example 1

Here is the table of heights of 30 boys.

Calculate an estimate for the median.

$\frac{1}{2}$ of 30 = 15, so the median is the mean of the 15th and 16th heights.

To find the 15th and 16th heights, complete a running total table.

Class interval Height, h (cm)	Frequency (f)
$120 \leqslant h < 130$	3
$130 \leqslant h < 140$	7
$140 \leqslant h < 150$	8
$150 \leqslant h < 160$	12

Class interval Height, h (cm)	Frequency (f)	Running total	Interpretation
$120 \leqslant h < 130$	3	**3**	3 shortest heights < 130 cm
$130 \leqslant h < 140$	7	3 + 7 = **10**	10 shortest heights < 140 cm
$140 \leqslant h < 150$	8	10 + 8 = **18**	18 shortest heights < 150 cm
$150 \leqslant h < 160$	12	18 + 12 = **30**	All 30 heights < 160 cm

The 15th and 16th heights are both in the class interval $140 \leqslant h < 150$.
So the median height lies between 140 and 150 cm.
They are the 5th and 6th heights in this interval.

Assume that the heights of the 8 boys in the class interval $140 \leqslant h < 150$ are evenly spread throughout the interval.

So 8 heights are evenly spread over 10 cm.
So there is one height every 10 ÷ 8 = 1.25 cm.

The 15th height is 140 + (5 × 1.25) = 146.25 cm.
The 16th height is 140 + (6 × 1.25) = 147.5 cm.

The median lies halfway between the 15th and 16th heights.

So an estimate of the median = (146.25 + 147.5) ÷ 2 = 146.875 cm
= 147 cm (to the nearest cm)

When data is grouped, you can also:

- **find the modal class**, which is the class interval with the highest frequency;
- **calculate an estimate of the range** by finding the difference between the largest value in the highest class interval and the smallest value in the lowest class interval.

Example 2

Here is the table of heights of 30 boys.

Class interval Height, h (cm)	Frequency (f)
$120 \leqslant h < 130$	3
$130 \leqslant h < 140$	7
$140 \leqslant h < 150$	8
$150 \leqslant h < 160$	12

a What is the modal class?

$150 \leqslant h < 160$

b Calculate an estimate of the range.

Minimum possible value = 120 cm
Maximum possible value = 160 cm
Estimate of the range = 160 − 120 = 40 cm

For each set of data in **Exercise 3**, questions 1, 2 and 4, and **Exercise 4**, questions 1 and 2:

  i find the modal class;

 ii calculate an estimate of the range;

iii calculate an estimate of the median.

Points to remember

- The **median** value in a set of n ordered values is:
  - the $\frac{1}{2}(n + 1)$th value when n is odd;
  - the mean of the $\frac{1}{2}n$th and $(\frac{1}{2}n + 1)$th values when n is even.
- For grouped data, you can work out which interval contains the median by using the running total of the frequencies.
- To estimate the median, assume that the data is evenly spread throughout the class interval in which the median occurs.
- The **modal class** of a set of grouped data is the class interval with the greatest frequency.
- The **spread** of a set of grouped data can be estimated by making an estimate of the **range**.
- **Measures of average** (mean, median, mode) and **spread** (range) can be estimated from a frequency polygon.

6 Correlation

This lesson will help you to draw and use scatter graphs and lines of best fit and understand correlation.

Exercise 6

A **scatter graph** is used to find out whether there is a relationship between two variables.

For example, the scatter graph on the left below shows the marks of 12 pupils in two maths tests, Paper 1 (calculator not allowed) and Paper 2 (calculator allowed).

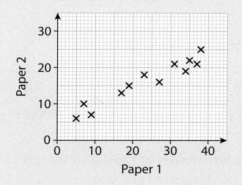 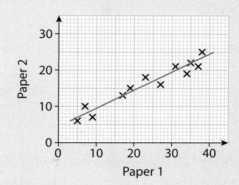

A **line of best fit** is a straight line that represents the best estimate of the relationship between the two variables.

The line of best fit for the maths test scores is shown on the right above.

When you draw a line of best fit, use a ruler. Draw a line that has roughly equal numbers of points on each side of it. Aim to keep all the points as close to the line as possible.

The pattern of the crosses and the line of best fit on the scatter graph suggests that there is a relationship between the marks in the two tests. One way of describing this relationship is:

> As the Paper 1 mark increases, the Paper 2 mark increases.

Correlation is a measure of the strength of the relationship between two variables. If the points are all close to the line of best fit, the correlation is called high or strong.

When one quantity increases as the other increases, the correlation is positive.
When one quantity decreases as the other increases, the correlation is negative.

High positive correlation

Low positive correlation

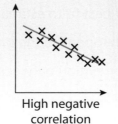
High negative correlation

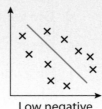
Low negative correlation

Lines of best fit can be used to make estimates.

For example, to estimate the Paper 2 mark of a pupil whose Paper 1 mark is 13, draw a vertical line up from 13 to the line of best fit.

Then draw a horizontal line across and read off the Paper 2 mark, 11.

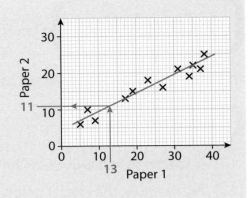

You will need some graph paper.

1   This table shows the ages of 10 children and their times to run 100 metres.

Age	8	4	11	8	6	7	5	4	10	10
Time (seconds)	17	23	14	15	20	20	22	26	13	16

a   On graph paper, copy and complete this scatter graph to represent the data in the table. The first five points have already been plotted to help you.

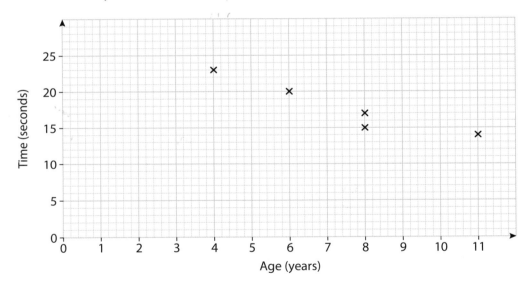

Age (years)

b   Use your ruler to draw a line of best fit.

c   Use your line of best fit to estimate the time that a child aged 9 takes to run 100 m.

d   Use your line of best fit to estimate the time that a child aged 2 takes to run 100 m.

e   Describe what happens to the time taken to run 100 m as the children's ages increase.

f   Describe the correlation between a child's age and the time taken to run 100 m. Choose from:

    A   Positive correlation   B   Negative correlation   C   No correlation

2 Jack sells ice creams. The table shows the weekly rainfall and the number of ice creams he sells each week for a 13-week period.

Rainfall (mm)	20	28	18	24	30	26	27	21	16	29	19	27	23
Number of ice creams	70	86	58	76	97	91	82	65	58	91	63	93	79

a On graph paper, copy and complete this scatter graph to represent the data in the table. The first two points have already been plotted to help you.

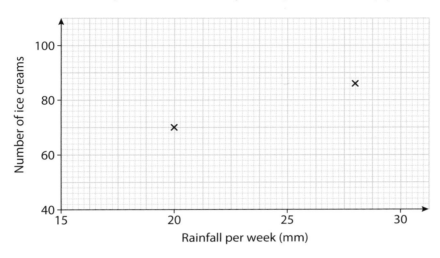

b Use your ruler to draw a line of best fit.

c Estimate the number of ice creams that Jack will sell in a week with 25 mm of rainfall.

d Describe what happens to the number of ice creams sold as the weekly rainfall increases.

e Describe the correlation between the weekly rainfall and the number of ice creams sold.

3 For each pair of variables, write whether you think they have a positive correlation, a negative correlation or no correlation. Give your reasons for each answer.

a The distance an aeroplane travels and the amount of fuel used.

b A pupil's shoe size and their mark in a maths test.

c The age of a car and its value.

d The age of an adult female and her height.

e The maximum air temperature and the number of hours of sunshine for a day in May in the UK.

f The number of hours of sunshine and the millimetres of rainfall per month in the UK.

4 Here is a scatter graph with one axis labelled 'Weight'.

a Describe the type of correlation.

b From this list, choose an appropriate label for the other axis.

   A shoe size

   B length of hair

   C waist measurement

   D mark in a spelling test

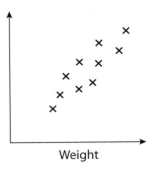

Weight

5 The table shows the outdoor temperature, in °C, at noon on ten winter days and the number of units of electricity used in heating a house on each of those days.

Noon temperature (°C)	9	2	0	4	11	10	12	5	3	1
Units of electricity used	25	39	44	34	23	24	21	32	36	42

a On graph paper, copy the grid below.
Draw a scatter graph and line of best fit to represent the information in the table.

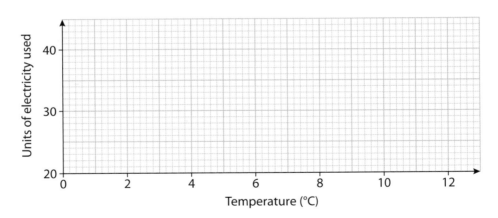

b Describe what happens to the number of units of electricity used as the temperature rises.

c Describe the correlation between the number of units of electricity used and the outdoor temperature.

d Use your line of best fit to estimate:

   i the number of units of electricity used when the outdoor temperature was 7°C;

   ii the outdoor temperature when 35 units of electricity were used.

6 Yehuda measures the current that flows through a circuit as the voltage is increased from 0 volts to 100 volts. He represents the results of his experiment on this scatter graph.

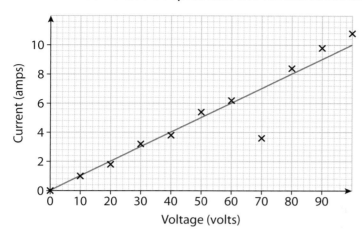

a Yehuda has plotted one of his points incorrectly. Use the line of best fit to estimate the coordinates of the point that Yehuda should have plotted.

b Show that the line of best fit passes through the point representing the mean voltage and the mean current.

Extension problem

7 The tread on a tyre and the distance travelled by that tyre are recorded.
The table shows the results for a sample of 8 tyres.

Distance (km)	14 000	16 000	18 000	20 000	24 000	25 000	27 000	29 000
Tread (mm)	5.8	5.6	5.1	4.4	4.3	3.7	3.6	3.1

a On graph paper, copy this grid.
Draw a scatter graph and line of best fit to represent this information.

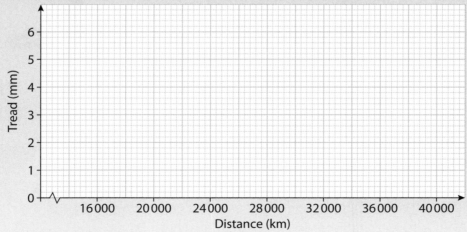

b Tyres with a tread of less than 1.6 mm are illegal.
Estimate how many kilometres a car with a tyre of tread 1.7 mm is able to travel before its tyres are illegal.
Explain why your estimate might be unreliable.

Points to remember

- A **scatter graph** is used to show whether there is a relationship between two variables.
- A **line of best fit** is a straight line that represents the best estimate of the relationship between the two variables on a scatter graph.
- When you draw a line of best fit, there should be roughly equal numbers of points on the scatter graph on each side of it.
- **Correlation** is a measure of the strength of the relationship between two variables. High correlation occurs when there is a close relationship and the points of the scatter graph lie close to the line of best fit.
- The correlation is positive when an increase in one variable results in an increase in the other, and negative when an increase in one variable results in a decrease in the other.

7 Statistical investigation

Did you know that...?

George Horace Gallup (1901–1984) was an American pioneer of survey sampling techniques and the inventor of the surveys of public opinion called Gallup Polls.

Gallup Polls are widely regarded as reliable measures of people's views. Results, analyses, and videos are published daily on Gallup.com.

Dr Gallup founded the American Institute of Public Opinion in 1935. To ensure his independence and objectivity, he resolved that he would not carry out any survey that was paid for or sponsored in any way by special interest groups such as political parties, a principle that Gallup upholds to this day.

In 1936, he achieved national recognition in the USA by correctly predicting, from the replies of a carefully chosen sample of 5000, the result of that year's presidential election.

Dr George Gallup in 1941

This double lesson will help you to carry out a statistical investigation.

Exercise 7

The purpose of **statistical enquiry** is to check whether or not a hypothesis is true.

A **hypothesis** is a statement that may or may not be true.

To carry out a statistical enquiry follow the **data handling cycle** shown on the right.

Specify the problem and plan

- Choose the problem, decide on the population to be investigated and write a hypothesis.
- Decide what data to collect, how much to collect, and how and when to collect it.

Collect data from a variety of sources

- Decide how to choose a sample to represent the population.
- Decide on the degree of accuracy needed for any measurements to be made.
- Design any questionnaire, data collection sheet or tally chart, or observation form.
- Collect the data from primary or secondary sources:
  - **primary** data is collected first-hand as part of a survey, experiment or investigation;
  - **secondary** data exists already.

Process and represent the data

- Organise and represent the data in appropriate tables, diagrams, graphs and charts.
- Work out measures of average and spread.

Interpret and discuss data

- Compare the general shape of distributions, and measures of average and spread.
- Comment on correlation if appropriate.

Evaluate results

- Decide whether or not the hypothesis is true.

You may need the Excel file **Test scores** if you work on question 1e.

(1) Work in a group of three or four to do one of the following.

  a Compare people's hand spans with their shoe sizes.

  b Compare the reaction times of two different groups of pupils.

  c Investigate pupils' ability to estimate the lengths of lines (straight or curved) and the sizes of angles.

  d Compare the word lengths and sentence lengths in a newspaper and a magazine, or in two different newspapers.

  e Compare percentage scores in tests or exams in different subjects, e.g. English, French, music, maths and science. You may need the Excel file **Test scores** for this.

  f Choose your own investigation.

(2) Working individually, write a report of your investigation.

  a Describe:

   ◉ the problem you tackled, your hypothesis and your plan of action;

   ◉ how you chose a representative sample;

   ◉ how you collected your data;

   ◉ how you made sure that you minimised any bias.

  b Include, and explain:

   ◉ the tables, diagrams, graphs and charts that you drew to represent the data;

   ◉ the measures of average and range that you calculated.

  c Give:

   ◉ an analysis of your results;

   ◉ a conclusion about your original hypothesis.

Extension problems

(3) a List any factors that could have affected your results.

  b Describe how you could overcome these in future, e.g. by increasing the size of your sample or by changing the way that you chose your sample.

(4) Choose a different investigation from those in question 1.

  Write a plan of how you would carry out your investigation, including how to overcome any problems that you met in your first investigation.

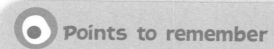

Points to remember

⊙ To carry out a **statistical investigation** follow the steps in the **data handling cycle**.

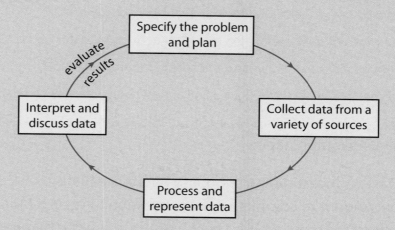

How well are you doing?

Can you:

- describe how to select a sample so that bias is minimised?

- interpret a frequency polygon to represent grouped data?

- estimate measures of average and spread for grouped data?

- interpret a scatter graph, draw a line of best fit and identify correlation?

You will need graph paper.

1. David is investigating shopping habits. He plans to ask 30 people at a local newsagent to complete a short questionnaire on a Monday morning.
   Give three reasons why David's results might be biased.

2. This table shows the numbers of workers of different ages at two factories.

Age	25–29	30–34	35–39	40–44	45–49	50–54	55–59
Factory A	2	4	8	16	11	7	2
Factory B	3	9	16	12	8	2	0

The diagram shows a frequency polygon for Factory A.

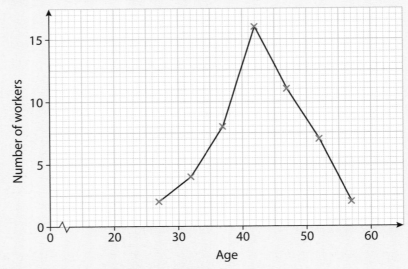

a Copy the frequency polygon on graph paper.
   Draw a frequency polygon for Factory B on the same diagram.

b What do the frequency polygons tell you about the ages of the workers at the two factories?

A customer at a supermarket complains to the manager about the waiting times at the checkouts. The manager records the waiting times of 100 customers at one checkout. The frequency diagram shows the results.

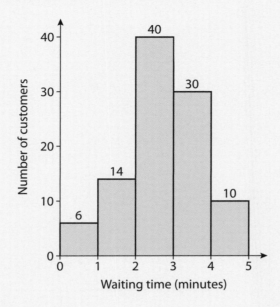

a Calculate an estimate of the mean waiting time per customer.
Show your working.
Copy and complete the table below to help you with the calculation.

Waiting time (t, minutes)	Midpoint of bar (x)	Number of customers (f)	$f \times x$
$0 < t \leqslant 1$	0.5	6	3
$1 < t \leqslant 2$			
$2 < t \leqslant 3$			
$3 < t \leqslant 4$			
$4 < t \leqslant 5$			
		100	

b Use the graph to calculate an estimate of the median waiting time per customer.
Show your working.

c The manager wants to improve the survey.
She records the waiting times of more customers.
Give a different way the manager could improve the survey.

The scatter graph shows information about trees called poplars.

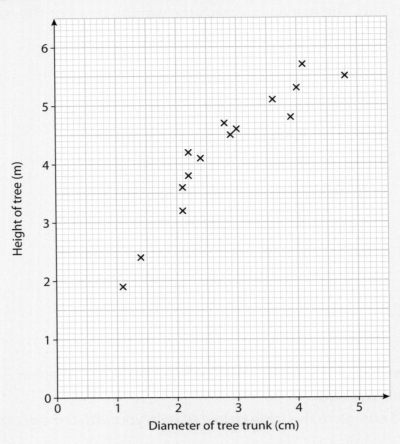

a What does the scatter graph show about the relationship between the diameter of the tree trunk and the height of the tree?

b The height of a different tree is 3 m. The diameter of its trunk is 5 cm.
Use the graph to explain why this tree is not likely to be a poplar.

c Another tree is a poplar. The diameter of its trunk is 3.2 cm.
Estimate the height of this tree.

d Below are some statements about drawing lines of best fit on scatter graphs.
For each statement, state whether the statement is True or False.

Lines of best fit must always…

   i go through the origin;

  ii have a positive gradient;

 iii join the smallest and the largest values;

 iv pass through every point on the graph.

Trigonometry 2

This unit will help you to:

- use Pythagoras' theorem to calculate the lengths of sides of right-angled triangles;
- use trigonometry to find unknown lengths and angles in right-angled triangles;
- solve problems using properties of angles, parallel lines, triangles and other polygons, explaining your reasoning.

1 Using Pythagoras' theorem 1

 Did you know that...?

There are more than 300 proofs of Pythagoras' theorem.

James Garfield (1831–1881) was President of the USA for six months in 1881 before he was assassinated.

Five years before he became President, he discovered a proof of Pythagoras' theorem, based on this diagram.

Can you see how the proof works?

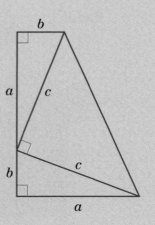

This lesson will help you to find the length of the hypotenuse in a right-angled triangle.

Exercise 1

Pythagoras' theorem

In **any** right-angled triangle, the square of the longest side is the sum of the squares of the other two sides.

This can be written $a^2 + b^2 = c^2$.

c is the longest side of the triangle and is called the **hypotenuse**. The hypotenuse is always opposite the right angle.

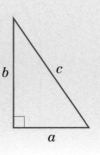

Example

Find the length x in the triangle below.

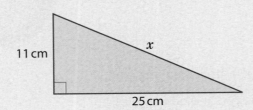

11 cm

x

25 cm

Using Pythagoras' theorem:

$$11^2 + 25^2 = x^2$$

$$121 + 625 = x^2$$

$$746 = x^2$$

$$\sqrt{746} = x$$

$$x = 27.3 \text{ cm (to 3 s.f.)}$$

You need a calculator. Give your answers to 3 significant figures.
Work with a partner for question 1.

① The diagrams show four proofs of Pythagoras' theorem.

Each of you should pick a different proof.
Individually, write an explanation of how your diagram proves Pythagoras' theorem.
Now try to explain your diagram to your partner.

Proof 1

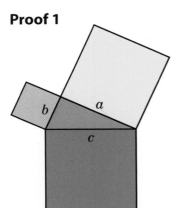

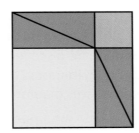

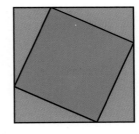

Proof 2

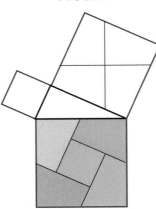

Proof 3

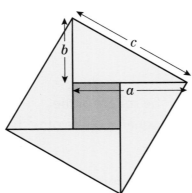

Proof 4

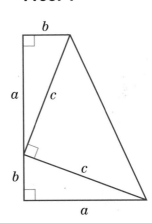

2 Find the lengths marked by the letters a, b, c and d in these diagrams.

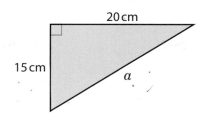

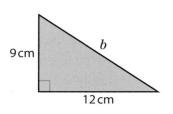

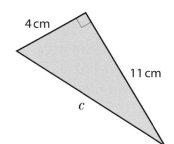

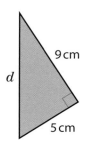

3 Peter walks 65 m west and then 90 m south. How far is he from his starting position? Draw a sketch to help you.

4 Calculate the perimeter of this trapezium.

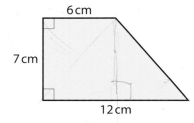

5 Find the length of a side of this rhombus.

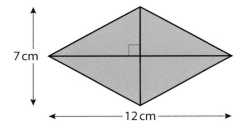

6 Find the lengths of a, b, c and d in this diagram.

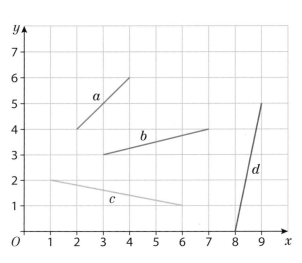

Extension problems

7 A plane flies 75 km due east from airport A to airport B.
It then flies due north for 140 km to airport C.
Finally, it flies directly back to airport A.

Calculate the direct distance from airport C to airport A.
Give your answer to the nearest kilometre.

8 A hockey pitch is 90 m long and 75 m wide.
Calculate the length of a diagonal of the pitch.
Give your answer to the nearest metre.

⦿ Points to remember

- ⦿ **Pythagorean triples** are sets of three integers that satisfy the relationship $a^2 + b^2 = c^2$: for example, 3, 4, 5 or 5, 12, 13.
- ⦿ **Pythagoras' theorem** can be written as a formula, $a^2 + b^2 = c^2$, where a and b are the lengths of the two shorter sides of a right-angled triangle and c is the length of the hypotenuse.
- ⦿ If you know the lengths of the two shorter sides of a right-angled triangle, use Pythagoras' theorem to find the length of the hypotenuse.

2 Using Pythagoras' theorem 2

This lesson will help you to find the length of a shorter side in a right-angled triangle.

Exercise 2

Pythagoras' theorem can also be used to find the length of one of the shorter sides in a right-angled triangle. Remember to solve the equation correctly.

Example

Find length z.

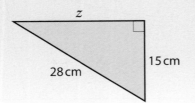

28 cm, 15 cm, z

Using Pythagoras' theorem:

$$15^2 + z^2 = 28^2$$
$$225 + z^2 = 784$$
$$z^2 = 784 - 225$$
$$z^2 = 559$$
$$z = \sqrt{559} = 23.6 \text{ cm (to 3 s.f.)}$$

You need a calculator. Give your answers to 3 significant figures.

1 Find the lengths marked by the letters a, b, c and d in these diagrams.

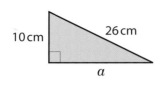 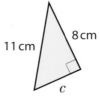 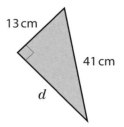

2 Sketch and solve these problems.

a A 3 m ladder is leaning against a wall.
The foot of the ladder is 2 m away from the foot of the wall.
How far up the wall does the ladder reach?

b A 5 m ladder is leaning against a wall.
The foot of the ladder is 3 m away from the foot of the wall.
How far up the wall does the ladder reach?

c A 7.5 m ladder is leaning against a wall.
The foot of the ladder is 4.5 m away from the foot of the wall.
How far up the wall does the ladder reach?

3 Find the perpendicular heights of these triangles.

a An equilateral triangle with side 7 cm.

b An isosceles triangle with base 9 cm and two equal sides 12 cm long.

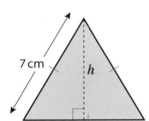 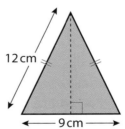

4 Find whole-number lengths that satisfy these right-angled triangles.
There may be more than one answer.

a 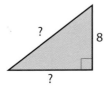 **b** 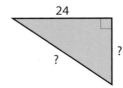 **c**

5 The diagonal of a square measures 16 cm.
What is the area of the square?

6 What is the length of the diagonal of a square with the given area?

a 25 cm²   b 49 cm²   c 60 cm²

Extension problems

7 The size of a television screen is measured by the length of the diagonal in inches.

a Find the diagonal length for a television 16″ wide and 9″ high.

b Modern screens have a width:height ratio of 16:9.

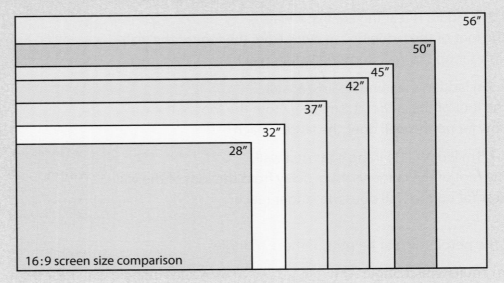

16:9 screen size comparison

c Find the dimensions for the 28″, 42″ and 56″ screens.

> **Hint**   What do you notice about all the rectangles?

8 A cupboard in a small room is in the position shown.
Is the room wide enough to move the cupboard to the new position?

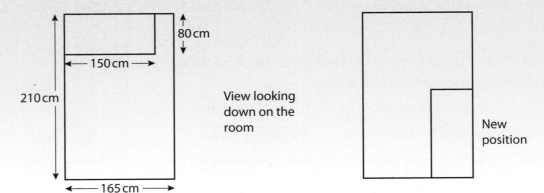

View looking down on the room

New position

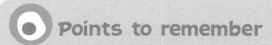

Points to remember

⊙ **Pythagoras' theorem** can be written as a formula, $a^2 + b^2 = c^2$, where a and b are the lengths of the two shorter sides of a right-angled triangle and c is the length of the hypotenuse.

⊙ If you know the lengths of any two sides of a right-angled triangle, use Pythagoras' theorem to find the length of the third side.

3 Triangles

This lesson will help you to use what you know about triangles to classify them.

Exercise 3

There are lots of ways you can find out more about a triangle.

For example, you could **draw** an accurate diagram, **measure** or **calculate** some angles, **classify** the triangle according to its type, and use **Pythagoras' theorem** to see if it is right-angled.

Work in a group of 3 or 4. Each group will need a large piece of paper, compasses, ruler, pencil scissors, glue and a calculator.

① The table below contains several sets of three numbers.
The numbers in each set are the lengths of the sides of a triangle.

6, 6, 8.5	5, 12, 13	10, 7, 10	8, 11, 20
6, 7, 8	7, 7, 7	7, 9, 14	6, 6, 11

Pick a set of three numbers. Find out as much as you can about the triangle that has those numbers as its side lengths. For example:

◎ What kind of triangle is it? How do you know?

◎ What is its area?

◎ How can you test whether or not the triangle is right-angled?

◎ What can you find out about its angles?

Now try the other sets of three numbers. Are the other triangles the same or different?

Record your findings, and your justifications for them, on the large sheet of paper.

2 Try applying Pythagoras' theorem to each triangle.
How can you tell if a triangle is obtuse-angled or acute-angled using Pythagoras' theorem?

Points to remember

⊙ Three given lengths may or may not form the sides of a triangle.

⊙ If the sum of the two shorter sides $a + b$ is less than the longest side c, you cannot make a triangle.

⊙ You can use Pythagoras' theorem to check the angle properties of a triangle with longest side c:
 – if $c^2 > a^2 + b^2$, the triangle is obtuse-angled;
 – if $c^2 < a^2 + b^2$, the triangle is acute-angled;
 – if $c^2 = a^2 + b^2$, the triangle is right-angled.

4 Spirals

Did you know that...?

Theodorus was a Greek mathematician who lived in the fifth century BC. He was a follower of Pythagoras and one of Plato's teachers. Plato gave him credit for proving that the square roots of 3, 5, 6, 7, 8, 10, 11, 12, 13, 14, 15 and 17 are irrational. Little else is known about him.

Many people have tried to determine how Theodorus proved his results. Some suggest that he used a spiral called the **Wheel of Theodorus**, which is constructed from right-angled triangles with hypotenuse lengths equal to $\sqrt{2}, \sqrt{3}, \sqrt{4}, \ldots$, up to $\sqrt{17}$.

The Wheel of Theodorus looks like the spiral on a nautilus shell.

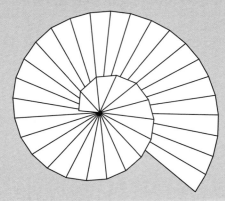

This lesson will help you to use Pythagoras' theorem and square roots to explore spirals.

Exercise 4

Spirals occur in both the natural and man-made worlds.

There are lots of different ways of drawing spirals. In this exercise you will look at spirals that are formed from triangles.

When a square root is not an integer or a terminating decimal, you can give its exact value by leaving the root sign in place, for example $\sqrt{2}$, $\sqrt{3}$. This is called writing it as a **surd**.

You need plain paper, a ruler, set square, protractor and a sharp pencil.

(1) Follow these instructions to draw an accurate copy of the **Wheel of Theodorus**.

- Draw two line segments at right angles, each the same length (perhaps 2 cm). Call this length 1 unit.

  Join the ends of the lines to form the hypotenuse of a right-angled triangle.

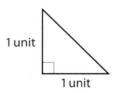

- Draw a line segment of length 1 unit at right angles to the hypotenuse.

  Use the first hypotenuse and the new line segment to make a second right-angled triangle.

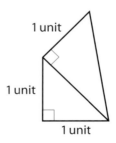

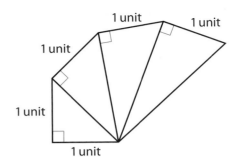

◎ Draw a line segment of length 1 unit at right angles to the second hypotenuse.

Use the second hypotenuse and the new line segment to make a third right-angled triangle.

Continue in the same way until you have drawn at least 12 triangles.

2 a Measure the lengths of the hypotenuses of the triangles that you drew in question 1.

   b Now use Pythagoras' theorem to work out the lengths of the hypotenuses. Leave the square root signs in place.

   c What do you notice about the lengths when they are written in this way?

3 Look at this spiral:

   a Describe how it is constructed.

   b Work out all the lengths in the spiral.

      Leave the square root signs in place.

   c Which of these lengths are whole numbers?

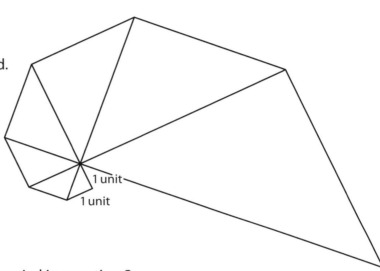

4 Make an accurate drawing of the spiral in question 3.

5 Design your own spiral based on right-angled triangles.

◉ Points to remember

⊙ A **spiral** is a curve which starts from a central point and which gets progressively further away as it revolves around the point.

⊙ Some spirals can be constructed from right-angled triangles.

⊙ Decimals that neither terminate nor recur are called **irrational numbers**, e.g. π, $\sqrt{2}$.

⊙ When a square root is not an integer or a terminating decimal, you can leave the root sign in place. This is called writing it as a **surd**.

5 Using the trigonometric ratios

This lesson will help you to use the sine, cosine and tangent ratios to find unknown lengths in right-angled triangles.

Exercise 5

The **hypotenuse** of a right-angled triangle is opposite the right angle.
The side opposite the angle marked x is the **opposite** side.
The side next to this angle is the **adjacent** side.

$$\sin x = \frac{\text{opposite}}{\text{hypotenuse}} \qquad \cos x = \frac{\text{adjacent}}{\text{hypotenuse}} \qquad \tan x = \frac{\text{opposite}}{\text{adjacent}}$$

Example 1

Find length b.

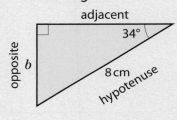

$$\sin x = \frac{\text{opposite}}{\text{hypotenuse}}$$

Sketch the triangle, label the sides and write down the ratio.

$$\sin 34° = \frac{b}{8}$$

Substitute values you know.

$$0.559 = \frac{b}{8}$$

Calculate sin of the angle.

$$b = 4.47 \text{ cm (to 3 s.f.)}$$

Solve the equation.

Example 2

Find length a.

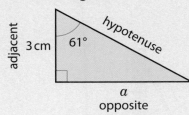

$$\tan x = \frac{\text{opposite}}{\text{adjacent}}$$

Sketch the triangle, label the sides and write down the ratio.

$$\tan 61° = \frac{a}{3}$$

Substitute values you know.

$$1.80 = \frac{a}{3}$$

Calculate tan of the angle.

$$a = 5.41 \text{ cm (to 3 s.f.)}$$

Solve the equation.

Example 3

Find length c.

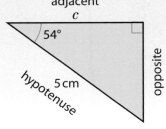

$$\cos x = \frac{\text{adjacent}}{\text{hypotenuse}}$$

Sketch the triangle, label the sides and write down the ratio.

$$\cos 54° = \frac{c}{5}$$

Substitute values you know.

$$0.588 = \frac{c}{5}$$

Calculate cos of the angle.

$$c = 2.94 \text{ cm (to 3 s.f.)}$$

Solve the equation.

You need a calculator. Give your answers correct to 3 significant figures.
Make a sketch of the triangle in each problem. Remember to show your working.

1 Use the tangent ratio to find the lengths marked with letters.

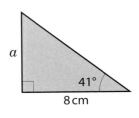 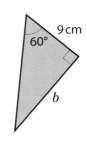 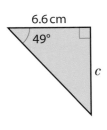 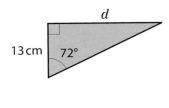

2 Use the sine ratio to find the missing lengths.

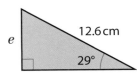 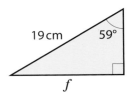 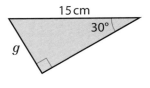 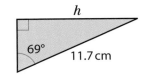

3 Use the cosine ratio to find the missing lengths.

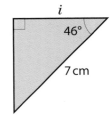 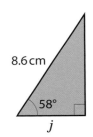 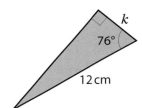 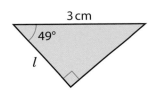

4 a A ladder is placed against a vertical wall.
      The ladder is 6 m long.
      It makes an angle of 65° with the ground.

      How far from the foot of the wall
      is the foot of the ladder?

      Use the cosine ratio.

   b A ladder is placed against a vertical wall.
      Its foot is 2.6 m from the wall.
      It makes an angle of 65° with the ground.

      How far up the wall does the ladder reach?

      Use the tangent ratio.

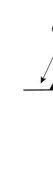

c A ladder is placed against a vertical wall.
The ladder is 4 m long.
It makes an angle of 65° with the ground.

How far up the wall does the ladder reach?

Use the sine ratio.

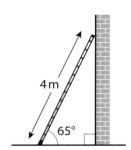

Extension problem

 Calculate the length of the hypotenuse in each of these triangles.

a

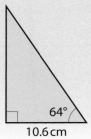

64°
10.6 cm

b

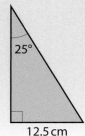

25°
12.5 cm

Points to remember

⊙ Use the **sine**, **cosine** and **tangent** ratios to find unknown lengths in right-angled triangles.

⊙ Choose the correct ratio to use to solve each problem.

$$\sin x = \frac{\text{opposite}}{\text{hypotenuse}} \qquad \cos x = \frac{\text{adjacent}}{\text{hypotenuse}} \qquad \tan x = \frac{\text{opposite}}{\text{adjacent}}$$

---

6 Choosing between sine, cosine and tangent

This lesson will help you to choose which trigonometric ratio to use to find unknown lengths in right-angled triangles.

Exercise 6

The three trigonometric ratios are:

$$\sin x = \frac{\text{opp}}{\text{hyp}} \qquad \cos x = \frac{\text{adj}}{\text{hyp}} \qquad \tan x = \frac{\text{opp}}{\text{adj}}$$

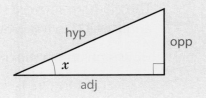

To decide which one to use, choose the ratio that refers
to the side you are given and the side that you want to find.

Example 1 Find length x.

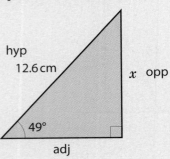

You need to find the opposite side. You know the hypotenuse, so use the sine ratio.

$$\sin = \frac{\text{opp}}{\text{hyp}}$$

$$\sin 49° = \frac{x}{12.6}$$

$$0.755 = \frac{x}{12.6}$$

$$x = 9.51 \text{ cm (to 3 s.f.)}$$

Example 2 Find length y.

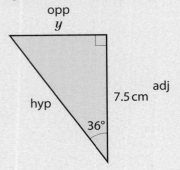

You need to find the opposite side. You know the adjacent side, so use the tan ratio.

$$\tan x = \frac{\text{opp}}{\text{adj}}$$

$$\tan 36° = \frac{y}{7.5}$$

$$0.727 = \frac{x}{12.6}$$

$$y = 5.45 \text{ cm (to 3 s.f.)}$$

You need a calculator. Give all your answers correct to 3 significant figures.
Make a sketch of the triangle in each problem. Remember to show your working.

1. Find the lengths a, b, c, d, e and f.

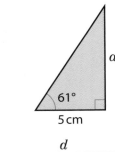
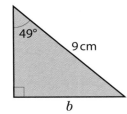
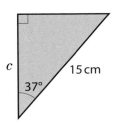

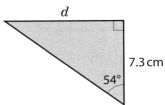
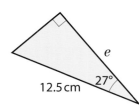
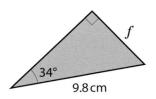

2. The diagram shows a slide 10 m long at an angle of 37° to the ground.

   How high above the ground is the top of the slide?

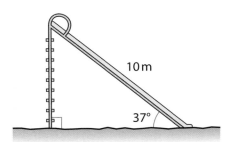

3 The diagram shows a flag pole held up by a guy rope on horizontal ground.

The peg at the bottom of the guy rope is 3.2 m away from the base of the flag pole.
The rope makes an angle of 42° with the ground.

Find the height of the flag pole.

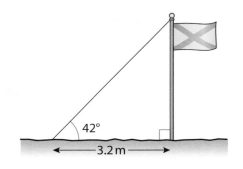

4 The short side of a rectangular field is 160 m long.
A path runs straight across the diagonal of the field.
The path makes an angle of 52° with the short side of the field.

Find the length of the long side of the field.

Extension problems

5
   a Find the length BC in the diagram.

   b Find the length BD in the diagram.

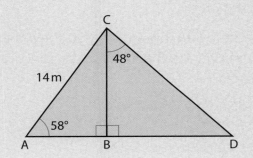

6 **a** Find the length BC in the diagram.

   b Find the length AC in the diagram.

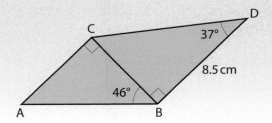

7 Finding unknown angles

This lesson will help you to choose and use the sine, cosine and tangent ratios to find unknown angles in right-angled triangles.

Exercise 7

You can use sine, cosine and tangent to find the size of an angle in a right-angled triangle.

Choose the ratio that refers to the two sides relative to the unknown angle.

Example

Find angle b.

Sketch the triangle.

Label the sides.

You want to find the angle b. You know the adjacent side and the hypotenuse, so use the cosine ratio.

Write down the cosine ratio.

$$\cos = \frac{\text{adj}}{\text{hyp}}$$

Substitute values you know.

$$\cos b = \frac{7.5}{16.1} = 0.4658\ldots$$

Use your calculator to find $\cos^{-1} 0.4658\ldots$ which is $62.235\ldots°$

$$b = 62.235\ldots°$$

Round this to 1 decimal place.

$$b = 62.2° \text{ (to 1 d.p.)}$$

You need a calculator. Give all your answers correct to 1 decimal place.
Make a sketch of the triangle in each problem. Remember to show your working.

1. For this triangle, what is:

   a $\sin x$

   b $\cos x$

   c $\tan x$?

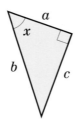

2. What is:

   a x when $\sin x° = 0.8$

   b y when $\cos y° = 0.12$

   c z when $\tan z° = 1.59$?

3 Find each angle marked with a letter.
Give your answers correct to 1 decimal place.

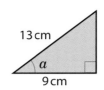
13 cm
a
9 cm

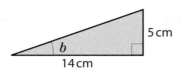
5 cm
b
14 cm

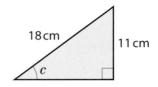
18 cm
11 cm
c

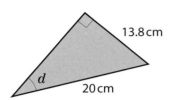
13.8 cm
d
20 cm

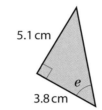
5.1 cm
3.8 cm
e

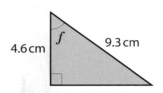
4.6 cm
f
9.3 cm

4 Find the value of x and the value of y when:

a $\sin x° = 0.2$, $\cos y° = 0.2$

b $\sin x° = 0.5$, $\cos y° = 0.5$

c $\sin x° = 0.7$, $\cos y° = 0.7$

What do you notice about these pairs of answers?
Explain why.

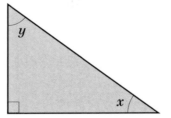
y
x

5 A ladder 3 m long is leaning against a vertical wall.

Its foot is on horizontal ground 1.2 m away from the foot of the wall.

a What angle does the ladder make with the wall?

b What angle does the ladder make with the ground?

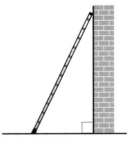

Extension problems

6 Sand Bay is 8 km east and 5 km north of Bleadon.

Ella wants to sail directly from Bleadon to Sand Bay.
On what bearing should she sail?
Show your working.

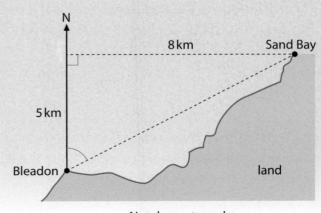
N
8 km   Sand Bay
5 km
Bleadon   land
Not drawn to scale

7 In triangle ACD the point B lies on AD so
that CB and AD are perpendicular.

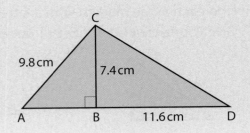

a In triangle ABC, calculate the size
of angle BAC.

b In triangle BCD, calculate the size
of angle BDC.

c Use your answers to parts **a** and **b** to calculate the size of angle ACD.
Show your working.

Points to remember

⊙ **To find an unknown angle** of a right-angled triangle:

- given two sides, choose the ratio that refers to the two sides relative to
the unknown angle;

- given the right angle and one other angle, use the angle sum of a
triangle to find the third angle.

---

8 Using trigonometry to solve problems

This lesson will help you to solve problems using Pythagoras' theorem and trigonometry.

Exercise 8

Use **trigonometry** to find angles and lengths in right-angled triangles.

The side opposite the right angle is the hypotenuse **(hyp)**.
The side opposite the angle marked x is the opposite side **(opp)**.
The side next to this angle is the adjacent side **(adj)**.

$$\sin x = \frac{\text{opp}}{\text{hyp}} \qquad \cos x = \frac{\text{adj}}{\text{hyp}} \qquad \tan x = \frac{\text{opp}}{\text{adj}}$$

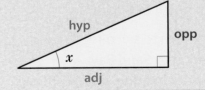

Use **Pythagoras' theorem** to find the length of the
third side of a right-angled triangle when the lengths
of the other two sides are known.

$$a^2 + b^2 = c^2$$

You need a calculator. Make a sketch of the triangle in each problem and show your working.
When your answer is a length or distance, give it correct to 3 significant figures.
When your answer is an angle, give it correct to 1 decimal place.

1. a Selima cycles 5 km west and then 8 km north.
      How far is she from her starting point?

   b Selima then cycles another 7 m north.
      How much further from her starting point is she now?

2. A theme park slide begins at the top of a vertical high
   tower. The slide is 220 m long.
   It makes an angle of 31° with the ground.
   How far is the base of the tower from the end of the slide?

3. Zahir is flying his kite on a string 28 m long.
   The string makes an angle of 41° with the ground.
   What is the vertical height of the kite above the ground?

4. Emma is 1.54 m tall.
   At a particular time of day her shadow when she stands upright is 2.41 m long.
   Find the distance between the top of Emma's head and the end of her shadow.

5. A small ramp is built to fill in a step.
   The ramp makes an angle of 15° with the ground.
   The foot of the ramp is 2 m away from the foot of the step.
   What is the height of the step?

6. a Calculate the length of the line marked x.

   b Work out the size of the angle marked y.

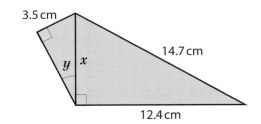

7. A volleyball net attached to two posts is
   anchored by two guy ropes to one peg.

   The peg is 1.54 m from the foot of
   the post.
   The shorter guy rope is 2.1 m long.
   The net is 1 m deep.

   a Find the total height of the post.

   b Find the length of the other
      guy rope.

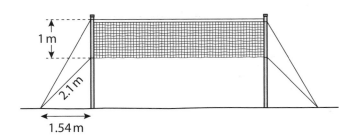

8 A regular octagon is cut from a square of card.

The octagon has side length 5 cm.

What is the area of the triangle of card that is cut from each corner?

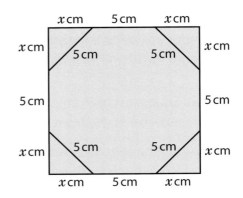

9 The diagram shows a circle with centre O and radius 7 cm.

Find the length of the chord AB.

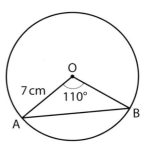

10 For safety, the foot of a 6 m ladder leaning against a wall must be placed between 1.5 m and 2.2 m from the foot of the wall.

a What is the maximum angle that the ladder can make with the wall?

b What is the maximum angle that the ladder can make with the ground?

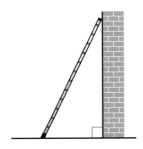

Extension problems

11 A slide 5 m long is reached by a ladder.
The slide makes an angle of 30° with the ground.

a How high is the top of the ladder above the ground?

b How long is the ladder?

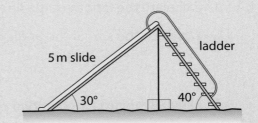

12 The diagram shows a regular pentagon with side length 8 cm.

Calculate the length of a diagonal.

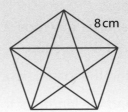

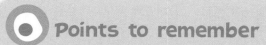

Points to remember

⊙ Draw a sketch of the triangle in the problem.

⊙ Mark on the sketch all the known sides and angles, including the units.

⊙ Identify the unknown side or angle by labelling it with a letter, such as x.

⊙ Label the sides in relation to the given or unknown angle: **opp**osite, **adj**acent, **hyp**otenuse.

⊙ Decide and write down the trigonometric ratio that you need to use to solve the problem.

⊙ Substitute values you know and solve the equation.

⊙ Give your answer to a suitable degree of accuracy (usually three significant figures for lengths and one decimal place for angles).

How well are you doing?

1 *1997 level 7*

Calculate the area of this triangle.

Show your working.

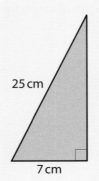

25 cm

7 cm

Not drawn accurately

2 *2006 level 7*

The diagram shows a square with side length 5 cm.

The length of the diagonal is y cm.

Show that the value of y is $\sqrt{50}$.

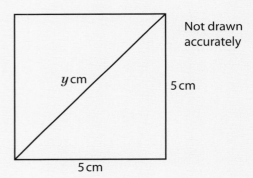

Not drawn accurately

y cm

5 cm

5 cm

3 *2000 level 7*

ABC and ACD are both right-angled triangles.

a Explain why the length of AC is 10 cm.

b Calculate the length of AD.

Show your working.

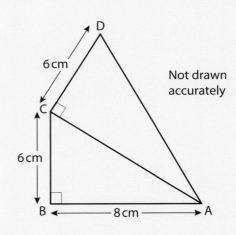

D

6 cm

C

6 cm

B

8 cm

A

Not drawn accurately

4 *2008 level 7*

Look at this triangle.

Work out length DF.

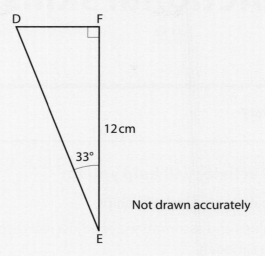

12 cm

33°

Not drawn accurately

5 *2005 level 8*

a Calculate the length w.

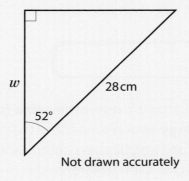

w

28 cm

52°

Not drawn accurately

b Calculate the size of angle x.

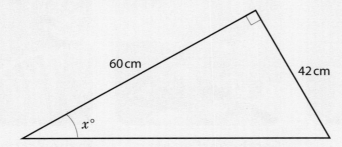

60 cm

42 cm

$x°$

Not drawn accurately

Functional skills 7

Solar power

This group activity will help you to:

- examine patterns and relationships;
- change values and assumptions or adjust relationships to see the effects on answers in a model;
- find and interpret results and draw conclusions;
- consider how appropriate and accurate results and conclusions are;
- communicate results and solutions.

Background

Energy sources such as coal, oil and gas are **non-renewable forms of energy**. One day, they will run out. **Renewable energy sources** are those that will not run out. Examples are solar power, wind power, hydropower, biomass energy and geothermal power. These sources of power don't have the same environmental impact as traditional fuels.

Solar power uses the sun to provide electricity.

Geothermal power is generated by hot springs.

Hydroelectric power is generated by water.

Electric consumption over h hours by an appliance of w watts is $\frac{wh}{1000}$ kilowatt hours.

A typical cost for electricity is 20.9p per kilowatt hour.

Problems

Here is some information about **solar panels** and the **wattage of household appliances**.

Size of panel (mm²)	Power (watts)	Price (£)
200 × 350	5	55
520 × 350	20	140
640 × 650	50	230
1000 × 650	85	370
1420 × 650	130	530
1420 × 990	200	800

Appliance	Power (watts)
Clock radio	10
Washing machine	350–500
Tumble dryer	1800–5000
Dishwasher	1200–2400
Boiler	750
Hairdryer	1200–1875
Iron	1000–1800
Microwave	750–1100
Computer	280
TV	130
Toaster	800–1400
DVD player	20–25

Work in a small group.

1. The Channel Islands are the sunniest place in the UK, with approximately 1800 hours of sunshine per year. The Shetland Isles are the least sunny, with 960 hours of sunshine on average per year.

   a John lives in Liverpool. He has a small solar panel which produces 40 watts of power. Estimate how much electricity John's solar panel produces on a sunny day.

   b Estimate how much solar power saves John in electricity costs in a year.

2. Investigate how much money your family could save by installing solar panels on the outside of your home. You might like to consider some of these questions:
   - How much energy does your household use in a year?
   - How much solar energy could you generate in a year?
   - How much would this save in electricity charges?
   - How long would it be before the solar panels paid for themselves?

3. Discuss and make notes on the advantages and disadvantages of solar power and any other sources of renewable energy that might be suitable for home use.

Be prepared to discuss your considerations with other groups.

Using algebra

This unit will help you to:

- solve problems involving the properties of linear graphs;
- use ICT to generate graphs;
- draw accurate quadratic graphs;
- use graphs to estimate the solutions of equations and find them to a given number of decimal places using trial and improvement;
- interpret graphs of real-life situations;
- investigate problems involving quadratic sequences.

1 Properties of linear graphs

This lesson will remind you about the graphs of linear functions and their inverses.

Exercise 1

The **normal form** of a linear equation is $y = ax + b$.

The **gradient** of the graph of this equation is a straight line with gradient a and **intercept** on the y-axis at $(0, b)$.

The graph on the right is of $y = 3x - 1$.

Its gradient is **3** and the intercept on the y-axis is $(0, -1)$.

If you know that the gradient of a line is a, and its y-intercept is b, you can write its equation as $y = ax + b$.

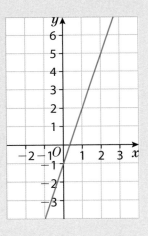

Example 1

Write the equation $3y - 9x + 21 = 0$ in its normal form.

Divide each term by 3 $y - 3x + 7 = 0$

Add $3x$ $y + 7 = 3x$

Subtract 7 $y = 3x - 7$

Example 2

a What is the equation of the inverse function for $y = 4x + 5$?

The function in x is: $\qquad$ $x \rightarrow \boxed{\times 4} \rightarrow \boxed{+5} \rightarrow 4x + 5$

The inverse function is: $\qquad$ $\dfrac{x - 5}{4} \leftarrow \boxed{\div 4} \leftarrow \boxed{-5} \leftarrow x$

The equation of the inverse function is $y = \dfrac{x - 5}{4}$, or $x = 4y + 5$.

This is similar to the original equation with x replaced by y and y replaced by x.

b Draw the graph of $y = 4x + 5$ and its inverse.

The red line is the graph of $y = 4x + 5$.

The blue line is the graph of the inverse function:

$x = 4y + 5$

The green line is the graph of $y = x$.

You can see that the blue line is the reflection of
the red line in the green line.

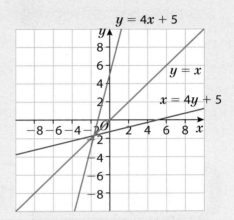

You need a copy of **A6.4 Resource sheet 1.1** for sketching graphs.
Use a new grid for each sketch of a graph, and label each line with its equation.
You will need a computer graph plotter or graphics calculator for the extension problem.

1 Write the gradient and intercept on the y-axis for the graph of each equation.
Then sketch the graph.

   a $y = x + 7$ **b** $y = -x$ **c** $y = 2x + 1$

   d $y = 0.5x - 2$ **e** $y = -8x - 11$ **f** $y = -6x + 4$

2 Rearrange each equation in its normal form.
Write the gradient and intercept on the y-axis for the graph of each equation.
Then sketch the graph.

   a $y - x = 1$ **b** $y + 2x - 4 = 0$ **c** $x - y = 2$

   d $y - 3x - 5 = 0$ **e** $5y - 30x = 25$ **f** $12x = 3y - 27$

3 On the same axes, sketch the graph of each function and its inverse.

   a $x \rightarrow \boxed{+3} \rightarrow x + 3$ **b** $x \rightarrow \boxed{\times 3} \rightarrow 3x$ **c** $x \rightarrow \boxed{\div 2} \rightarrow \dfrac{x}{2}$

   d $x \rightarrow \boxed{-9} \rightarrow x - 9$ **e** $x \rightarrow \boxed{\times 3} \rightarrow \boxed{+4} \rightarrow 3x + 4$ **f** $x \rightarrow \boxed{-1} \rightarrow \boxed{\times 2} \rightarrow 2(x - 1)$

Extension problem

 a Use a computer or graphics calculator to draw the graph of $y = -x + 3$.

b What is the equation of the reflection of this graph in the line $y = x$?

c What does this tell you about the inverse function?

d Write the general equation of any line with this property.

Points to remember

- The **normal form** of a linear equation is $y = ax + b$.
- The straight line graph $y = ax + b$ has **gradient** a and **intercept** on the y-axis at $(0, b)$.
- The graph of the **inverse** of a linear function is a reflection in the line $y = x$.

2 Parallel and perpendicular lines

This lesson will help you to find the equations of parallel and perpendicular lines.

Exercise 2

Parallel lines have the same gradients. For example, the three lines $y = 2x - 3, y = 2x - 2$ and $y = 2x + 4$ are parallel since the gradient of each line is **2**.

Any line **parallel** to $y = 2x - 2$ is of the form $y = 2x + b$.

The diagram shows a pair of perpendicular lines.

The blue line $y = 2x - 2$ has a positive gradient of **2**.
The red line $y = -\frac{1}{2}x + 3$ has a negative gradient of $-\frac{1}{2}$.

Multiplying the gradients gives -1.

Any line **perpendicular** to $y = 2x - 2$ is of the form $y = -\frac{1}{2}x + b$.

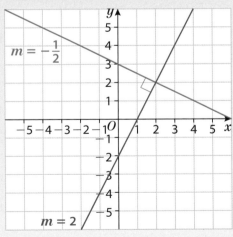

Example 1

A line is parallel to $y = 4x - 11$ and intersects the y-axis at $(0, 18)$.
What is its equation?

The gradient of the line is 4, and the y-intercept is 18.
So the equation of the line is $y = 4x + 18$.

Example 2

A line is perpendicular to $y = 4x - 11$ and passes through $(8, 4)$. What is its equation?

The gradient of the line is $-\frac{1}{4}$, so the equation of the line is $y = -\frac{1}{4}x + b$.

Calculate b by substituting $x = 8$, $y = 4$ in $y = -\frac{1}{4}x + b$, which gives $b = 6$.

So the equation of the line is $y = -\frac{1}{4}x + 6$.

1 **a** A line is parallel to $y = 3x + 11$ and intersects the y-axis at $(0, -6)$.
What is its equation?

b A line is parallel to $y = -8x + 1$ and intersects the y-axis at $(0, 7)$.
What is its equation?

c A line intersects the y-axis at $(0, 4)$ and is parallel to the line through $(1, 1)$ and $(3, 5)$.
What is its equation?

d A line passes through $(1, -2)$ and is parallel to the line through $(1, 4)$ and $(2, 7)$.
What is its equation?

2 The equation of a line is $y = 3x - 7$.
What are the equations of the lines parallel to this line that pass through these points?

a $(1, 7)$ **b** $(2, 4)$ **c** $(-1, 6)$ **d** $(3, 4)$

3 **a** What is the equation of the red line?

b What is the equation of the line parallel to the red line that passes through point A?

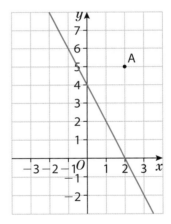

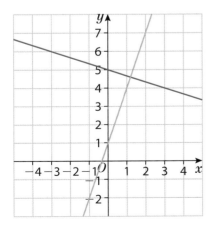

4 **a** What is the gradient of the orange line?

b What is the gradient of the green line?

c What is the angle between the orange and green lines? Explain how you know.

5 a A line is perpendicular to $y = 2x + 6$ and intersects the y-axis at $(0, 8)$.
What is its equation?

b A line is perpendicular to $y = -0.5x + 9$ and intersects the y-axis at $(0, -3)$.
What is its equation?

c A line passing through $(0, 15)$ is perpendicular to the line through $(2, 5)$ and $(3, 8)$.
What is its equation?

d A line passing through $(1, 7)$ is perpendicular to the line passing through $(2, 6)$ and $(6, 5)$.
What is its equation?

6 In each question, you are given the coordinates of four points: **A**, **B**, **C** and **D**.
Decide whether the line segments AB and CD are parallel, perpendicular or neither.

a A is $(1, 1)$, **B** is $(3, 5)$, **C** is $(2, 1)$ and **D** is $(-2, 3)$.

b A is $(-3, 1)$, **B** is $(-1, 9)$, **C** is $(0, 1)$ and **D** is $(4, 17)$.

c A is $(-3, -1)$, **B** is $(2, 3)$, **C** is $(0, 5)$ and **D** is $(-1, 2)$.

d A is $(2, 1)$, **B** is $(3, 6)$, **C** is $(2, 3)$ and **D** is $(-3, 4)$.

Extension problem

7 Prove that the triangle formed by the three lines $y - 3x + 2 = 0$, $3y + x - 21 = 0$ and
$2y - x - 2 = 0$ is a right-angled triangle.

Points to remember

- **Parallel lines** have the same gradient.
- Any line parallel to $y = 5x + 2$ has a gradient of 5
  and is of the form $y = 5x + b$.
- Any line **perpendicular** to $y = 5x + 2$ has a gradient of $-\frac{1}{5}$
  and is of the form $y = -\frac{x}{5} + b$.

---

3 Generating quadratic graphs with ICT

This lesson will help you to generate and investigate quadratic graphs.

Exercise 3

The **normal form** of a **quadratic equation** is $y = ax^2 + bx + c$.

The graph of a quadratic equation is a **U-shaped curve**.

Example 1

Generate the curves:

a $y = x^2 + 2x - 3$ (red curve)

b $y = x^2 + 2x + 1$ (purple curve)

c $y = x^2 + 2x + 4$ (blue curve)

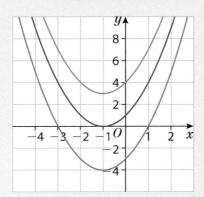

Example 2

Generate the curves:

a $y = -x^2 + 2x - 3$ (green curve)

b $y = -x^2 + 2x + 1$ (brown curve)

c $y = -x^2 + 2x + 4$ (yellow curve)

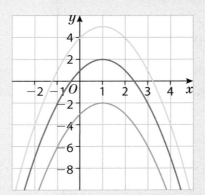

You need a computer graph plotter or a graphics calculator.
You also need copies of **A6.4 Resource sheet 3.1** for sketching graphs.

① Investigate graphs of the form $y = x^2 + c$.
Use ICT to generate the graphs of the equations below.
Sketch the graphs on the same set of axes on **Resource sheet 3.1**.
In the space provided write some comments describing the graphs.

a $y = x^2$ **b** $y = x^2 + 2$ **c** $y = x^2 - 1$

d $y = x^2 - 9$ **e** $y = x^2 + 7$ **f** $y = x^2 + 10$

② Investigate graphs of the form $y = -x^2 + c$.
Use ICT to generate the graphs of the equations below.
Use a new grid on **Resource sheet 3.1**. Sketch the graphs on the same set of axes.
In the space provided explain how these graphs differ from those in question 1.

a $y = -x^2$ **b** $y = -x^2 + 2$ **c** $y = -x^2 - 1$

d $y = -x^2 - 9$ **e** $y = -x^2 + 7$ **f** $y = -x^2 + 10$

③ Investigate graphs of the form $y = x^2 + bx$.
Use ICT to generate the graphs of the equations below.
Use a new grid on **Resource sheet 3.1**. Sketch the graphs on the same set of axes.
In the space provided explain what you notice about the graphs.

a $y = x^2 + x$ **b** $y = x^2 + 2x$ **c** $y = x^2 + 3x$

d $y = x^2 + 4x$ **e** $y = x^2 - x$ **f** $y = x^2 - 2x$

4 Investigate graphs of the form $y = ax^2$.
Use ICT to generate the graphs of the equations below.
Use a new grid on **Resource sheet 3.1**. Sketch the graphs on the same set of axes.
In the space provided explain what you notice about the graphs.

a $y = x^2$
b $y = 2x^2$
c $y = 3x^2$
d $y = -x^2$
e $y = -2x^2$
f $y = -3x^2$

Extension problem

5 Investigate further quadratic graphs of the form $y = ax^2 + bx + c$,
where a, b and c are any real numbers.

⊙ Points to remember

- A **quadratic equation** is one in which the highest power of x is x^2.
- The **normal form** of a quadratic equation is $y = ax^2 + bx + c$.
- The graph of a quadratic equation is a symmetrical U-shaped curve. When a is negative the U-shaped curve is reflected in the x-axis.
- A quadratic graph may cut or touch the x-axis at two points, one point or not at all.
- The **turning point** shows the **minimum or maximum** value of y for the equation.

4 Generating cubic graphs with ICT

ⓘ Did you know that...?

Girolano Cardano (1501−1576), an Italian mathematician, published books on how to solve cubic equations. However, another Italian mathematician, **Nicolo Tartaglia** (1500–1557), claimed that the ideas had been stolen from him.

Academics in the 16th and 17th centuries were very competitive over their mathematical discoveries. Sometimes they would not publish their work because they were afraid that someone else would use it to find even better solutions.

Girolano Cardano

This lesson will help you to generate and investigate cubic graphs.

Exercise 4

A **cubic equation** is one containing an x^3 term.

The **normal form** of a cubic equation is $y = ax^3 + bx^2 + cx + d$.

The graph of a cubic equation is an **S-shaped curve**.

Example 1

Generate the curve

$y = x^3 - 5x^2 + 3x + 6$.

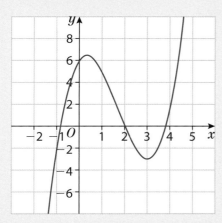

Example 2

Generate the curve

$y = -x^3 - 3x^2 + 3x + 6$.

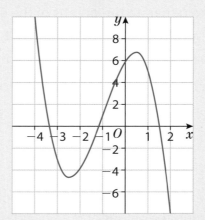

You will need computer graphing software or a graphics calculator.

You will also need copies of **A6.4 Resource sheet 3.1**.

1. Investigate graphs of the form $y = x^3 + d$.

   Use ICT to generate the graphs of the equations below.

   Sketch the graphs on the same set of axes on **Resource sheet 3.1**.

   In the space provided write some comments describing the graphs.

   a $y = x^3$ b $y = x^3 + 1$ c $y = x^3 + 2$

   d $y = x^3 + 3$ e $y = x^3 - 1$ f $y = x^3 - 2$

2. Investigate graphs of the form $y = -x^3 + d$.

   Use ICT to generate the graphs of the equations below.

   Use a new grid on **Resource sheet 3.1**. Sketch the graphs on the same set of axes.

   In the space provided explain how these graphs differ from those in question 1.

   a $y = -x^3$ b $y = -x^3 + 1$ c $y = -x^3 + 2$

   d $y = -x^3 + 3$ e $y = -x^3 - 1$ f $y = -x^3 - 2$

3   Investigate graphs of the form $y = x^3 + cx$.
    Use ICT to generate the graphs of the equations below.
    Use a new grid on **Resource sheet 3.1**. Sketch the graphs on the same set of axes.
    In the space provided explain what you notice about the graphs.

    a $y = x^3 + x$ b $y = x^3 + 2x$ c $y = x^3 + 3x$

    d $y = x^3 - x$ e $y = x^3 - 2x$ f $y = x^3 - 3x$

4   Investigate graphs of $y = x^3 + bx^2$.
    Use ICT to generate the graphs of the equations below.
    Use a new grid on **Resource sheet 3.1**. Sketch the graphs on the same set of axes.
    In the space provided explain what you notice about the graphs.

    a $y = x^3 + x^2$ b $y = x^3 + 2x^2$ c $y = x^3 + 3x^2$

    d $y = x^3 - x^2$ e $y = x^3 - 2x^2$ f $y = x^3 - 3x^2$

Extension problems

5   Continue to investigate cubic graphs of the form $y = ax^3 + bx^2 + cx + d$
    by changing the values of a, b, c and d.
    Sketch the graphs and make some notes about what you notice.

6   Investigate graphs of polynomial equations of the form:

    $$y = ax^n + bx^{n-1} + cx^{n-2} + dx^{n-3} + \ldots$$

    where a, b, c, d are constants and n is any positive integer.

    Are there any common characteristics?

Points to remember

⊙ A **cubic equation** is one in which the highest power of x is x^3.
⊙ The normal form of a cubic equation is $y = ax^3 + bx^2 + cx + d$.
⊙ The graph of a cubic function is an S-shaped curve.
⊙ A cubic graph may cut or touch the x-axis at three points or one point.
⊙ A cubic graph has two turning points or no turning point.

5 Drawing graphs

Did you know that...?

Johann Bernoulli (1667–1748) came from a family of mathematicians. There was open hostility between him and his older brother Jacob over using each other's ideas.

Bernoulli made an important contribution to the study of equations.

He also became famous for applying mathematics to medicine.

This lesson will help you to draw quadratic graphs.

Exercise 5

Example

Draw an accurate graph of $y = x^2 + 2x - 1$.

First, complete a table of values.

x	-4	-3	-2	-1	0	1	2
y	7	2	-1	-2	-1	2	7

Notice that the values are symmetrical about $x = -1$.

Draw axes with x from -4 to 2 and y from -2 to 8 on graph paper. Mark the coordinate pairs.

Draw a smooth curve joining the points you have marked.

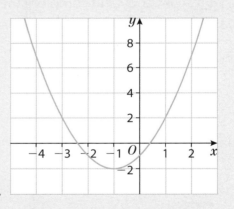

You will need 2 mm graph paper and a sharp pencil.
Before you draw an accurate graph, do a quick sketch to get an idea of what it should look like.

1. **a** Copy and complete this table of values for the equation $y = x^2$.

x	-3	-2	-1	0	1	2	3
y							

 b Draw the graph of $y = x^2$.

② a Copy and complete this table of values for the equation $y = x^2 + 3x$.

x	−5	−4	−3	−2	−1	0	1	2
y								

b Draw the graph of $y = x^2 + 3x$.

③ a Copy and complete this table of values for the equation $y = -x^2 + 4x - 1$.

x	−1	0	1	2	3	4	5
y							

b Draw the graph of $y = -x^2 + 4x + 1$.

④ a Copy and complete this table of values for the equation $y = x^3 - 12x$.

x	−4	−3	−2	−1	0	1	2	3	4
y		9			0			−9	16

b Draw the graph of $y = x^3 - 12x$.

⑤ a Copy and complete this table of values for the equation $y = x^2 + 3x + 5$.

x	−5	−4	−3	−2	−1	0	1	2
y								

b Draw the graph of $y = x^2 + 3x + 5$.

Extension problem

⑥ a Draw the graph of $y = x^2 + 2x - 8$.

b What is the equation of the axis of symmetry?

c What is the minimum y-value on the graph?

Points to remember

⊙ To draw the graph of a **linear function**, you need only plot the coordinates of three points.

⊙ To draw the graph of a **quadratic function**, you need to plot enough points to be able to draw a smooth curve.

6 Using graphs to help solve equations

This lesson will help you to use graphs to solve quadratic and cubic equations.

Exercise 6

When you want to solve an equation such as $x^2 + x + 1 = 0$, first draw the graph of $y = x^2 + x + 1$. Estimate where the graph crosses the x-axis.

Use this value of x as a starting point for finding the solution using **trial and improvement**.

Example

Solve the equation $x^2 + x - 8 = 0$.

Draw the graph of $y = x^2 + x - 8$.
Use the graph to get a first estimate for the two solutions by looking at points where $y = 0$.

Estimate: $x = -3.3$ or 2.3

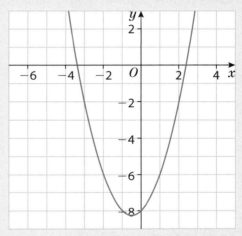

Try	$x^2 + x - 8$	
2.3	-0.41	too small
2.4	0.16	too big
2.35	-0.1275	too small
2.37	-0.0131	too small
2.38	0.0444	too big
2.375	0.015625	too big

The solution lies between 2.37 and 2.375. All numbers lying between these two values round to 2.37 to two decimal places.

So $x = 2.37$ to two decimal places.

Work in the same way to get the other solution ($x = -3.37$ to two decimal places).

You need a computer graph plotter or a graphics calculator.

1. Solve each pair of simultaneous equations by drawing their graphs.

   a $3x + 2y = 12$
      $4x - y = 5$

   b $2x - 5y = 3$
      $3x + 7y = 19$

2. Solve each quadratic equation using trial and improvement.
   Draw a graph to get a first estimate for each solution.

   a $3x^2 + 4x - 9 = 0$

   b $2x^2 - 3x - 6 = 0$

3 A cuboid has a square cross-section of side x cm.
Its length is 6 cm.
It has a total surface area of 50 cm^2.

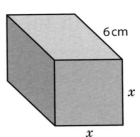

Form an equation in x.

Solve your equation, giving your answer to 2 decimal places.

 4 This trapezium has area 40 cm^2.

Form an equation in x.

Solve your equation, giving your answer to 2 decimal places.

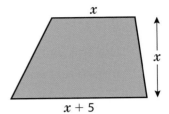

 5 **a** One of the solutions to the equation $x^3 - 5x = 0$ is at $x = 0$.

By drawing the graph of $y = x^3 - 5x$ estimate the two other solutions to one decimal place.

b Use the method of trial and improvement to find these two solutions to two decimal places.

 6 Write the equation of the graph that you would draw to help you solve these equations.

a $x^3 + 3x - 4 = 10$ **b** $x^3 - 5x + 7 = 3$

Extension problems

You need the Excel spreadsheet **Trial and improvement** for question 7.

 7 **a** Look at this cubic equation.

$$2x^3 - x^2 - 10 = 100$$

Draw an appropriate graph to help you find a first estimate of a solution.

b Explain why there is only one solution to this equation.

c Use the spreadsheet **Trial and improvement** to find this solution correct to two decimal places.

 8 **a** Draw the graph of $y = x^2 + 2x - 3$.

b Use the graph to solve the equation $x^2 + 2x - 3 = 0$.

c What line would you draw on the graph to solve the equation $x^2 + 2x - 6 = 0$?

d What line would you draw on the graph to solve the equation $x^2 + 2x - 20 = 0$?

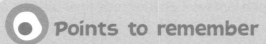

Points to remember

- ⊙ Equations can be represented as **graphs**.
- ⊙ You can read **integer solutions** to equations and **first estimates** directly from graphs.
- ⊙ Use **trial and improvement** to find solutions of equations to a given number of decimal places.
- ⊙ You can use graphs as a visual check of algebraic solutions to equations.

7 Interpreting graphs

This lesson will help you to interpret graphs of real-life situations.

Exercise 7

Graphs are used to represent data in all areas of life. Sometimes they are used to provide a visual picture of information.

At other times they are used to look for relationships between two variables.

Occasionally graphs are used to misrepresent data.

You should always check the axes and their scales before attempting to interpret a graph.

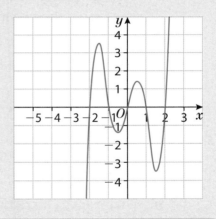

1. This graph is used to convert temperatures in degrees Celsius to degrees Fahrenheit and vice versa.

   a Central heating manufacturers recommend that room temperatures are set at 20°C.
   Estimate this temperature in degrees Fahrenheit.

   b Sam's grandmother says that the day she got married the temperature was 75°F.
   Estimate this in degrees Celsius.

   c Estimate the gradient of the graph.

   d What is the equation relating the temperature in degrees Fahrenheit, F, and the temperature in degrees Celsius, C?

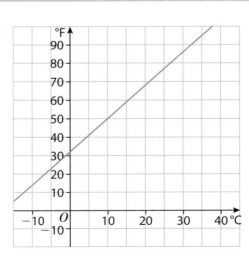

2 This shows the journey of the Smith family when they rode their bicycles along a track.

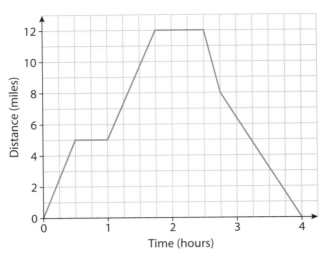

a The Smiths set out at 10:15 hours.
At what time did they arrive at their first stop?

b How far did they travel between their first and second stop?

c After their second stop they started on the return journey.
How far did they go in the first quarter of an hour?

d What speed did they do in that leg of their journey?

e At what time did the Smiths get back to the starting point?

3 This graph shows the sales figures for a group of supermarkets.

a What does each point on the *y*-axis represent?

b What was the increase in sales from the second to the third month?

c What was the percentage increase in sales from the third to the fourth month?

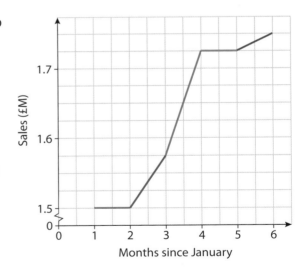

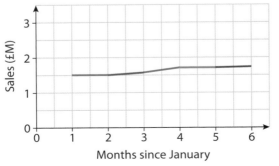

d A competitor showed the same information on a different graph.

Explain why this graph is not a good representation of the figures.

4 This graph shows the relationship between the radius and area of a circle.

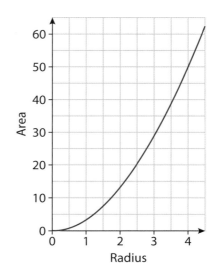

a Estimate the area of the circle when the radius is 3.

b Ned is cutting out circular badges from plastic squares that are 4 cm by 4 cm.

Estimate the greatest area of a badge.

c A water pipe needs to have a cross-sectional area of 50 cm².

Estimate its diameter.

5 A rectangular birthday card has area 10 cm², length x and height y.

The graph on the right shows the relationship between x and y.

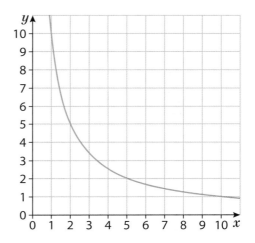

a Use the graph to find the value of x when the height $y = 5$.

b Use the graph to estimate the values of x and y for a square card.

c What is the equation of the graph?

d What is the relationship between x and y?

6 This graph shows the relationship between the radius and volume of a sphere.

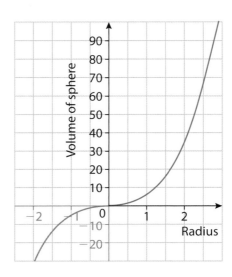

a Estimate the volume when the radius is 2.

b Estimate the radius when the volume is 60.

c Is the graph linear, quadratic or cubic?

d Why do you think the left-hand side of the graph is faded to grey?

(7) A car travels between two towns that are 100 km apart.

When the journey time is 2 hours, the car's average speed is 50 km/h.
The journey time is different at different average speeds.

Copy the grid on the right.

Show the relationship between journey time and average speed by sketching a graph on your grid.

Extension problem

(8) Look at the two graphs below.

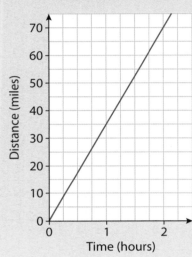

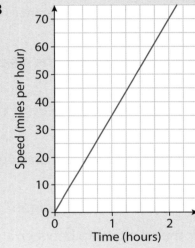

a Describe what the graph represents in graph A.

b Describe what the graph represents in graph B.

c What does the gradient of graph A represent?

d What does the gradient of graph B represent?

e How could you use graph B to work out the distance travelled after 2 hours?

Points to remember

⊙ When you interpret a **'real-life' graph**:
  – look at the labels and decide what is represented on each axis;
  – work out the scale on each axis;
  – look at the shape of the graph and think about what happens to one variable as the other variable increases.

This lesson will help you to use mathematics to carry out investigations.

Exercise 8

When you carry out an investigation, try to work **systematically** and **methodically**.

Example

Barry works at a supermarket. He creates displays of tin cans in the shape of a triangle. Find a rule relating the number of rows in the triangle n to the number of cans c.

Start by considering smaller numbers of rows and try to find a pattern.

Draw the triangles and put the results in a table.

Number of rows	Number of cans
1	1
2	$3 = 1 + 2$
3	$6 = 3 + 3$
4	$10 = 6 + 4$
5	$15 = 10 + 5$

Make a conjecture, e.g.

'I think that there will be $15 + 6 = 21$ pieces when there are 6 rows.'

Test this by drawing. The conjecture is correct.

Try to explain or justify the pattern, e.g.

'A new triangle with n rows adds another n cans to the previous triangle.'

Look at the differences between the terms. The second differences are constant, so the sequence is a quadratic sequence. The formula for the nth term is $T_n = an^2 + bn + c$. So:

$$T_1 = a + b + c = 1 \qquad T_2 = 4a + 2b + c = 3 \qquad T_3 = 9a + 3b + c = 6$$

Solve these equations to find $a = \frac{1}{2}$, $b = \frac{1}{2}$ and $c = 1$, so $c = \frac{1}{2}n^2 + \frac{1}{2}n + 1 = \frac{1}{2}n(n + 1)$.

The number of cans c in a triangle with n rows is given by $c = \frac{1}{2}n(n + 1)$.

You could extend this investigation by considering other arrangements of cans, e.g. a 3D arrangement of cans in the shape of a tetrahedron.

① **Painted cube**

Centimetre cubes are joined together to make larger cubes.
Imagine a 3 by 3 cube dipped in red paint.

a How many of the smaller cubes would have 3 faces painted red?

b How many of the smaller cubes would have 2 faces painted red?

c How many of the smaller cubes would have 1 face painted red?

d How many of the smaller cubes would have 0 faces painted red?

e Imagine a 4 by 4 cube, then a 5 by 5 cube, … n by n cube.

  Investigate how many faces of the smaller cubes are painted red when the cubes are dipped in paint.

② **Diagonals of polygons**

A triangle has 0 diagonals.
A square has 2 diagonals.
A regular pentagon has 5 diagonals.

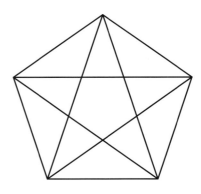

a How many diagonals does a hexagon have?

b How many diagonals does a heptagon have?

c How many diagonals does an n-sided polygon have?

③ **Crossing lines**

Straight lines are drawn, as in the diagram, so that they cross every other line.
No two straight lines can cross in the same place.
This gives the maximum number of crossings possible.

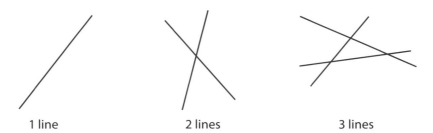

1 line   2 lines   3 lines

There are no crossings with one straight line, 1 crossing with two straight lines, 3 crossings with three straight lines.

a How many crossings will there be with 4 straight lines?

b How many crossings will there be with 10 straight lines?

c How many crossings will there be with n straight lines?

4 On 1 April, Chris said that he would do the housework for his parents.

He said that he wanted 1p for the first day, 2p for the second day, 4p for the third day, 8p for the fourth day and so on.

a How much does Chris want on the tenth day?

b How much does he want on the 30 April?

c Do you think that this was an April Fool's joke? Explain your answer.

⦿ **Points to remember**

⊙ Read through the problem.

⊙ Decide what mathematics you are going to use.

⊙ Define any variables.

⊙ Use mathematics to model the problem, e.g. draw a diagram, write an equation or draw a graph.

⊙ Solve the problem.

⊙ Interpret the solution in terms of the original investigation.

⊙ Justify or prove the results.

⊙ Ask your own 'what if' questions.

How well are you doing?

Can you:

- solve problems involving the properties of linear graphs?
- draw accurate quadratic graphs?
- use graphs to estimate the solutions of equations?
- use trial and improvement to find the solution to an equation to a given number of decimal places?
- interpret graphs of real-life situations?
- investigate problems involving quadratic sequences?

Using algebra (calculator allowed)

You need graph paper for questions 2, 3, 4 and 5.

1 *2006 Mental Test level 7*

Sketch the straight line with equation $y = x + 2$.

2 *GCSE 1388 January 2005*

A straight line passes through the points (0, 5) and (3, 17).
Find the equation of the straight line.

3 Find graphically the solution of the simultaneous equations:

$x + y = -2$

$y = x - 4$

4 *GCSE 1385 June 1998*

a Draw the graph of $y = x^2 - x - 4$. Use values of x between -2 and $+3$.

b Use your graph to write down an estimate for:

   i the minimum value of y;

   ii the solutions of the equation $x^2 - x - 4 = 0$.

5 *2002 level 7*

a Each point on the straight line $x + y = 12$ has an x-coordinate and a y-coordinate that add together to make 12.
Draw the straight line $x + y = 12$.

b Plot on a coordinate grid at least 6 points whose x-coordinate and y-coordinate multiply together to make 12.
Then draw the curve $xy = 12$.

6 The graph shows $y = x^3 + 2x + 10$.

From the graph, estimate the solution to $x^3 + 2x + 10 = 0$.

Use trial and improvement to find the solution, giving your answer to 2 decimal places.

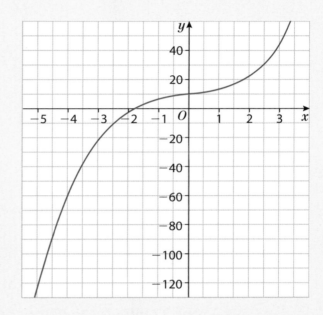

7 These patterns are made from matches.

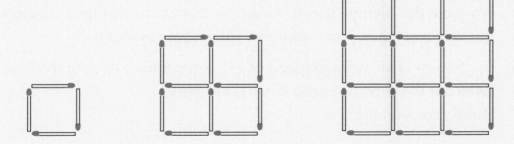

a How many matches are there in the 1st, 2nd and 3rd patterns?

b How many matches are there in the 10th pattern?

c How many matches are there in the nth pattern?

Two buses travel along the same route from the Town Hall to the Red Lion, 8 km away, and back again.

This simplified graph shows the journeys. P and Q mark two points on the graph.

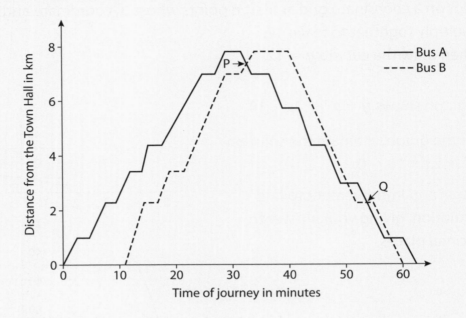

a Describe briefly what happened at point P.

b Describe briefly what happened at point Q.

c Bus A took 27 minutes to get to the Red Lion.
Work out the average speed in km per hour.

d Bus A stopped several times on the way to the Red Lion.
The average time for a stop was 2 minutes.
Work out the average speed using only that amount of time during which the bus was moving in your calculation. Show your working.

e Bus B went at an average speed of 21.5 km per hour back to the Town Hall.
Work out the average speed in miles per hour.
Show your working.

Probability 2

This unit will help you to:

- use tree diagrams to represent the outcomes of combined independent events;
- know when to add and when to multiply two probabilities;
- use relative frequency as an estimate of probability and compare the outcomes of experiments.

1 Tree diagrams 1

This lesson helps you to use tree diagrams to represent the outcomes of combined events.

Exercise 1

Tree diagrams show the outcomes when two or more events occur at the same time or one after the other.

Each set of branches on a tree diagram represents all the possible outcomes of an event. Tree diagrams help you to work out the probability of two or more combined events.

For example:

An ice cream van sells two flavours of ice cream – Raspberry (**R**) and Blueberry (**B**).

Two customers chosen at random buy an ice cream.

The tree diagram shows the four different ways that two customers can choose two different flavours. The four equally likely outcomes are:

First customer	Second customer	Possible choices of flavour
	R	R and R
R	B	R and B
	R	B and R
B	B	B and B

    R and **R**

    R and **B**

    B and **R**

    B and **B**.

The probability of each outcome is $\frac{1}{4}$.

The probability that the customers buy different flavours is:

    P(**R** and **B**) + P(**B** and **R**) = $\frac{1}{4} + \frac{1}{4} = \frac{1}{2}$

Example

One raspberry ice cream is sold for every **two** blueberry ice creams.

First customer	Second customer	Possible choices of flavour

R
   R   R and R
   B   R and B
   B   R and B

B
   R   B and R
   B   B and B
   B   B and B

B
   R   B and R
   B   B and B
   B   B and B

Each of the nine outcomes is equally likely.

Each outcome has a probability of $\frac{1}{9}$.

The probability of choosing each of the four possible combinations is shown in this table.

Ice cream choice	Number of outcomes	Probability
R and **R**	1	$\frac{1}{9}$
R and **B**	2	$\frac{2}{9}$
B and **R**	2	$\frac{2}{9}$
B and **B**	4	$\frac{4}{9}$

a What is the probability of the two customers choosing different flavours?

P(**R** and **B** or **B** and **R**) = P(**R** and **B**) + P(**B** and **R**)

$$= \frac{2}{9} + \frac{2}{9} = \frac{4}{9}$$

b What is the probability of the customers choosing at least one blueberry ice cream?

P(**R** and **B** or **B** and **R** or **B** and **B**) = P(**R** and **B**) + P(**B** and **R**) + P(**B** and **B**)

$$= \frac{2}{9} + \frac{2}{9} + \frac{4}{9} = \frac{8}{9}$$

This can also be worked out like this:

P(**R** and **B** or **B** and **R** or **B** and **B**) = 1 − P(**R** and **R**)

$$= 1 - \frac{1}{9} = \frac{8}{9}$$

1 An ice cream kiosk sells two flavours of ice cream, vanilla (**V**) and chocolate (**C**).
Two people chosen at random buy an ice cream.

    a Copy and complete this tree diagram to show the flavours that they can choose.

    b Assuming that choices of flavour are made at random, work out the probability that the people buy these combinations of flavours:

       i two vanilla ice creams

      ii two chocolate ice creams

     iii two ice creams with the same flavour

     iv one chocolate and one vanilla ice cream

      v at least one chocolate ice cream

First customer	Second customer	Possible choices of flavour
	V	V and V
	C	

2 A kiosk sells three flavours of ice cream, vanilla (**V**), chocolate (**C**) and strawberry (**S**).
Two customers chosen at random buy an ice cream.

    a Copy and complete this tree diagram to show the flavours that they can choose.

    b Assuming that choices of flavour are made at random, work out the probability that these combinations of flavours are sold.

       i two vanilla ice creams

      ii two chocolate ice creams

     iii two strawberry ice creams

     iv two ice creams with the same flavour

      v one vanilla and one chocolate ice cream

     vi one chocolate and one strawberry ice cream

    vii two ice creams with different flavours

   viii exactly one strawberry ice cream

     ix exactly one vanilla ice cream or exactly one chocolate ice cream

      x at least one chocolate ice cream

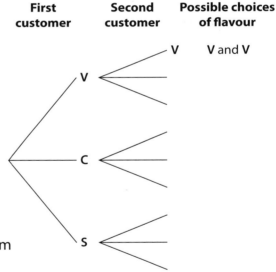

First customer	Second customer	Possible choices of flavour
	V	V and V
	C	
	S	

3 The kiosk in question 2 actually sells two chocolate ice creams for every one vanilla ice cream and one strawberry ice cream.

Two customers chosen at random buy an ice cream.

a Copy and complete this tree diagram to show the flavours that they can choose.

b Work out the probability that these combinations of flavours are sold.

  i two vanilla ice creams

  ii two chocolate ice creams

  iii two strawberry ice creams

  iv two ice creams of the same flavour

  v one vanilla and one chocolate ice cream

  vi two ice creams with different flavours

  vii exactly one strawberry ice cream

  viii exactly one chocolate ice cream

  ix exactly one vanilla ice cream or exactly one chocolate ice cream

  x at least one chocolate ice cream

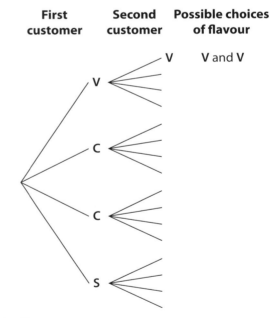

First customer	Second customer	Possible choices of flavour
	V	V and V
V		
C		
C		
S		

c Are these combined outcomes mutually exclusive?

  Two vanilla ice creams   Two strawberry ice creams

  Explain your answer.

d Are these combined outcomes mutually exclusive?

  Exactly one vanilla ice cream   Exactly one strawberry ice cream

  Explain your answer.

4 An ice cream van sells two flavours of ice cream, chocolate (**C**) and strawberry (**S**). Three customers chosen at random buy an ice cream.

a Copy and complete this tree diagram to show the flavours they can choose.

First customer	Second customer	Third customer	Possible choices of flavour

C ⟨ C ⟨ C — C, C and C

C

S

b Explain why each of the possible choices of flavours are mutually exclusive.

c Assuming that choices of flavour are made at random, work out the probability that these combinations of flavours are sold.

i   three chocolate ice creams

ii   three strawberry ice creams

iii   three ice creams of the same flavour

iv   one strawberry and two chocolate ice creams

v   one chocolate and two strawberry ice creams

vi   three ice creams each with a different flavour

vii   at least one strawberry ice cream

viii   at least one chocolate ice cream

Extension problem

 5 You need a copy of **S6.4 Resource sheet 1.1**.

The ice cream van in question 4 sells twice as many strawberry ice creams as it does chocolate ice creams. Three customers chosen at random buy an ice cream.

a Complete the tree diagram and the list of choices of flavours on the resource sheet.

b Explain why each of the choices in the list is mutually exclusive.

c Work out the probability of these combinations of flavours being sold.

   i three chocolate ice creams

   ii three strawberry ice creams

   iii three ice creams of the same flavour

   iv exactly one chocolate ice cream

   v exactly one strawberry ice cream

   vi exactly one chocolate ice cream or exactly one strawberry ice cream

   vii at least one chocolate ice cream

   viii at least one strawberry ice cream

Points to remember

- **Mutually exclusive** outcomes of an event or of combined events cannot occur at the same time.
- If **A** and **B** are two mutually exclusive outcomes of an event then:

   $P(\textbf{A or B}) = P(\textbf{A}) + P(\textbf{B})$

- You can use **tree diagrams** to represent mutually exclusive outcomes of combined events and their probabilities.

2 Tree diagrams 2

This lesson helps you to use a tree diagram in a practical situation — traffic flowing through a simple network of roads — and to calculate the probability that a vehicle will take a particular route.

Exercise 2

Networks of roads can be represented on a tree diagram.

The relative frequency of traffic turning, say, left or right at a junction in the network can be worked out from a traffic survey.

If a large number of vehicles is observed in the traffic survey, then the relative frequency gives a good estimate of the probability of a vehicle turning left or right.

Example

Traffic enters a network of roads at **A** and approaches a junction.
Vehicles either go left (**L**) or right (**R**), as shown by the arrows.

Junction

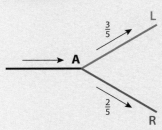

Tree diagram

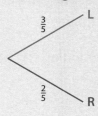

From the relative frequencies in a traffic survey, at junction A the probability that a car turns left P(**L**) is $\frac{3}{5}$ and the probability that a car turns right P(**R**) is $\frac{2}{5}$.

Both the vehicles turning left and those turning right approach a second junction where, again, they either go left (**L**) or right (**R**).

Network

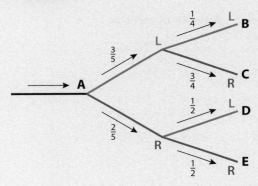

Tree diagram

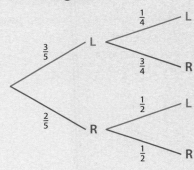

After turning **left** at the first junction, at the second junction:

$$P(\mathbf{L}) = \tfrac{1}{4} \quad P(\mathbf{R}) = \tfrac{3}{4}$$

After turning **right** at the first junction, at the second junction:

$$P(\mathbf{L}) = \tfrac{1}{2} \quad P(\mathbf{R}) = \tfrac{1}{2}$$

This information is shown on both a diagram of the network and a tree diagram.

To get to **B** vehicles go **L** and **L**. To get to **C** vehicles go **L** and **R**.
To get to **D** vehicles go **R** and **L**. To get to **E** vehicles go **R** and **R**.

a What happens if 100 vehicles travel through the network?

First junction

Of the **100** cars that enter the network, on average:

$\frac{3}{5} \times 100 = 60$ cars go left (**L**) $\frac{2}{5} \times 100 = 40$ cars go right (**R**)

Second junction

Of the **60** cars that go left (**L**) at the first junction, on average:

$\frac{1}{4} \times 60 = 15$ cars go left (**L**) $\frac{3}{4} \times 60 = 45$ cars go right (**R**)

Of the **40** cars that go right (**R**) at the first junction, on average:

$\frac{1}{2} \times 40 = 20$ cars go left (**L**) $\frac{1}{2} \times 40 = 20$ cars go right (**R**)

This information can be shown on the network and a tree diagram.

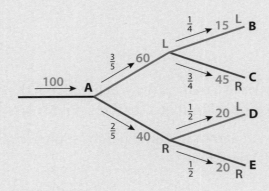

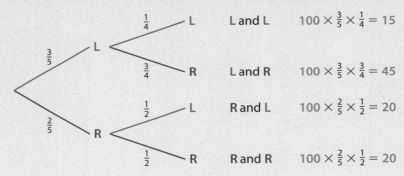

First junction	Second junction	Outcomes	Number of vehicles

b Using the numbers of vehicles on the tree diagram, estimate these probabilities of a vehicle taking each route through the network.

P(**L** and **L**) = $\frac{15}{100}$ = 0.15 (or $\frac{3}{20}$)   P(**L** and **R**) = $\frac{45}{100}$ = 0.45 (or $\frac{9}{20}$)

P(**R** and **L**) = $\frac{20}{100}$ = 0.2 (or $\frac{1}{5}$)   P(**R** and **R**) = $\frac{20}{100}$ = 0.2 (or $\frac{1}{5}$)

On each branch of a tree diagram **all mutually exclusive** outcomes are included, so the sum of the probabilities is 1.

L and **L**, **L** and **R**, **R** and **L** and **R** and **R** are **all** the mutually exclusive combined outcomes, so the sum of their probabilities is 1.

$$P(\textbf{L and L}) + P(\textbf{L and R}) + P(\textbf{R and L}) + P(\textbf{R and R}) = \frac{15}{100} + \frac{45}{100} + \frac{20}{100} + \frac{20}{100}$$

$$= \frac{100}{100} = 1$$

① Traffic travels through this network of roads.

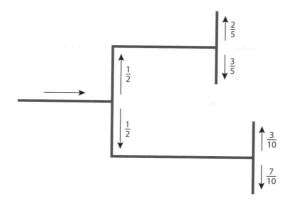

The probability that traffic turns in the direction of the arrows is shown at each junction.

a Copy and complete this tree diagram to represent the network.

b 100 vehicles enter the network. On average, how many vehicles take these routes through the network?

   i **L** and **L**   ii **L** and **R**

  iii **R** and **L**   iv **R** and **R**

c Work out these probabilities.

   i P(**L** and **L**)   ii P(**L** and **R**)   iii P(**R** and **L**)   iv P(**R** and **R**)

② The tree diagram represents a network of roads.

The probability of a vehicle travelling along a particular route in the network is shown on the tree diagram.

For example, the probability of a vehicle turning left at the first junction is $\frac{3}{10}$.

100 vehicles enter the network.

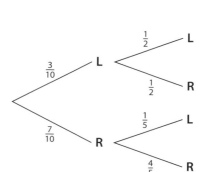

a On average, how many vehicles take these routes through the network?

   i **L** and **L**   ii **L** and **R**

  iii **R** and **L**   iv **R** and **R**

b Work out these probabilities:

   i P(**L** and **L**)   ii P(**L** and **R**)

  iii P(**R** and **L**)   iv P(**R** and **R**)

(3) Repeat question 2 for the networks of roads represented by these tree diagrams.

a

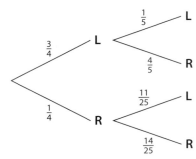

b

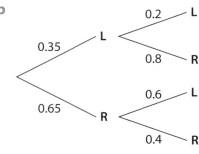

(4) The tree diagram represents a network of roads.

The probability of a vehicle travelling along a particular route in the network is shown on the tree diagram.

For example, the probability of a vehicle turning left at the first junction is $\frac{7}{20}$.

100 vehicles enter the network.

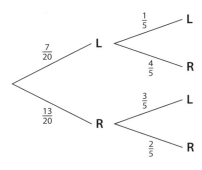

a Explain why the sum of the probabilities on each set of branches of the tree diagram is 1.

b On average, how many vehicles are likely to:

  i turn left at the first junction

  ii take the route **L** and **L** through the network

  iii take the route **R** and **R** through the network?

c A vehicle that goes **L** and **R** or **R** and **L** goes to the motorway. How many of the 100 vehicles go to the motorway?

d Work out these probabilities.

  i P(**L** and **L**)   ii P(**R** and **R**)   iii P(goes to the motorway)

e Explain why these outcomes are mutually exclusive:

  Going **L** and **L**   Going **R** and **R**

f Explain why P(**R** and **L or R** and **R**) = P(**R** and **L**) + P(**R** and **R**).

g Explain why P(**L** and **L**) + P(**L** and **R**) + P(**R** and **L**) + P(**R** and **R**) = 1.

Extension problem

  Traffic enters this network of roads.

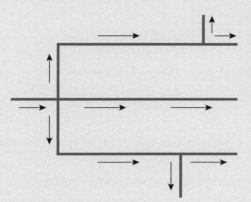

The arrows show the direction that traffic travels through the network.

The tree diagram represents the network.
The probability of a vehicle taking a particular route at each junction of the network is shown on the tree diagram.

a Copy the tree diagram and complete the probabilities on each set of branches.

b Work out these probabilities.

   i   P(**L** and **L**)   ii   P(**L** and **R**)

  iii   P(**R** and **L**)   iv   P(**R** and **R**)

c Show that the sum of the probabilities you worked out in part **b** is 0.85.
Give a reason for this result.

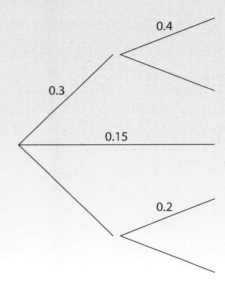

Points to remember

- The probabilities of the outcomes of each event can be written on the branches of a **tree diagram**.
- Each set of branches should include all the mutually exclusive outcomes of the event.
- The sum of the probabilities on each set of branches is 1.
- Use the probabilities on the branches to work out the probabilities of combined outcomes.
- The sum of the probabilities of all the mutually exclusive combined outcomes is 1.

3 Tree diagrams 3

This lesson helps you understand

- ◉ when events are independent;
- ◉ how to work with probabilities associated with independent mutually exclusive events, using tree diagrams to help work out probabilities where appropriate.

Exercise 3

Tree diagrams are particularly useful for working out probabilities when combined events are not equally likely. Multiply the probabilities on the branches for each combined outcome.

Example 1

An ice cream kiosk sells twice as many strawberry (**S**) as chocolate (**C**) ice creams.

a What is the probability of selling **i** a strawberry ice cream and **ii** a chocolate ice cream?

$P(\mathbf{S}) = \frac{2}{3}$ $P(\mathbf{C}) = \frac{1}{3}$

b Draw a tree diagram to show the possible ways that two customers can buy an ice cream. Work out the probability of each outcome.

First customer	Second customer	Possible ice cream choices	Probabilities
	$\frac{1}{3}$ C	C and C	$\frac{1}{3} \times \frac{1}{3} = \frac{1}{9}$
$\frac{1}{3}$ C	$\frac{2}{3}$ S	C and S	$\frac{1}{3} \times \frac{2}{3} = \frac{2}{9}$
$\frac{2}{3}$ S	$\frac{1}{3}$ C	S and C	$\frac{2}{3} \times \frac{1}{3} = \frac{2}{9}$
	$\frac{2}{3}$ S	S and S	$\frac{2}{3} \times \frac{2}{3} = \frac{4}{9}$

Notice that:

$P(\mathbf{C} \text{ and } \mathbf{C}) + P(\mathbf{C} \text{ and } \mathbf{S}) + P(\mathbf{S} \text{ and } \mathbf{C}) + P(\mathbf{S} \text{ and } \mathbf{S}) = \frac{1}{9} + \frac{2}{9} + \frac{2}{9} + \frac{4}{9} = \frac{9}{9} = 1$

c What is the probability of selling two ice creams of different flavours?

$P(\mathbf{C} \text{ and } \mathbf{S} \text{ or } \mathbf{S} \text{ and } \mathbf{C}) = P(\mathbf{C} \text{ and } \mathbf{S}) + P(\mathbf{S} \text{ and } \mathbf{C}) = \frac{2}{9} + \frac{2}{9} = \frac{4}{9}$

d What is the probability that two customers buy at least one strawberry ice cream?

$P(\mathbf{C} \text{ and } \mathbf{S} \text{ or } \mathbf{S} \text{ and } \mathbf{C} \text{ or } \mathbf{S} \text{ and } \mathbf{S}) = P(\mathbf{C} \text{ and } \mathbf{S}) + P(\mathbf{S} \text{ and } \mathbf{C}) + P(\mathbf{S} \text{ and } \mathbf{S})$

$= \frac{2}{9} + \frac{2}{9} + \frac{4}{9} = \frac{8}{9}$

Independent and mutually exclusive events

Compare the probabilities on the branches on these tree diagrams.

Ice cream

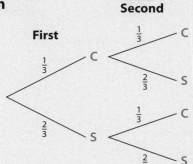

Road network

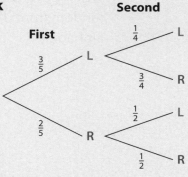

In the **ice cream** example, the probabilities for the second choice of ice cream do not depend on the choice of the first ice cream. Events like this are **independent**.

The combined outcomes for the ice cream example are:

   C and C   C and S   S and C   S and S

These outcomes cannot occur at the same time so they are **mutually exclusive**.

In the **road network**, the probabilities for left and right at the second junction depend upon whether a vehicle goes left or right at the first junction. The events are **not independent**.

Example 2

A counter is taken at random from a bag containing 7 red (**R**) and 3 blue (**B**) counters. The counter is replaced and another counter is taken at random.

a Draw a tree diagram to show the combined outcomes and the probability calculations.

First pick	Second pick	Outcomes	Probabilities
	$\frac{7}{10}$ R	R and R	$\frac{7}{10} \times \frac{7}{10} = \frac{49}{100}$
R			
$\frac{7}{10}$	$\frac{3}{10}$ B	R and B	$\frac{7}{10} \times \frac{3}{10} = \frac{21}{100}$
	$\frac{7}{10}$ R	B and R	$\frac{3}{10} \times \frac{7}{10} = \frac{21}{100}$
B $\frac{3}{10}$			
	$\frac{3}{10}$ B	B and B	$\frac{3}{10} \times \frac{3}{10} = \frac{9}{100}$

b Are the two events independent?

The outcomes of the second pick are **not** influenced by the outcomes of the first so the events are **independent**.

c What is the probability that the counters have the same colour?

P(**R** and **R** or **B** and **B**) = P(**R** and **R**) + P(**B** and **B**) = $\frac{49}{100} + \frac{9}{100} = \frac{58}{100} = \frac{29}{50}$

1 a For each of these pairs of **independent** events copy and complete the tree diagrams, the combined outcomes and their probabilities.

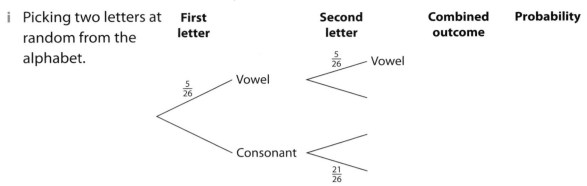

i Picking two letters at random from the alphabet.

First letter	Second letter	Combined outcome	Probability

$\frac{5}{26}$ — Vowel

$\frac{5}{26}$ — Vowel

Consonant

$\frac{21}{26}$

ii Leaving a light on in two different rooms of a house.

First room	Second room	Combined outcome	Probability

0.2 — On

0.2

2 Ian and Tara play a game with a box containing one red counter and two blue counters.

In the game Ian and Tara take it in turns to choose a counter at random.
After each choice the counter is put back in the box.
The game stops after three counters have been chosen.

Ian scores a point for every **Red** counter that is chosen.
Tara scores a point for every **Blue** counter that is chosen.

a Copy and complete the tree diagram to show all the outcomes of choosing 3 counters.
Work out the probability of each combined outcome.

First choice	Second choice	Third choice	Combined outcome	Probability

$\frac{1}{3}$ R

b Work out the probability that: i Ian scores 3 points

                               ii Ian scores 1 point more than Tara

                               iii Tara scores at least 1 point

c Work out the probability that Tara scores more points that Ian and wins the game.

3 Two shops, A and B, sell ice cream of different flavours.
The probabilities of each different flavour for each shop are shown in the table.

Flavour	Vanilla (V)	Chocolate (C)	Strawberry (S)
Shop A	$\frac{2}{5}$	$\frac{3}{5}$	
Shop B	$\frac{1}{2}$	$\frac{1}{3}$	

A customer, chosen at random, buys an ice cream from shop A.
A different customer, chosen at random, buys an ice cream from shop B.

a Work out the probability that Shop A sells strawberry ice cream.

b Work out the probability that Shop B sells strawberry ice cream.

c Copy and complete this tree diagram together with a list of **all** the possible choices of ice cream the two customers can buy.

Write the probabilities of each outcome on the branches of the diagram.

d Explain why the two events are independent.

e Work out the probability that the customers buy at least one vanilla ice cream.

f Work out the probability that the two customers buy the same flavour ice cream.

4 A bag contains 5 red balls (**R**) and 3 blue balls (**B**).

A ball is taken at random from the bag and its colour is recorded.
The ball is replaced.
A second ball is taken at random from the bag and its colour recorded.

a Draw a tree diagram to show all the possible outcomes of these two events.
Write the probabilities of each outcome on the branches of the diagram.

b Explain why the events are independent.

c Work out:
   i P(**R** and **R**)   **ii** P(**B** and **B**)
  iii The probability that the balls have the same colour.
  iv The probability that the balls are a different colour.

d Explain why P(**R** and **R**) + P(**R** and **B**) + P(**B** and **R**) + P(**B** and **B**) = 1.

Extension problem

5 Aftab gets a lift to school on each day of the week except Monday.

On Mondays the probability that he is late for school is $\frac{2}{5}$.

On Tuesdays the probability that he is late for school is $\frac{1}{10}$.

a Draw a tree diagram to show whether Aftab is late or not on a Monday and a Tuesday in any school week. Assuming that being late on Monday and Tuesday are independent events, write the probabilities of each outcome on the branches of the diagram.

b Work out the probability that Aftab is late on either a Monday or Tuesday of a school week.

c Estimate the number of times that Aftab is likely to be late on either a Monday or Tuesday in a school year of 39 weeks.

Points to remember

⊙ When one event happening does not affect the probability of another event happening, the events are independent.

⊙ The probabilities of the outcomes of combined independent events can be worked out from a tree diagram.

⊙ Multiply the probabilities on the branches that represent each combined outcome, so when A and B are the outcomes of two independent events:

$$P(A \text{ and } B) = P(A) \times P(B)$$

4 Relative frequency and probability

Did you know that...?

The law of large numbers is one of the basic laws of probability.

It is sometimes called Bernoulli's law after **Jacob Bernoulli** (1654–1705), the mathematician who first proved it in 1713.

Put simply, the law of large numbers states that there is always a 'guaranteed' long-term result for a random event.

For example after a large number of throws of a fair coin, more or less half the results are heads and half are tails.

Jacob Bernoulli

This lesson will help you to compare probabilities worked out from relative frequency with theoretical probability for probability trials involving combined events.

You can use the results of a probability experiment based on repeated trials to check if the trial is **fair**. Compare the **relative frequency** of an outcome with its **theoretical probability**.

$$\text{Relative frequency} = \frac{\text{number of times the outcome occurs}}{\text{total number of trials in the experiment}}$$

For example, three coins are thrown and the number of heads obtained is recorded.

The tree diagram shows that there are eight possible combined outcomes.

Coin 1	Coin 2	Coin 3	Outcome	Probabilities
		H	HHH	$\frac{1}{8}$
	H	T	HHT	$\frac{1}{8}$
H		H	HTH	$\frac{1}{8}$
	T	T	HTT	$\frac{1}{8}$
		H	THH	$\frac{1}{8}$
	H	T	THT	$\frac{1}{8}$
T		H	TTH	$\frac{1}{8}$
	T	T	TTT	$\frac{1}{8}$

If the trial is fair, then the theoretical probability of each outcome is $\frac{1}{8}$ or 0.125. The **relative frequency** of each outcome should be approximately equal to the **theoretical probability** of each outcome after a large number of trials.

The trial is carried out 200 times. The results are shown in this frequency table.

Outcome	Tally	Frequency	Relative frequency	Theoretical probability
HHH	IIII IIII IIII IIII III	23	0.115	0.125
HHT	IIII IIII IIII IIII IIII I	26	0.13	0.125
HTH	IIII IIII IIII IIII IIII II	27	0.135	0.125
HTT	IIII IIII IIII IIII III	23	0.115	0.125
THH	IIII IIII IIII IIII III	23	0.115	0.125
THT	IIII IIII IIII IIII IIII I	26	0.13	0.125
TTH	IIII IIII IIII IIII IIII IIII	29	0.145	0.125
TTT	IIII IIII IIII IIII IIII III	23	0.115	0.125

For each outcome, the relative frequency is close to the theoretical probability, so the trial is a fair one.

Another way to look at the results is to draw a **relative frequency graph**. For one particular outcome, record its frequency after 20, 40, 60, … trials and calculate the relative frequencies.

For example, the table shows the frequencies and relative frequencies for throwing three heads.

Number of trials	Tally	Cumulative frequency	Relative frequency
20	||	2	0.1
40	|||||		6	0.15
60	|||||		6	0.1
80	||||| ||	7	0.088
100	||||| |||	8	0.08
120	||||| ||||| ||	12	0.1
140	||||| ||||| |||||		16	0.114
160	||||| ||||| ||||| |||	18	0.113
180	||||| ||||| ||||| ||||| |||	23	0.128
200	||||| ||||| ||||| ||||| |||	23	0.115

The graph shows the relative frequency for throwing three heads.

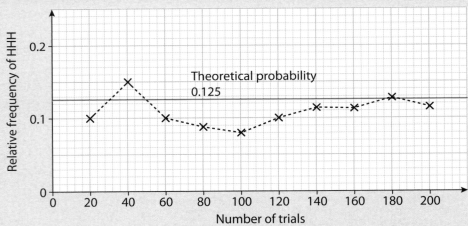

As the number of trials increases the graph gets closer to the limit of 0.125, which is the theoretical probability.

This shows that a good estimate of the limit of the relative frequency of throwing three heads is the theoretical probability of throwing three heads.

This suggests that the trial is fair.

You need copies of **S6.4 Resource sheets 4.2 and 4.3**.

1 You need a copy of **Resource sheet 4.2**.

Three dice numbered from 1 to 6 are rolled. The number of sixes is recorded.

a Copy and complete this tree diagram to show the outcomes of the trial.

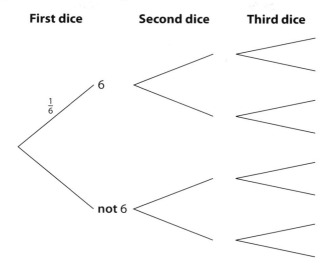

b Use the tree diagram to work out the probability of rolling one or two sixes.
Write this probability as a decimal to 2 decimal places.

c **Resource sheet 4.2** shows a large number of the results of the trial.

Choose any 200 consecutive trials from the resource sheet.

Copy and complete this frequency table.

Outcome	Tally	Frequency	Relative frequency	Theoretical probability
1 or 2 sixes				
not 1 or 2 sixes				

d Copy and complete this table for the number of times one or two sixes are rolled.

Number of trials	Tally	Cumulative frequency	Relative frequency
20			
40			
60			
...			

Draw a relative frequency graph to show how the relative frequency of 1 or 2 sixes changes as the number of trials increases.

e Is the trial fair? Justify your conclusion.

② You need a copy of **Resource sheet 4.3**.

A dice is rolled repeatedly until a 6 is scored. The number of rolls to score a 6 is recorded.

a Copy and complete this tree diagram to show the outcome of the trial for three rolls of the dice.

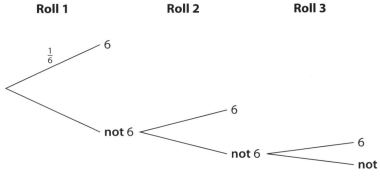

b Use the tree diagram to work out the probability of rolling a six with one **or** two **or** three rolls of the dice. Write this probability as a decimal to 2 decimal places.

c **Resource sheet 4.3** shows 120 results of the trial.

On the resource sheet, fill in the columns giving the number of rolls of the dice. The first few have been done for you.

Use all the results to copy and complete this frequency table.

Outcome	Tally	Frequency	Relative frequency	Theoretical probability
6 rolled in up to three rolls				
6 **not** in up to three rolls				

d Copy and complete this table for getting a 6 with three or fewer rolls of the dice.

Number of trials	Tally	Cumulative frequency	Relative frequency
20			
40			
60			

Draw a relative frequency graph to show how the relative frequency of rolling a six in three or fewer rolls changes as the number of trials increases.

e Is the trial fair? Justify your conclusion.

⊙ **Points to remember**

⊙ You can test whether or not a trial is fair by comparing the **relative frequency** of outcomes from the trial with the **theoretical probability** of the outcomes, provided that the number of trials is large.

How well are you doing?

Probability 2 (calculator allowed)

1 *GCSE 1387 June 2003*

Julie does a statistical experiment.
She throws a dice 600 times. She scores six 200 times.

a Is the dice fair? Explain your answer.

b Julie then throws a fair red dice once and a fair blue dice once.
Copy and complete the probability tree diagram to show the outcomes.
Label clearly the branches of the probability tree diagram.

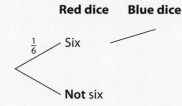

c i Julie throws a fair red dice once and a fair blue dice once.
Calculate the probability that Julie gets a six on both the red dice and the
blue dice.

ii Calculate the probability that Julie gets at least one six.

2 A box of counters contains 2 red counters (**R**) and 3 blue counters (**B**).
A counter is picked at random from the box.
The counter is replaced and a second counter is picked at random from the box.

a Explain why the first pick and the second pick are independent events.

b Copy and complete this tree diagram to show all the possible outcomes.

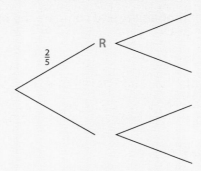

First counter   Second counter   Outcomes

c Use the tree diagram to work out the probability of picking:

i two red counters;

ii first a blue and then a red counter;

iii first a red and then a blue counter;

iv two blue counters.

d Work out the probability that the two counters have the same colour.

e The trial is carried out 500 times.
Estimate how many times the counters are likely to be a different colour.

3 *2001 level 8*

a A fair coin is thrown. When it lands it shows heads or tails.

Game: Throw the coin three times.

Player A wins one point each time the coin shows a head.
Player B wins one point each time the coin shows a tail.

Show that the probability that player A scores three points is $\frac{1}{8}$.

b What is the probability that player B scores exactly two points?
Show your working.

Using and applying maths

This unit will help you to:

- do some research to find out how different cultures have influenced the development and history of mathematics;
- be aware of some current applications of mathematics;
- use your mathematical knowledge to solve unfamiliar problems;
- work logically and use mathematical reasoning;
- solve problems by breaking them into parts;
- find counter-examples to prove that a statement is not true;
- appreciate the difference between evidence and proof.

1 The history of pi

Did you know that...?

Throughout history, mathematicians from many different countries have discovered approximations for π, including the Greek **Archimedes** (c. 287–212 BC).

Archimedes came from a noble family. He was the leading scientist and mathematician of his time.

He used geometrical methods to measure curves and the areas and volumes of solids, using a very close approximation of pi. His value for π is correct to 3 decimal places.

This lesson will help you to appreciate how different cultures have influenced the development and history of mathematics.

Exercise 1

1. Look on the Internet to find the current world record for the greatest number of decimal places for which π has been calculated.

2. Write down the value of π to 30 places.

(3) Pi day is celebrated each year in the United States. When is it?

(4) A magazine for Key Stage 3 pupils intends to publish a series of articles about π or the mathematicians associated with its history.

Do some Internet research to find out more information about one of them.
Make notes while you do this.
Your teacher will suggest some useful websites.

For homework, you are to write an article for the magazine based on your notes.

⊙ Points to remember

- ⊙ People from many different cultures have contributed to work on π throughout the ages.
- ⊙ The Internet is a useful source of information about mathematics and its history but it is important to find the best website.
- ⊙ It is often necessary to narrow down an Internet search so that it results in **a** less information, and **b** more relevant information.

---

2 Limits of sequences

This lesson will help you to use your mathematical knowledge to solve unfamiliar problems, work logically and use mathematical reasoning.

Exercise 2

Some sequences come to an end after so many terms. These are called **finite sequences**.

Sequences that go on for ever are called **infinite sequences**.

When the terms of an infinite sequence get closer and closer to a particular number, that number is called the **limit** of the sequence.

Example

The first term of a sequence is 3. The term-to-term rule is 'divide by 2, then add 3'.

a What are the first 12 terms of the sequence?

3, 4.5, 5.25, 5.625, 5.8125, 5.906 25, 5.953 125,
5.976 562 5, 5.988 281 25, 5.994 140 625, 5.997 070 313, 5.998 535 157

b What do you think the limit of the sequence will be?

The terms appear to be getting closer and closer to 6 so the limit of the sequence is 6.

Investigation 1

1. A rule to get the next number in a number sequence is:

> Look at the last number.
> If it is a multiple of 4, divide by 2.
> If it is not a multiple of 4, add 3.

a What are the next five numbers in this sequence?
10, 13, 16, 8, ☐, ☐, ☐, ☐, ☐

b Work out the 500th number in the sequence.
Show how you worked it out.

c Here is another sequence of numbers that follows the same rule.
☐, ☐, ☐, 14, 17, 20, 10, 13

The first, second and third numbers are missing.
What could they be?
Give all the possible answers.

Investigation 2

2. The first term of a sequence is 1.
The term-to-term rule is: 'add 3 and divide by 2'.

a Find the first 10 terms generated by this sequence. Use a calculator or a spreadsheet.

b To what value does this sequence get closer and closer?

c Use the same term-to-term rule with different starting numbers.
What do you notice?

3. Change the term-to-term rule in question 2 to: 'add 4 and divide by 2'.
Repeat parts **a**, **b** and **c** of question 2.

4. What do you think the limit will be for the rule 'add 8 and divide by 2'?

5 What will be the limit of the sequence if the rule is 'add N and divide by 2'?

6 Investigate the term-to-term rule 'add N and divide by 3' for different starting numbers.

Extension problem

7 The first term of a sequence is 1.
The term-to-term rule is 'divide by 3 and add 2'.

Investigate the sequence by varying the number that you add each time.

Find a rule for predicting the limit of the sequence 'divide by 3 and add N'.

Points to remember

⊙ You can use a term-to-term rule to generate a sequence.

⊙ Sequences that go on for ever are called **infinite sequences**.

⊙ In some infinite sequences, the terms get closer and closer to a certain number, which is called the **limit** of the sequence.

3 Investigating paper sizes

This lesson will help you to use mathematical reasoning to solve unfamiliar problems.

Exercise 3

There is an international standard for **paper sizes**. The largest size is A0. Successive paper sizes (A1 to A10) are defined by halving the preceding paper size parallel to its shorter side. The most frequently used paper size is A4.

The linking of paper sizes in this way was first suggested in 1768 by the German scientist **Georg Lichtenberg**.

At the start of the 20th century, **Dr Walter Porstmann** turned the idea into a proper system of standard paper sizes, which was introduced in Germany in 1922.

This standard has now been adopted by all countries in the world except the USA and Canada.

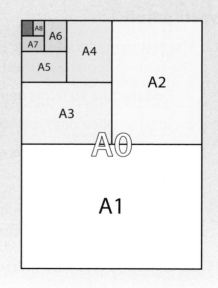

Investigation 1

① You need three paper rectangles size A4, A5 and A6.

  a Measure and write down the length and width of each rectangle.

  b For each rectangle, write the ratio width : length as a unitary ratio ($1 : \frac{length}{width}$).
  What do you notice?

  c Use your calculator to find the value of the square root of 2.
  How close are the ratios in part **b** to $1 : \sqrt{2}$?

  d Are your three rectangles similar rectangles?
  Write **Yes** or **No**. Explain your answer.

  e Use your measurements from part **a** to calculate the approximate dimensions of A3, A2, A1 and A0 size paper.

  f Work out the approximate area of A0 size paper. What do you notice?

  g The definition of the standard size for a sheet of A0 paper is:

  – its area is 1 square metre;

  – the ratio of its length to its width is $1 : \sqrt{2}$.

  Use this definition to calculate the actual dimensions of A0 paper.

Investigation 2

② Make three right-angled triangles from the largest square you can cut from A4 paper: one large (size 1), one medium (size 2) and one small (size 3).

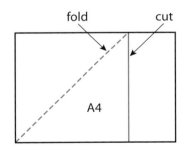
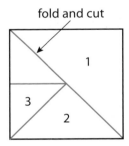

  a Measure and write down the length of the hypotenuse and shortest side for each of the three triangles.

  b For each triangle, divide the length of the hypotenuse by the length of the shortest side. What do you notice?

  c Use your calculator to find the value of the square root of 2.
  How close is this to the result of each division in part **b**?

  d Work out: $\dfrac{\text{length of hypotenuse of large triangle}}{\text{length of hypotenuse of medium triangle}}$

  and: $\dfrac{\text{length of hypotenuse of medium triangle}}{\text{length of hypotenuse of small triangle}}$.

  What do you notice?

⊙ A **ratio** compares two or more quantities.

⊙ Ratios are simplified like fractions.

⊙ The ratio $a:b$ can be stated in the form of the **unitary ratio** $1:\frac{b}{a}$.

⊙ To compare ratios, write them as unitary ratios.

⊙ Corresponding sides of similar shapes are in the same ratio.

4 Proof

This lesson will help you to use mathematical reasoning, know the difference between evidence and proof and find a counter-example to prove that a statement is not true.

Exercise 4A

One way to prove that a statement is **not true** is to find just one example where the result does not work. This is called finding a **counter-example**.

Example

Emma says that when n is an even number, $\frac{1}{2}n + 5$ is even.
Show that she is wrong.

Try $n = 2$ $\frac{1}{2}n + 5 = 1 + 5 = 6$, which is even.

Try $n = 10$ $\frac{1}{2}n + 5 = 5 + 5 = 10$, which is even.

Try $n = 4$ $\frac{1}{2}n + 5 = 2 + 5 = 7$, which is not even.

This is a counter-example, so Emma is wrong.

① p and q are both prime numbers.
Give an example to show that $p + q$ is not always an even number.

②   Rose says that $a^3 + 2$ is never a multiple of 3.
Show that Rose is wrong.

③ Nerissa says that when z is an even number,
$z^2 + \frac{1}{2}z$ is always odd.
Explain why Nerissa is wrong.

④ m is an odd number and n is an even number.
Tariq says that $m + n - 1$ cannot be a prime number.
Explain why Tariq is wrong.

⑤ Jack says that the square root of a number is
always less than the number.

Is Jack correct? Write **Yes** or **No**.
Explain your reasoning.

⑥ Anita says:

'When you cut a piece off a shape, you reduce its
area and perimeter.'

Is Anita correct? Write **Yes** or **No**.
Explain your reasoning.

Exercise 4B

Showing that a statement is true in a particular case doesn't prove that it is always true.
It verifies that the statement is true in only that particular cases.

You can use step-by-step reasoning, or algebra, to **prove** that a statement is true.

Example

Think of a positive number.
Multiply it by 3, add 5, double the result, subtract 4, then divide by 6.
Subtract the original number.
Prove that you always end up with 1.

You can verify the result for the particular
case when the number is 5 like this.

Start with 5.
Multiply by 3 gives 15.
Add 5 gives 20.
Double the result gives 40.
Subtract 4 gives 36.
Divide by 6 gives 6.

The right-hand column shows that the result is
true when the number is 5.

Subtract the original number gives 1.

You can prove the result is true for all positive numbers like this.

Let the number be n.
Multiply by 3 gives $3n$.
Add 5 gives $3n + 5$.
Double the result gives $6n + 10$.
Subtract 4 gives $6n + 6 = 6(n + 1)$.

The right-hand column proves that you always get the answer 1.

Divide by 6 gives $n + 1$.
Subtract the original number gives 1.

1. a is an odd number and b is an even number.

    a   Explain why $a + b + 1$ is always an even number.

    b   Explain why $ab - 1$ is always an odd number.

2. n is a positive integer.
      Prove that $n(n + 1)$ must be even.

3. p is an odd number.
      Explain why $p^2 + 1$ is always even.

4. p is an odd number and q is an even number.
      Explain why $(p + q)(p - q)$ is always an odd number.

5.   Explain why the sum of three consecutive numbers is always a multiple of 3.

6.   Prove that the sum of four consecutive numbers is always even.

7.   Ruth says: 'The number of edges of a prism is always a multiple of 3.'

      Is Ruth correct? Write **Yes** or **No**.
      Explain your reasoning.

⊙ Points to remember

- ⊙ You can verify that an expression or formula is true or not true for a particular number by substituting that number into the expression or formula.
- ⊙ Verifying that a statement is true in particular cases does not prove it is always true.
- ⊙ You can **prove** that a statement is true by using step-by-step reasoning.
- ⊙ You can prove that a statement is not true by finding just one **counter-example**.

5 Maths in our lives

This lesson will help you to appreciate some ways in which maths is used at home and work.

Exercise 5

Maths is used in many different ways in our lives at home, school and work.

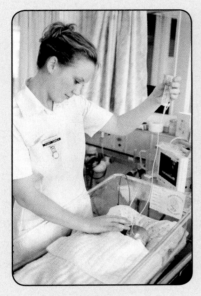
Nurse

Football player

Architect

① **a** Do some Internet research.
Find out more about how maths is used in three different occupations.
Make notes while you do this.
Your teacher will suggest some useful websites.

b Prepare three PowerPoint slides, one on each of the occupations.
Be prepared to show your slides to the rest of the class at the end of the lesson.

> ### ◉ Points to remember
>
> ⊙ The use of maths is widespread in everyday life, from children's toys and games, to driving and shopping, and practical tasks around the home or garden.
> ⊙ Many different occupations use mathematics in some way, sometimes in ways that are not immediately obvious.

How well are you doing?

Can you:

- use your mathematical knowledge to solve unfamiliar problems?
- work logically and use mathematical reasoning?
- solve problems by breaking them into parts?
- find counter-examples to prove that a statement is not true?
- appreciate the difference between evidence and proof?

Using and applying maths (no calculator)

1 *2005 level 7*

A three-digit number is multiplied by a two-digit number.
Write the minimum number and the maximum number of digits that the answer could have. Show your working.

2 *2003 level 7*

a Which of these two statements is true?

A When x is even, $(x-2)^2$ is even.

B When x is even, $(x-2)^2$ is odd.

Show how you know it is true for **all** even values of x.

b Which of these two statements is true?

C When x is even, $(x-1)(x+1)$ is even.

D When x is odd, $(x-1)(x+1)$ is even.

Show how you know it is true for **all** even values of x.

3 *1999 level 7*

Each term of a number sequence is made by adding 1 to the numerator and 2 to the denominator of the previous term.
Here is the beginning of the number sequence:

$$\frac{1}{3}, \quad \frac{2}{5}, \quad \frac{3}{7}, \quad \frac{4}{9}, \quad \frac{5}{11}, \quad \cdots$$

a Write an expression for the nth term of the sequence.

b The first five terms of the sequence are shown on the graph.

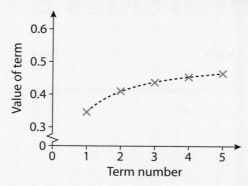

The sequence goes on and on for ever.

Which of the four graphs below shows how the sequence continues?

A

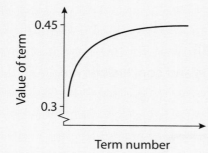

B

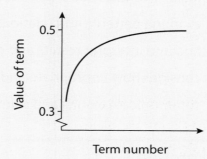

C

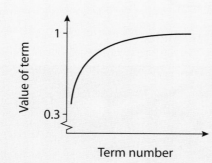

D

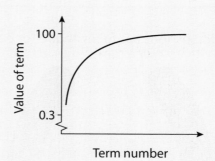

Using and applying maths (calculator allowed)

4 *2005 level 7*

In one week Jamal watched television for **26 hours**.
In that week:

> He watched television for the same length of time
> on Monday, Tuesday, Wednesday and Thursday.
> On each of Friday, Saturday and Sunday, he
> watched television for twice as long as on Monday.

How long did he spend watching television on Saturday?
Write your answer in hours and minutes.

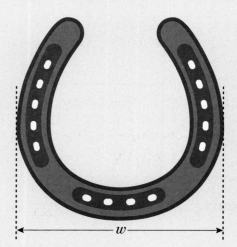

FS 6.8

Functional skills 8

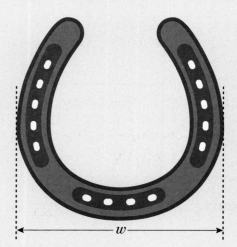

Horseshoes

This group activity will help you to:

- ⊙ recognise that aspects of a situation can be represented using mathematics;
- ⊙ make an initial model of a situation using suitable forms of representation;
- ⊙ examine patterns and relationships;
- ⊙ find and interpret results and draw conclusions;
- ⊙ consider how appropriate and accurate results and conclusions are;
- ⊙ communicate results and solutions.

Background

Horseshoes are tailor-made for each horse by blacksmiths.

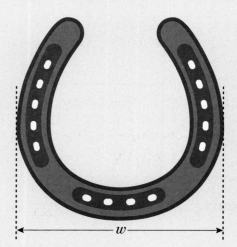

The blacksmith takes a straight strip of iron and bends it into a horseshoe shape. The blacksmith need to know the perimeter of the horse's hoof so that he knows what length of iron to use, but this is difficult to measure.

Instead, the blacksmith measures the width of the hoof in inches (w) and estimates the length in inches of the iron strip (L) using a simple formula:

$$L = 2w + 2$$

Problems

The table shows some data for the hooves of 11 horses. All the measurements are in inches.

The perimeter measurement is around the outside of the horseshoe.

Horse	Fore hoof		Hind hoof	
	Width (inches)	Perimeter (inches)	Width (inches)	Perimeter (inches)
Sparkle	5.25	14.5	5	14
Sapphire	6.25	16	5.5	15.25
Ruby	6	16	5.75	15
Louis	5.75	14.5	5.25	13.5
Dobbin	6	15	5.5	14
Heidi	5.5	14.5	5	13.5
Sky	5.25	14	5.25	13.75
Blossom	4.75	12.75	4.5	12.5
Lucky	5.5	15	5.25	14.5
Trigger	5	14	5	13.5
Caspian	5	13.5	5	13.25

When he makes horseshoes, the blacksmith uses an iron strip $1\frac{1}{2}$ inches shorter than the perimeter of the hoof to allow for the gap in the horseshoe.

Work with a partner.

1 Draw up a new table showing the width (w) and length of iron strip (L) for the 22 horseshoes.

2 a Draw a graph showing the data in your table.

b On the same axes, draw the graph of the blacksmith's formula.

c Is the blacksmith's formula a good one? Give your reasons.

Be prepared to discuss your conclusions with other groups.

Revision unit 1

This unit will help you to:

- revise your work during the year so far;
- answer questions like those in tests and examinations;
- help you to decide whether you are achieving National Curriculum level 7.

1 Fractions and percentages

This lesson will remind you how to solve problems involving fractions or percentages.

Exercise 1

When you **add or subtract mixed numbers**, deal with whole numbers first.

Example 1

Work out $2\frac{3}{4} + 3\frac{7}{12}$.

$2\frac{3}{4} + 3\frac{7}{12} = 5\frac{3}{4} + \frac{7}{12}$ Add the whole numbers.

$\qquad = 5\frac{9}{12} + \frac{7}{12}$ Form common denominator.

$\qquad = 5\frac{16}{12}$ Add the two fractions.

$\qquad = 6\frac{4}{12}$ Change $\frac{16}{12}$ to $1\frac{4}{12}$.

$\qquad = 6\frac{1}{3}$ Simplify by cancelling.

Example 2

Work out $4\frac{5}{12} - 2\frac{3}{4}$.

$4\frac{5}{12} - 2\frac{3}{4} = 2\frac{5}{12} - \frac{3}{4}$ Subtract the whole numbers.

$\qquad = 2\frac{5}{12} - \frac{9}{12}$ Form common denominator.

$\qquad = 1\frac{17}{12} - \frac{9}{12}$ Change 1 whole to $\frac{12}{12}$.

$\qquad = 1\frac{8}{12}$ Subtract the fractions.

$\qquad = 1\frac{2}{3}$ Simplify by cancelling.

To **multiply fractions**, cancel, then multiply the numerators and multiply the denominators.

Example 3

$$\frac{21}{40} \times \frac{15}{28} = \frac{3\ \cancel{21}}{8\ \cancel{40}} \times \frac{\cancel{15}^{\ 3}}{\cancel{28}^{\ 4}} \quad \text{Cancel.}$$

$$= \frac{3 \times 3}{8 \times 4} \quad \text{Multiply the numerators and multiply the denominators.}$$

$$= \frac{9}{32}$$

To **divide fractions**, turn the divisor upside down and multiply by it.

Example 4

$$\frac{5}{14} \div \frac{10}{21} = \frac{5}{14} \times \frac{21}{10} \quad \text{Turn the dividing fraction upside down and multiply.}$$

$$= \frac{\cancel{5}^{\ 1}}{\cancel{14}_{\ 2}} \times \frac{\cancel{21}^{\ 3}}{\cancel{10}_{\ 2}} \quad \text{Cancel the 21 and 14 by 7, and the 5 and 10 by 5.}$$

$$= \frac{1 \times 3}{2 \times 2} \quad \text{Multiply the numerators and multiply the denominators.}$$

$$= \frac{3}{4}$$

To find the percentage that a is of b, work out $\frac{a}{b} \times 100$.

Example 5

Sam scored 21 out of 35 marks in a test. What was his percentage score?

Calculate the percentage that is equivalent to the fraction $\frac{21}{35}$:

$$\frac{21}{35} \times 100 = \frac{3}{5} \times 100 = 3 \times 20 = 60 \quad \textbf{Answer } 60\%$$

Example 6

Ros spent 7% of her savings on a camera costing £84.
How much did Ros have in savings?

First find 1% by dividing 84 by 7, then find 100% by multiplying by 100.

$$\frac{84}{7} \times 100 = \frac{12}{1} \times 100 = 1200 \quad \textbf{Answer } £1200$$

Answer questions 1–5 **without using your calculator**.

(1) *1996 level 6*

12 500 people visited the museum in 2009.
This is an increase of a quarter on 2008.
How many visitors were there in 2008?

② *2002 level 6*

In Class 8, 80% of the pupils like crisps.
75% of the pupils who like crisps also like chocolate.
In Class 8, what percentage of the pupils like both crisps and chocolate?

③ *1999 level 6*

In a magazine there are three adverts
on the same page. In total, what fraction
of the page do the three adverts use?
Show your working.

> **Advert 1** uses $\frac{1}{4}$ of the page.
>
> **Advert 2** uses $\frac{1}{8}$ of the page.
>
> **Advert 3** uses $\frac{1}{16}$ of the page.

④ *2004 level 6*

  a Calculate $\frac{5}{6} \times \frac{3}{5}$. Show your working.
     Write your answer as a fraction in its simplest form.

  b Four-fifths of the members of a club are female.
     Three-quarters of these females are over 20 years old.
     What fraction of the members of the club are females over 20 years old?
     Show your working.

⑤ Work out, giving your answers as mixed numbers:

  a $1\frac{2}{3} \times 2\frac{3}{10}$

  b $4\frac{2}{3} \div 1\frac{2}{5}$

For questions 6–13 you may **use a calculator**.

⑥ *2002 level 7*

The diagram shows a square and a circle.
The circle touches the edges of the square.

What percentage of the diagram is shaded?
Show your working.

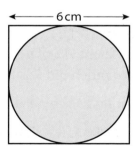

⑦ *GCSE 1387 June 2003*

Ben bought a car for £12 000.
Each year the value of the car depreciated by 10%.
Work out the value of the car 2 years after he bought it.

8 *2002 level 7*

    a One calculation below gives the answer to the question:

      What is 70 increased by 9%?

      Write the correct one.

      $\boxed{70 \times 0.9}$ $\boxed{70 \times 1.9}$ $\boxed{70 \times 0.09}$ $\boxed{70 \times 1.09}$

    b Choose one of the other calculations.
      Write the calculation and a question about percentages that this calculation represents.

    c Now do the same for one of the remaining two calculations.

    d Copy and complete this sentence. Fill in the missing decimal number.

      To decrease by 14%, multiply by …

9 *GCSE 1385 June 2001*

In a sale all prices are reduced by 15%.

    a The normal price of a jacket is £42.
      Syreeta buys the jacket in the sale.
      Work out the sale price of the jacket.

    b In the same sale, Winston pays £15.64 for a shirt.
      Calculate the normal price of the shirt.

10 *2002 level 7*

$\frac{1}{3}, \frac{1}{8}, \frac{1}{5}$ are all examples of unit fractions.

The ancient Egyptians used only unit fractions.
For $\frac{3}{4}$, they wrote the sum $\frac{1}{2} + \frac{1}{4}$.

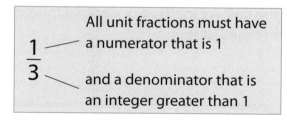

    a For what fraction did they write the sum $\frac{1}{2} + \frac{1}{5}$? Show your working.

    b They wrote $\frac{9}{20}$ as the sum of two unit fractions.
      One of them was $\frac{1}{4}$. What was the other? Show your working.

    c What is the biggest fraction you can make by adding two different unit fractions?
      Show your working.

(11) *2000 level 7*

A teacher said to a pupil: 'To the nearest per cent, $\frac{1}{6}$ is **17%**.'

The pupil said: 'So, to the nearest per cent, $\frac{2}{6}$ must be **34%**.'

Show that the pupil is wrong.

Extension problems

(12) *2004 level 8*

People were asked if they were considering changing what they eat.
29% of the people asked said yes.
Of these, 23% said they were considering becoming vegetarian.
What percentage of the people asked said they were considering becoming vegetarian?

(13) *2005 level 8*

Each side of a square is increased by 10%. By what percentage is the area increased?

Points to remember

⊙ To **add or subtract mixed numbers**, deal with whole numbers first.
⊙ To **multiply fractions**, cancel, then multiply the numerators and multiply the denominators.
⊙ To **divide fractions**, turn the divisor upside down and multiply by it.
⊙ When you **multiply or divide mixed numbers**, first convert them to improper fractions.
⊙ Use the **unitary method** or **decimal multipliers** to work out percentage changes.

2 Ratio and proportion

This lesson will remind you how to solve problems involving ratio or proportion.

Exercise 2

When a quantity is divided into two parts in the ratio $a:b$,
the two parts are the fractions $\dfrac{a}{a+b}$ and $\dfrac{b}{a+b}$ of the quantity.
Given a ratio and the size of one part, you can find the other part.

Example 1

Carol and Jim share a legacy in the ratio $5:7$.
Carol gets £16 000. How much does Jim get?

Carol gets $\frac{5}{12}$ of the legacy, which is £16 000.
For $\frac{1}{12}$, calculate £16 000 ÷ 5 = £3200.
For Jim's share of $\frac{7}{12}$ of the legacy, calculate £3200 × 7 = £22 400.

When you convert miles to kilometres, the ratio of miles : kilometres is always the same.
The number of kilometres is **directly proportional** to the number of miles.

miles : kilometres = $25:40$
$\qquad\qquad\qquad = 5:8$

miles : kilometres = $100:160$
$\qquad\qquad\qquad = 5:8$

miles : kilometres = $2.5:4$
$\qquad\qquad\qquad = 5:8$

miles	kilometres
5	8
25	40
100	160
2.5	4

Problems involving direct proportion can be solved using the **unitary method**.

Example 2

The mass of 60 ml of olive oil is 45 g.
What is the mass of 108 ml of olive oil?

1 ml of olive oil weighs 45 ÷ 60 = 0.75 g.
108 ml of olive oil weighs 0.75 × 108 = 81 g.

Answer questions 1–3 **without using your calculator**.

(1) *2003 Mental Test level 6*

Jenny and Mark share some money in the ratio $2:3$.
Jenny's share is £110.
How much is Mark's share?

(2) *2000 level 6*

Shortcrust pastry is made using flour, margarine and lard.
The flour, margarine and lard are mixed in the ratio $8:3:2$ by weight.
How many grams of margarine and lard are needed to mix with 200 grams of flour?

(3) *2001 level 6*

Children were asked to choose between a safari park and a zoo for a school trip.
The result of a vote was a ratio of $10:3$ in favour of going to a safari park.

130 children voted in favour of going to a safari park.
How many children voted in favour of going to the zoo?

For questions 4–13 you may **use a calculator**.

(4) *2003 level 6*

Paul is 14 years old. His sister is exactly 6 years younger, so this year she is 8 years old.
This year, the ratio of Paul's age to his sister's age is 14:8.
14 : 8 written as simply as possible is 7 : 4.

a When Paul is 21, what will be the ratio of Paul's age to his sister's age?
Write the ratio as simply as possible.

b When his sister is 36, what will be the ratio of Paul's age to his sister's age?
Write the ratio as simply as possible.

c Could the ratio of their ages ever be 7 : 7?
Write **Yes** or **No**. Explain how you know.

(5) *2005 level 6*

Each year, there is a men's tennis competition in Australia and another one in France.
The table shows how much money was paid to the winner in each country in 2002.

Country	Money
Australia	1 000 000 Australian dollars (£1 = 2.70 Australian dollars)
France	780 000 euros (£1 = 1.54 euros)

Which country paid more money? Show your working.

(6) *2001 level 6*

The labels on Yogurt A and Yogurt B show different information.

Yoghurt A	125 g
Each 125 g provides	
Energy	430 kJ
Protein	4.5 g
Carbohydrate	11.1 g
Fat	4.5 g

Yoghurt B	150 g
Each 150 g provides	
Energy	339 kJ
Protein	6.6 g
Carbohydrate	13.1 g
Fat	0.2 g

a How many grams of protein does 100 g of yoghurt A provide? Show your working.

b A boy eats the same amount of yoghurt A and yoghurt B.
Which yoghurt provides him with more carbohydrate? Show your working.

(7) *1997 level 7*

The table shows some information about pupils in a school.

	left-handed	right-handed
girls	32	180
boys	28	168

There are 408 pupils in the school.

a   What percentage of the pupils are boys? Show your working.

b   What is the ratio of left-handed pupils to right-handed pupils?
Write your ratio in the form 1 : ...   Show your working.

(8) *2008 level 7*

In a bag, there are red and blue cubes in
the ratio 4 : 7.

red : blue
4 : 7

I add 10 more red cubes to the bag.

Now there are red and blue cubes in the ratio 6 : 7.

How many blue cubes are in the bag?

red : blue
6 : 7

(9) *2008 level 7*

You can buy jars of the same jam in two sizes.

454 g for £1.59

340 g for £1.25

Which jar is better value for money? You must show working to explain your answer.

10 *GCSE 1385 November 2001*

Bill gave his three daughters a total of £32.40. The money was shared in the ratios 4 : 3 : 2. Jane had the largest share. Work out how much money Bill gave to Jane.

11 *GCSE 1388 January 2004*

The weight of a piece of wire is directly proportional to its length.
A piece of wire is 25 cm long and has a weight of 6 grams.
Calculate the weight of a 30 cm piece of the same wire.

Extension problems

12 *2002 level 8*

I fill a glass with orange juice and lemonade in the ratio 1 : 4.

I drink $\frac{1}{4}$ of the contents of the glass, then I fill the glass using orange juice.

Now what is the ratio of orange juice to lemonade in the glass?
Show your working, and write the ratio in its simplest form.

13 *1992 level 8*

These plant pots are mathematically similar. The internal dimensions are shown.

Calculate the value of m.
Show your working.

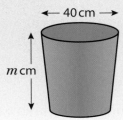
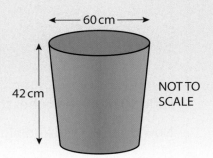

NOT TO SCALE

Points to remember

⊙ Two quantities a and b are **directly proportional** if their ratio $a:b$ stays the same as the quantities increase or decrease, so:
$\frac{a}{b} = k$, where k is constant

⊙ Use the **unitary method** to solve direct proportion problems by reducing the value of one of the variables to 1.

⊙ When a quantity is divided into two parts in the **ratio** $a:b$, the parts are $\frac{a}{a+b}$ and $\frac{b}{a+b}$ of the whole quantity.

3 Expressions and equations

This lesson will remind you how to work with algebraic expressions and formulae and solve simple linear equations.

Exercise 3

Example 1

What value of y makes $7y - 9$ equal to $5y + 7$?

$$7y - 9 = 5y + 7$$

Subtract $5y$ $2y - 9 = 7$

Add 9 $2y = 16$

Divide by 2 $y = 8$

Example 2

Work out $8(5x - 3)$.

Multiply everything inside the bracket by 8, so $8(5x - 3) = 40x - 24$.

Example 3

Work out $(x + 3)(x + 4)$.

Expand the brackets in the expression $(x + 3)(x + 4)$.

$\times$	x	$+$	4	
x	x^2	$+$	$4x$	$x^2 + 4x$
$+$				$+$
3	$3x$	$+$	12	$3x + 12$
				$x^2 + 7x + 12$

Alternatively, you can use the mnemonic **FOIL** as a quick method of expanding two brackets.

$(x + 3)(x + 4)$

First: $x \times x = x^2$

Outside: $x \times 4 = 4x$

Inside: $3 \times x = 3x$

Last: $3 \times 4 = 12$

$x^2 + 7x + 12$

Example 4

Work out the value of $y = \sqrt{(x - 2)(x - 3)(x - 4)}$ when $x = 7$.

Substitute $x = 7$ into the formula to get:

$$y = \sqrt{(7 - 2)(7 - 3)(7 - 4)} = \sqrt{5 \times 4 \times 3} = \sqrt{60} = 7.7 \text{ (to 1 d.p.)}$$

① *2004 level 7*

Look at these expressions.

$5y - 8$	$3y + 5$
first expression	second expression

What value of y makes the two expressions equal? Show your working.

② *2006 level 7*

Copy and complete these statements.
Write the missing operations ($+$ or $-$ or $\times$ or $\div$) in them.

a $a \ldots a = 0$

b $a \ldots a = 1$

c $a \ldots a = 2a$

d $a \ldots a = a^2$

③ *2006 level 7*

Look at this equation: $3a + 20 = 4a + k$

a If $a = 15$, find the value of k.

b If $a = -15$, find the value of k.

④ *2006 level 7*

Multiply out these expressions. Write your answers as simply as possible.

a $5(x + 2) + 3(7 + x)$

b $(x + 2)(x + 5)$

⑤ *1999 level 7*

Solve these equations. Show your working.

a $4 - 2y = 10 - 6y$

b $5y + 20 = 3(y - 4)$

c $\dfrac{9y}{2y + 1} = 9$

d $\dfrac{9}{y + 2} = y + 2$

⑥ *1998 level 7*

a Find the values of a and b when $p = 10$.

$$a = \frac{3p^3}{2}$$

$$b = \frac{2p^2(p - 3)}{7p}$$

b Simplify this expression as fully as possible: $\dfrac{3cd^2}{5cd}$

(7) *2005 level 7*

About 2000 years ago, Heron of Alexandria, a Greek mathematician, worked out this formula to find the area of any triangle.

A triangle has sides, in cm, of 3, 5 and 6. Use $a = 3$, $b = 5$ and $c = 6$ to work out the area of this triangle.

> For a triangle with sides a, b and c
>
> Area $= \sqrt{s(s-a)(s-b)(s-c)}$
>
> where $s = \dfrac{a+b+c}{2}$

(8) *GCSE 1387 November 2004*

  a Expand the brackets $p(q - p^2)$ **b** Expand and simplify $5(3p + 2) - 2(5p - 3)$

(9) *GCSE 1387 June 2005*

  a Expand and simplify $(x + 7)(x - 4)$ **b** Expand $y(y^3 + 2y)$

  c Factorise $p^2 + 6p$ **d** Factorise completely $6x^2 - 9xy$

(10) *GCSE 1388 March 2005*

Make p the subject of the formula $m = 3n + 2p$

(11) *GCSE 1387 June 2005*

  a Solve $4(x + 3) = 6$ **b** Make t the subject of the formula $v = u + 5t$

Extension problems

(12) *GCSE 1388 January 2003*

Make m the subject of the formula $2(2p - m) = 3 + 5m$

(13) *GCSE 1385 June 2001*

  a Simplify $(3xy^3)^4$ **b** Rearrange $\sqrt{\dfrac{x-4}{5}} = 2y$ to give x in terms of y.

◉ Points to remember

⊙ To find the value of an algebraic expression, substitute a value for each of the variables (letters).

⊙ A **linear equation**, such as $3x - 5 = 2x$, has a unique solution, i.e. $x = 5$.

⊙ To expand a bracket, multiply every term inside the bracket by the number outside, e.g. $5(3x + 4) = 15x + 20$.

⊙ To expand a pair of brackets, use a multiplication grid, or use FOIL, e.g. $(x + 3)(x + 2) = x^2 + 2x + 3x + 6 = x^2 + 5x + 6$.

4 Angles and triangles

This lesson will remind you how to use geometrical reasoning, Pythagoras' theorem and trigonometry to solve problems.

Exercise 4

The **hyp**otenuse of a right-angled triangle is opposite the right angle.
The side opposite the angle marked x is the **opp**osite side.
The side next to this angle is the **adj**acent side.

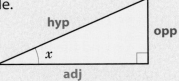

$$\sin x = \frac{\text{opp}}{\text{hyp}} \qquad \cos x = \frac{\text{adj}}{\text{hyp}} \qquad \tan x = \frac{\text{opp}}{\text{adj}}$$

There are sayings that help you to remember the trigonometric ratios. Here is a famous one:

Silly **O**ld **H**arry **C**hased **A H**orse **T**hrough **O**ur **A**ttic.

When you need to find a missing side in a right-angled triangle, label its sides in relation to the missing or given angle.

Example 1

Find the missing angle x in this right-angled triangle.

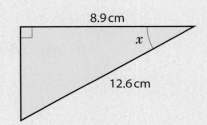

Identify the hypotenuse, opposite and adjacent sides.

You know the **hypotenuse** is 12.6 cm and the **adjacent** side is 8.9 cm, so use the cosine ratio:

$$\cos x = \frac{\text{adj}}{\text{hyp}} = \frac{8.9}{12.6}$$

Make sure that your calculator is in degrees mode.
You should see DEG in the display.

Work out 8.9 ÷ 12.6 on your calculator. The display will show .

To find the angle whose cosine is 0.706 349 206, use the $\cos^{-1}$ key.

On some calculators you press $\boxed{\text{SHIFT}}$ $\boxed{\cos^{-1}}$.

Check what to do with your own calculator.

The display should show $\boxed{45.06135229}$.

So angle $x = 45.1°$ (to 1 decimal place)

Example 2

Find the missing side g in this right-angled triangle.

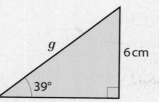

Identify the hypotenuse and the opposite side.

You know the **hypotenuse** g and the **opposite** side 6 cm, so use the sine ratio.

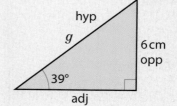

$$\sin 39° = \frac{\text{opp}}{\text{hyp}} = \frac{6}{g}$$

Rearrange the equation $g = \dfrac{6}{\sin 39°}$.

Make sure that your calculator is in degrees mode. Work out $6 \div \sin 39°$ on your calculator.

On some calculators you press ⑥ ➗ ③ ⑨ sin ⁼.

Check what to do with your own calculator.

The display should show ⌈ 9.534094374 ⌋.

So $g = 9.53$ cm (to 3 significant figures)

You can also use facts that you know about angles to find other angles. Always give the reason for each statement.

Example 3

Find angles a and b.

angle $a = 180 - 90 - 55 = 35°$ (angles in a triangle)
angle $b = 35°$ (alternate angles)

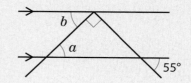

---

1 *2002 level 6*

The diagram shows a rectangle.

Work out the size of angle a.
Show your working.

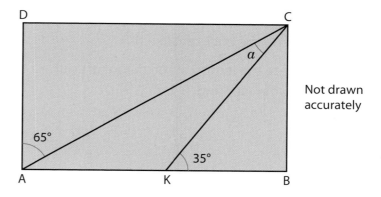

Not drawn accurately

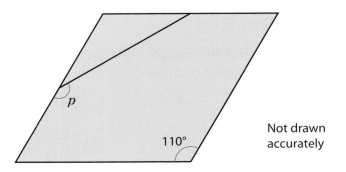

2 *2007 level 7*

The diagram shows a rhombus.

The midpoints of two of its sides are joined with a straight line.

What is the size of angle p?

Not drawn accurately

3 *2002 level 7*

The diagram shows a rectangle that just touches an equilateral triangle.

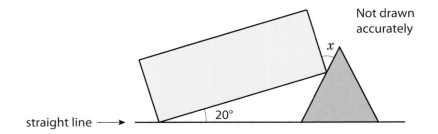

Not drawn accurately

a Find the size of the angle marked x. Show your working.

b Now the rectangle just touches the equilateral triangle so that ABC is a straight line.

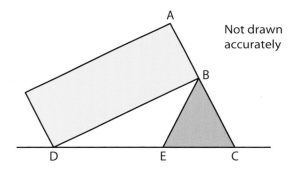

Not drawn accurately

Show that triangle BDE is isosceles.

4 *1995 level 7*

A cupboard needs to be strengthened by putting a strut on the back of it like this.

Calculate the length of the diagonal strut. Show your working.

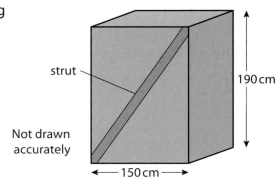

strut

190 cm

Not drawn accurately

150 cm

(5) *GCSE 1387 June 2006*

Calculate the length of the side marked x in this right-angled triangle.

Give your answer correct to 3 significant figures.

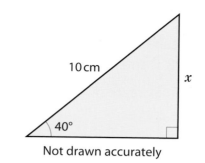

10 cm

x

40°

Not drawn accurately

(6) *GCSE 1387 November 2006*

Work out the value of x.
Give your answer correct to one decimal place.

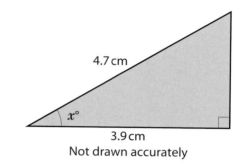

4.7 cm

$x°$

3.9 cm

Not drawn accurately

(7) *GCSE 1387 June 2007*

ABC is a right-angled triangle.

AC = 12 cm.
Angle ABC = 90°.
Angle ACB = 32°.

Calculate the length of AB.
Give your answer correct to 3 significant figures.

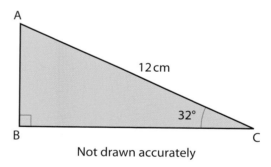

A

12 cm

32°

B

C

Not drawn accurately

(8) *GCSE 1387 November 2007*

PQR is a right-angled triangle.

PR = 12 cm.
QR = 4.5 cm.
Angle PRQ = 90°.

Work out the value of x.
Give your answer correct to one decimal place.

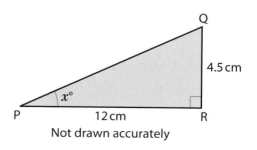

Q

4.5 cm

$x°$

P

12 cm

R

Not drawn accurately

Extension problems

9 *2008 level 8*

A cube is cut through four of its vertices, A, B, C and D, into two identical pieces.

The diagram on the right shows one of the pieces.

Find the length of the line AC.

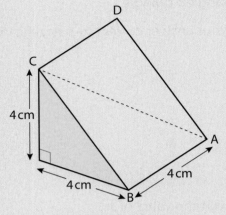

Not drawn accurately

10 *2001 level 8*

a On centimetre squared paper, draw a line AB.

Now draw a right-angled triangle with an area of 12 cm².

Use line AB as one side of the triangle.

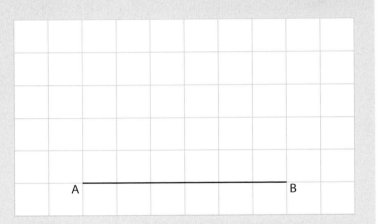

b Draw another line AB the same length as the first.
This time draw an isosceles triangle with an area of 12 cm².
Use line AB as one side of the triangle.

c Use Pythagoras' theorem to prove that AC is the same length as AB.
Show your working.

d Calculate the size of angle ABC.
Show your working.

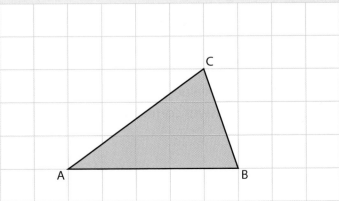

a Cape Point is 7.5 km east and 4.8 km north of Arton.

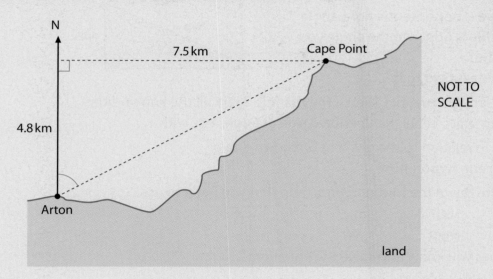

N

7.5 km   Cape Point

NOT TO
SCALE

4.8 km

Arton

land

Calculate the direct distance from Arton to Cape Point.
Show your working.

b Bargate is 6 km east and 4 km north of Cape Point.

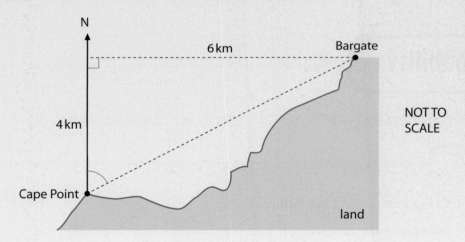

N

6 km   Bargate

NOT TO
SCALE

4 km

Cape Point

land

Steve wants to sail directly from Cape Point to Bargate.
On what bearing should he sail?
Show your working.

c Anna sails from Cape Point on a bearing of 048°.
She stops when she is due north of Bargate.

How far north of Bargate is Anna?
Show your working.

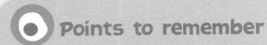

Points to remember

- ⊙ The **hypotenuse** is opposite the right angle. The **opposite** side is opposite the angle you know or must find. The **adjacent** side is next to it.

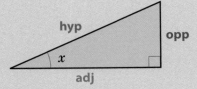

- ⊙ To solve a right-angled triangle, sketch the triangle. Mark all the known sides and angles, with units. Label the unknown side or angle, e.g. with x.

- ⊙ Label the sides in relation to the given or unknown angle: **opp**osite, **adj**acent, **hyp**otenuse.

- ⊙ Decide and write down the trigonometric ratio that you need to use.

- ⊙ $\sin x = \dfrac{\text{opp}}{\text{hyp}}$, $\text{os}\, x = \dfrac{\text{adj}}{\text{hyp}}$, $\tan x = \dfrac{\text{opp}}{\text{adj}}$

- ⊙ Substitute values you know and solve the equation.

- ⊙ Give your answer to a suitable degree of accuracy (3 s.f. for lengths and 1 d.p. for angles).

5 Probability

This lesson will remind you how to work out the probabilities of two independent events.

Exercise 5

The arrow on this fair spinner is spun twice.

The events are **independent** because the first spin of the arrow does not affect the probability of the outcomes from the second spin.

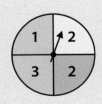

All the possible outcomes can be shown in a **two-way table**.

		1st spin			
		1	2	2	3
2nd spin	1	1 and 1	2 and 1	2 and 1	3 and 1
	2	1 and 2	2 and 2	2 and 2	3 and 2
	2	1 and 2	2 and 2	2 and 2	3 and 2
	3	1 and 3	2 and 3	2 and 3	3 and 3

Each entry in the table represents an equally likely outcome, so there are 16 equally likely outcomes. The probabilities of each outcome are:

P(**1** and **1**) $= \frac{1}{16}$ 　　 P(**1** and **2**) $= \frac{2}{16} = \frac{1}{8}$ 　　 P(**1** and **3**) $= \frac{1}{16}$

P(**2** and **1**) $= \frac{2}{16} = \frac{1}{8}$ 　　 P(**2** and **2**) $= \frac{4}{16} = \frac{1}{4}$ 　　 P(**2** and **3**) $= \frac{2}{16} = \frac{1}{8}$

P(**3** and **1**) $= \frac{1}{16}$ 　　 P(**3** and **2**) $= \frac{2}{16} = \frac{1}{8}$ 　　 P(**3** and **3**) $= \frac{1}{16}$

This **tree diagram** also shows all the possible outcomes.

The probabilities of each outcome for each spin are shown on the branches of the tree diagram.

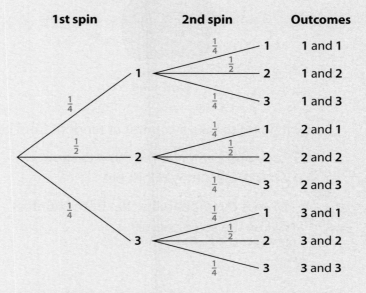

The probability of each **combined outcome** is shown in this table.

Outcome	1st spin	2nd spin	Calculation	Probability
1 and 1	P(**1**) $= \frac{1}{4}$	P(**1**) $= \frac{1}{4}$	$\frac{1}{4} \times \frac{1}{4}$	$\frac{1}{16}$
1 and 2	P(**1**) $= \frac{1}{4}$	P(**2**) $= \frac{1}{2}$	$\frac{1}{4} \times \frac{1}{2}$	$\frac{1}{8}$
1 and 3	P(**1**) $= \frac{1}{4}$	P(**3**) $= \frac{1}{4}$	$\frac{1}{4} \times \frac{1}{4}$	$\frac{1}{16}$
2 and 1	P(**2**) $= \frac{1}{2}$	P(**1**) $= \frac{1}{4}$	$\frac{1}{2} \times \frac{1}{4}$	$\frac{1}{8}$
2 and 2	P(**2**) $= \frac{1}{2}$	P(**2**) $= \frac{1}{2}$	$\frac{1}{2} \times \frac{1}{2}$	$\frac{1}{4}$
2 and 3	P(**2**) $= \frac{1}{2}$	P(**3**) $= \frac{1}{4}$	$\frac{1}{2} \times \frac{1}{4}$	$\frac{1}{8}$
3 and 1	P(**3**) $= \frac{1}{4}$	P(**1**) $= \frac{1}{4}$	$\frac{1}{4} \times \frac{1}{4}$	$\frac{1}{16}$
3 and 2	P(**3**) $= \frac{1}{4}$	P(**2**) $= \frac{1}{2}$	$\frac{1}{4} \times \frac{1}{2}$	$\frac{1}{8}$
3 and 3	P(**3**) $= \frac{1}{4}$	P(**3**) $= \frac{1}{4}$	$\frac{1}{4} \times \frac{1}{4}$	$\frac{1}{16}$

In general, in an experiment involving two **independent events**, if **A** is an outcome from one event and **B** is an outcome from the other event:

P(**A** and **B**) = P(**A**) × P(**B**)

① *Year 8 Optional Test level 6*

I have two bags of counters.

first bag

two counters,
1 blue, 1 red

second bag

three counters,
1 blue, 1 red, 1 yellow

I am going to take a counter at random from both bags.

a Copy and complete the table to show what colours they might be.

b What is the probability that both counters will be the same colour?

		1st bag	
		B	R
2nd bag	B	B and B	
	R		
	Y		

② Here are two sets of four cards.
Each set is numbered 1, 2, 3 and 4.

A card is selected at random from set A and a card is selected at random from set B.

The difference between the two numbers is worked out.

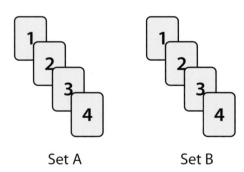

Set A   Set B

a Copy and complete the table on the right to show all the possible differences.

b Find the probability that the difference will be zero.

c Find the probability that the difference will not be 2.

		Set A			
		1	2	3	4
Set B	1	0			
	2				
	3				
	4				

3 *2004 level 7*

I have two fair 4-sided dice.

> One dice is numbered **2**, **4**, **6** and **8**
>
> The other is numbered **2**, **3**, **4** and **5**

I throw both dice and add the scores.
What is the probability that the total is even?
Show working to explain your answer.

4 **a** Copy and complete this tree diagram to
show all the possible ways that the two
counters can be taken from the bags in
question 1.

b Use the tree diagram to work out the
probability of taking one red and one
yellow counter.

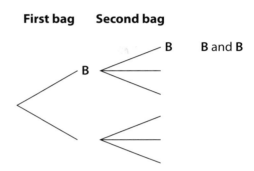

First bag   **Second bag**

B   B and B

B

5 *GCSE 1387 June 2007*

There are two sets of traffic lights on Georgina's route to school.
The probability that the first set of traffic lights will be red is 0.4.
The probability that the second set of traffic lights will be red is 0.3.

a Copy and complete the probability tree diagram.

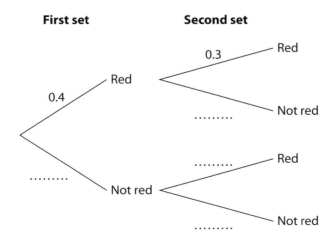

First set   **Second set**

0.4 Red

0.3 Red

.... Not red

....

.... Not red

Not red

.... Red

.... Not red

b Work out the probability that both sets of traffic lights will be red.

c Work out the probability that exactly one set of traffic lights will be red.

6 *GCSE 1388 March 2004*

Jacob has 2 bags of sweets.
Bag **P** contains 3 green sweets and 4 red sweets.
Bag **Q** contains 1 green sweet and 3 yellow sweets.

Jacob takes one sweet at random from each bag.

a Copy and complete the tree diagram.

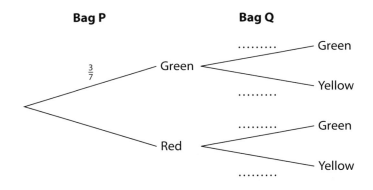

b Calculate the probability that Jacob will take 2 green sweets.

7 A spinner has the numbers 1, 2 and 3 on it.

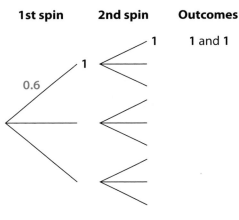

The probability of spinning the number 3 is 0.1.

The probability of spinning the number 1 is 0.6.

a Work out the probability of spinning the number 2.

b The spinner is spun twice and the numbers obtained are recorded.

Copy and complete this tree diagram to show the possible outcomes.

c Use the tree diagram to work out the probability of spinning:

  i 1 and 1   ii 2 and 3   iii 3 and 1

8 *GCSE 1387 June 2007*

Martin has a pencil case which contains 4 blue pens and 3 green pens.

Martin picks a pen at random from the pencil case. He notes its colour, and then replaces it. He does this two more times.

Work out the probability that when Martin takes three pens exactly two are the same colour.

Extension problems

 2000 level 8

John makes two clay pots.
Each pot is fired independently.
The probability that a pot cracks while it is being fired is 0.03.

a Calculate the probability that both of John's pots crack while being fired.

b Calculate the probability that only one of John's pots cracks while being fired.

Show your working.

 1999 level 8

On a road there are two sets of traffic lights.
The traffic lights work independently.

For each set of traffic lights, the probability that a driver will have to stop is 0.7.

a A woman is going to drive along the road.

   i What is the probability that she will have to stop at both sets of lights?

   ii What is the probability that she will have to stop at only one of the two sets of lights?

   Show your working.

b In one year, a man drives 200 times along the road.

   Calculate an estimate of the number of times he drives through both sets of traffic lights without stopping. Show your working.

 Points to remember

- **Mutually exclusive outcomes** cannot occur at the same time. If **A** and **B** are mutually exclusive, then:
    P(**A** or **B**) = P(**A**) + P(**B**)
- Two events are **independent** if one event occurring does not affect the probability of the other event occurring.
- Use **two-way tables** and **tree diagrams** to identify the possible outcomes of two independent events and work out their probabilities.
- If **A** is an outcome of one event and **B** is an outcome of an independent event, then:
    P(**A** and **B**) = P(**A**) × P(**B**)

Revision unit 2

This unit will help you to:

- revise your work during the year so far;
- answer questions like those in tests and examinations;
- help you to decide whether you are achieving National Curriculum level 7.

1 Decimals

This lesson will remind you about decimals, significant figures and standard form.

Exercise 1

You need to know how to use your calculator for complex calculations. Check that you can use these:

> bracket keys
> memory
> π key
> square root and square keys
> power and root keys
> fraction key

and that you know how to enter numbers in standard form.

Check that you also know how to:

- round a number to a given number of decimal places or significant figures;
- estimate the answer to decimal calculations;
- add, subtract, multiply and divide decimals without a calculator;
- convert between units of measurement and work out the limits for the accuracy of a measurement (half a unit in either direction).

Answer questions 1–5 **without using a calculator**.

1   *GCSE 1387 June 2007*

   a   Write 30 000 000 in standard form.

   b   Write 2×10^{-3} as an ordinary number.

2 *2001 level 6*

Write two decimals, each less than 1, which multiply to make 0.1.

$\square \times \square = 0.1$

3 *2003 level 6*

Calculate 57.3×2.1. Show your working.

4 *2000 level 7*

a Which of these is the best estimate of the answer to 32.7×0.48?

$$1.2 \qquad 1.6 \qquad 12 \qquad 16 \qquad 120 \qquad 160$$

b Estimate the answer to $\dfrac{39.93 \times 20.4}{4.96}$. Give your answer to 1 significant figure.

5 *GCSE 1387 June 2004*

a The area of a regular pentagon is $8560\,\text{mm}^2$.
   Change $8560\,\text{mm}^2$ to cm^2.

b Each side of another pentagon has a length of 101 mm, correct to the nearest millimetre.

   i Write down the least possible length of each side.

   ii Write down the greatest possible length of each side.

For questions 6–11 you may **use a calculator**.

6 *1995 level 7*

The diameter of a wheel on Harry's bicycle is 0.65 m.

Diagram NOT
accurately drawn

0.65 m

a Calculate the circumference of the wheel.
   Give your answer correct to 2 decimal places.

b Harry cycles 1000 metres.
   Calculate the number of turns the wheel makes.

(7) *2001 level 7*

Calculate the length of the unknown side of this right-angled triangle.

Show your working.

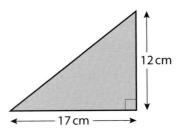

12 cm

17 cm

(8) *GCSE November 2003*

Use your calculator to work out the value of: $\dfrac{(7.91 - \sqrt[3]{81}) \times 4.32}{6.23 + 1.491}$.

Give your answer correct to 3 significant figures.

(9) *GCSE 1387 June 2004*

Martin cleaned his swimming pool.
He hired a cleaning machine to do this job.
The cost of hiring the cleaning machine was £35.50
for the first day, then £18.25 for each extra day.

a Martin's total cost of hiring the machine was £163.25.
For how many days did Martin hire the machine?

b Martin filled the pool with 54 000 gallons of water.
He paid £2.38 for each 1000 gallons of water.
Work out the total amount he paid for
54 000 gallons of water.

(10) *2001 level 7*

The table shows the average weekly earnings for men and women in 1956 and 1998.

	1956	1998
Men	£11.89	£420.30
Women	£6.16	£303.70

a For 1956, calculate the average weekly earnings for women as a percentage of the average weekly earnings for men.
Show your working and give your answer to 1 decimal place.

b For 1998, show that the average weekly earnings for women were a greater proportion of the average weekly earnings for men than they were in 1956.

Extension problem

 1997 level 8

Speed of light is about	1.1×10^9 km per hour
Speed of sound is about	1.2×10^3 km per hour

a Calculate the speed of light in km per second.
Give your answer in standard form. Show your working.

b How many times as fast as the speed of sound is the speed of light?
Give your answer to an appropriate degree of accuracy. Show your working.

c Gary sees a flash of lightning.
25 second later he hears the sound of thunder.
Calculate how far away he is from the lightning. Show your working.

 Points to remember

⊙ A number rounded to **one significant figure** has only one non-zero digit.

⊙ A number in **standard form** is of the form: $A \times 10^n$, where $1 \leqslant A < 10$ and n is an integer.

⊙ You can estimate answers by rounding numbers to one significant figure or another sensible approximation.

⊙ In an exact calculation, round the final answer, not the intermediate steps.

⊙ Measurements may be inaccurate by up to half a unit in either direction.

2 Sequences and graphs

This lesson will help you to find the nth term of a sequence and to work with graphs of linear equations.

Exercise 2

Example 1

Find the nth term of the sequence 5, 9, 13, 17, …

Sequence: 5   9   13   17
First difference: 4   4   4
The nth term is $4n + 1$.

Example 2

This graph shows the straight line with equation $y = 4x + 5$.

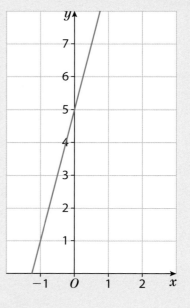

a A point on the line $y = 4x + 5$ has an x-coordinate of 30.
What is the y-coordinate of this point?

$y = 4 \times 30 + 5 = 125$

b A point on the line $y = 4x + 5$ has a y-coordinate of 45.
What is the x-coordinate of this point?

$45 = 4x + 5, x = 10$

c Is the point $(-8, -27)$ on the line $y = 4x + 5$?
Show how you know.

Yes. When $x = -8, y = 4 \times -8 + 5 = -27$.

d Write the coordinates of the point that lies on both
the straight lines $y = 4x + 5$ and $y = 6x - 3$.

Substitute $y = 4x + 5$ in $y = 6x - 3$, giving $4x + 5 = 6x - 3$.
So $2x = 8, x = 4$ and $y = 21$.

---

① *GCSE 1387 November 2003*

The first term of a sequence is 7. The rule for the sequence is: **Add 5 to the previous term**.

a Write down the second term and the third term of the sequence.

b Work out the 10th term of the sequence.

c Write down an expression, in terms of n, for the nth term of the sequence.

② *2006 level 7*

Look at these pairs of number sequences.
The second sequence is formed from the first sequence by adding
a number or multiplying by a number. Work out the missing nth terms.

a 5, 9, 13, 17, ... nth term is $4n + 1$

     6, 10, 14, 18, ... nth term is   ?

b 12, 18, 24, 30, ... nth term is $6n + 6$

     6, 9, 12, 15, ... nth term is   ?

c 2, 7, 12, 17, ... nth term is $5n - 3$

     4, 14, 24, 34, ... nth term is   ?

2006 level 7

Here are the rules for an algebra grid.

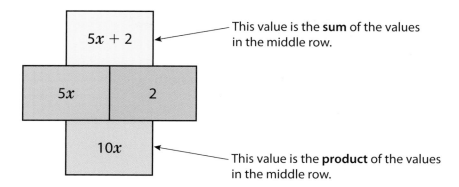

This value is the **sum** of the values in the middle row.

This value is the **product** of the values in the middle row.

Use these rules to copy and complete the grids below.
Write your expressions as simply as possible.

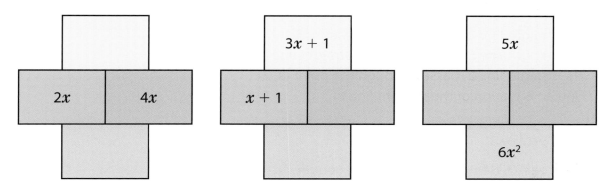

(4) *2005 level 6*

The graph shows a straight line.
The equation of the line is $y = 3x - 4$.

a   A point on the line $y = 3x - 4$
    has an x-coordinate of 50.
    What is the y-coordinate of this point?

b   A point on the line $y = 3x - 4$ has
    a y-coordinate of 50.
    What is the x-coordinate of this point?

c   Is the point $(-10, -34)$ on the line $y = 3x - 4$?
    Show how you know.

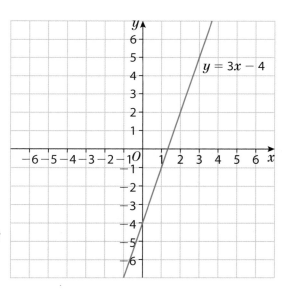

(5)   Write the equation of the straight line that joins these pairs of coordinates:

a   (1, 4) and (2, 8)   b   (1, 8) and (3, 0)   c   (1, 9) and (3, 3)

6 *2002 level 7*

The graph shows a straight line.
The equation of the line is $y = 3x$.

  a Does the point (25, 75) lie on the straight line
$y = 3x$? Explain how you know.

  b Write the coordinates of the point that lies on both
the straight lines $y = 4x + 1$ and $y = 6x - 4$.
Show your working.

  c Explain how you can tell there is no point that lies
on both the straight lines
$y = \frac{1}{2}x + 3$ and $y = \frac{1}{2}x + 5$.

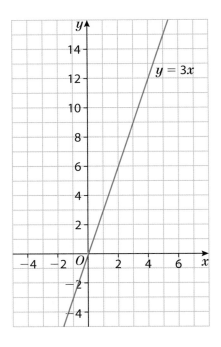

7 *GCSE 1387 November 2004*

The straight line L_1 has equation $y = 2x + 3$.
The straight line L_2 is parallel to the straight line L_1.
The straight line L_2 passes through the point (3, 2).
Find an equation of the straight line L_2.

Extension problem

8 Find the nth term for each quadratic sequence.

  a 13,   25,   41,   61,   85,   …

  b 12,   18,   26,   36,   48,   …

  c 7,   14,   27,   46,   71,   …

⊙ Points to remember

- The first difference between consecutive terms of a **linear sequence** is
constant. For example, in the linear sequence 5, 9, 13, 17, … , the first
difference is 4 and the nth term is $4n + 1$.
- The second difference between terms of a **quadratic sequence** is
constant. For example, in the quadratic sequence 1, 3, 6, 10, … , the
second difference is 1 and the nth term is $\frac{1}{2}n(n + 1)$.
- The **normal form** of the equation of a linear graph is $y = ax + b$, where a
is the gradient and $(0, b)$ is the intercept on the y-axis.
- Lines parallel to $y = ax + b$ also have gradient a.

3 Graphs and equations

This lesson will help you to interpret graphs of real-life situations and to solve equations using the method of trial and improvement.

Exercise 3

Example 1

Look at this graph.

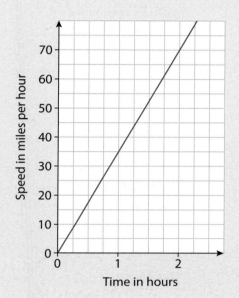

a What does the x-axis represent?

Time in hours

b What does each point on the x-axis represent?

A quarter of an hour

c What does the y-axis represent?

Speed in miles per hour

d How can you use the graph to work out the distance travelled in 2 hours?

Draw a vertical line from 2 on the x-axis to the graph and work out the area.

Example 2

Find to two decimal places the solution to $x^2 + 2x - 7 = 0$ that lies between 1 and 2.

x	y	
1	−4	too small
2	1	too big
1.5	−1.75	too small
1.7	−0.71	too small
1.8	−0.16	too small
1.9	0.41	too big
1.82	−0.0476	too small
1.83	0.0089	too big
1.825	−0.019 375	too small

$x = 1.83$ to 2 decimal places

You will need graph paper for question 2.

1 *2006 level 7*

The graph shows information about the
diameters and heights of a sample of
three types of tomato.

The dotted lines on the graph can be used
to decide which type of tomato each point is
likely to represent.

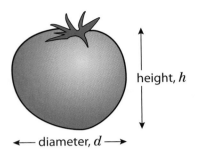

height, h

← diameter, d →

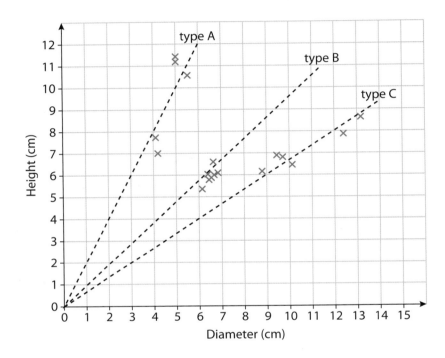

a The diameter of a tomato of type C is 11 cm. What would you expect its height to be?

b The diameter of a different tomato is 3.2 cm. Its height is 5.8 cm.
   Which of the three types of tomato is it most likely to be? Explain your answer.

c Which type of tomato is most nearly spherical in shape? Explain your answer.

d You can find the approximate volume of a tomato by using this formula:

$$V = \frac{1}{6}\pi d^2 h$$

V is the volume,
d is the diameter,
h is the height.

The diameter and the height of a tomato are both 3.5 cm.
What is the approximate volume of this tomato?

2 *2002 level 7*

Cars more than three years old must pass a test called an MOT.

The testers measure the right (R) and left (L) front wheel brakes. They give each brake a score out of 500. Then they use the graph.

For example:

A car has scores R = 300, L = 350. (300, 350) is in the white region, so the car passes this part of the test.

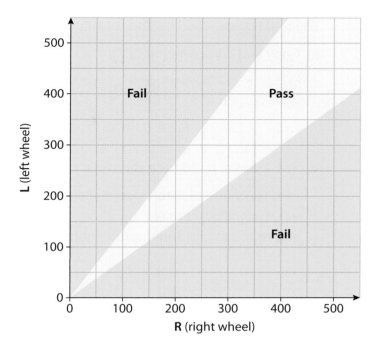

a   A man takes his car to be tested. He knows that L = 200.
   Approximately, between what values does R need to be for his car to pass this test?

b   A different part of the test uses R + L. To pass, R + L ⩾ 400.
   Copy the graph above. On the graph, draw the straight line R + L = 400.
   Then shade the region where the car fails, R + L < 400.

c   If L = 200, between what values does R need to be to pass **both** parts of the test?

3 *GCSE 1387 June 2007*

Judy drove from her home to the airport. She waited at the airport. Then she drove home.

Here is the distance–time graph for Judy's complete journey.

a   What is the distance from Judy's home to the airport?

b   For how many minutes did Judy wait at the airport?

c   Work out Judy's average speed on her journey home from the airport. Give your answer in kilometres per hour.

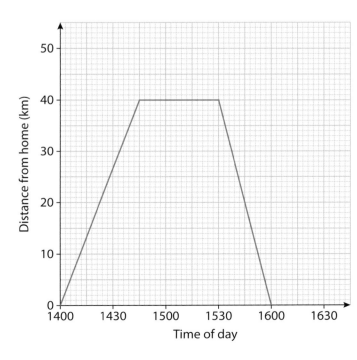

4 *1996 level 7*

The table below shows values of x and y for the equation $y = x^2 + x - 5$.

a Copy and complete the table.

x	-2	-1	0	1	2	3
y				-3	1	7

b The value of y is 0 for a value of x between 1 and 2.

Find the value of x, to 1 decimal place, that gives the value of y closest to 0.
You may use trial and improvement.

x	y
1	-3
2	1

5 *GCSE 1387 June 2007*

The equation $x^3 - x = 30$ has a solution between 3 and 4.
Use a trial and improvement method to find this solution. Give your answer correct to 1 decimal place.
You must show all your working.

6 *GCSE 1387 November 2004*

The equation $x^3 + 4x = 100$ has one solution which is a positive number.
Use the method of trial and improvement to find this solution. Give your answer correct to 1 decimal place.
You must show all your working.

7 *1995 level 7*

A robot accelerates at a constant rate, backwards or forwards.
When the robot moves, three equations connect:

- u its initial speed in m/s
- v its final speed in m/s
- a its acceleration in m/s^2
- s the distance travelled in m
- t the time taken in seconds

The equations are:

$$v = u + at \qquad v^2 = u^2 + 2as \qquad s = ut + \tfrac{1}{2}at^2$$

For a journey made by the robot:

$$u = 0.25 \, \text{m/s} \qquad t = 3.5 \, \text{seconds} \qquad a = -0.05 \, \text{m/s}^2$$

Use the appropriate equation to find:

a the distance travelled,

b the robot's final speed.

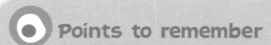

Points to remember

⊙ When you interpret **graphs of real-life situations**, always check what the axes represent and work out the scales on the axes.

⊙ You can use **trial and improvement** to solve equations methodically.

    – Start with an estimate. Substitute this and use the feedback to improve your next estimate.

    – Carry on until you have the required number of figures in the solution.

4 2D and 3D shapes

This lesson will remind you how to solve some problems involving 2D or 3D shapes.

Exercise 4

Example 1

Enlarge the triangle with scale factor 2 and centre O.

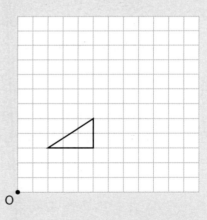

Choose any point A of the triangle. Join O, the centre of enlargement, to A and extend this line.

The scale factor is 2. O to A is 5 to the right and 3 up, so O to A' is 10 to the right and 6 up.

Mark A' on the diagram.

Either repeat the process to find the other two vertices of the enlarged triangle or draw it making its sides twice the length of those of the original triangle.

Always measure from the centre of enlargement.

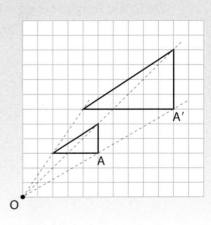

Example 2

Draw a plan, side and front elevation of this shape made from cubes.

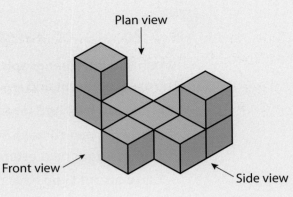

Plan view

Front view

Side view

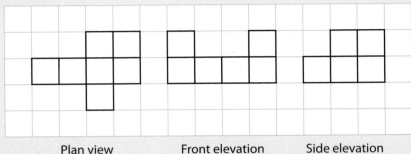

Plan view   Front elevation   Side elevation

Example 3

Calculate the area of the sector and the total perimeter.

Area of sector = (angle ÷ 360°) × area of circle
$$= 130° ÷ 360° × \pi × 9^2 = 91.9 \text{ cm}^2 \text{ (to 1 d.p.)}$$

The total perimeter = radius + radius + arc length
$$= 9 + 9 + 130° ÷ 360° × 2 × 9 × \pi$$
$$= 18 + 20.4 = 38.4 \text{ cm (to 1 d.p.)}$$

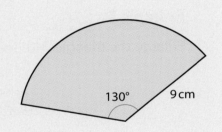

You need some squared paper.

1   *GCSE 1387 June 2007*

Describe fully the single transformation which maps triangle T onto triangle C.

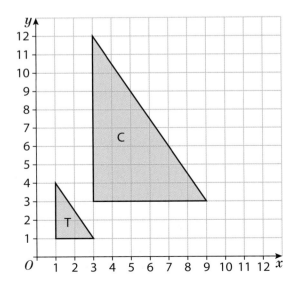

2 *GCSE 1387 June 2004*

Copy the grid and the triangle on squared paper. Mark point P with a cross.

Enlarge the shaded triangle by a scale factor 1.5, centre P.

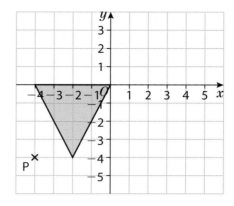

3 *2003 level 7*

Here are four pictures, A, B, C and D. They are not to scale.

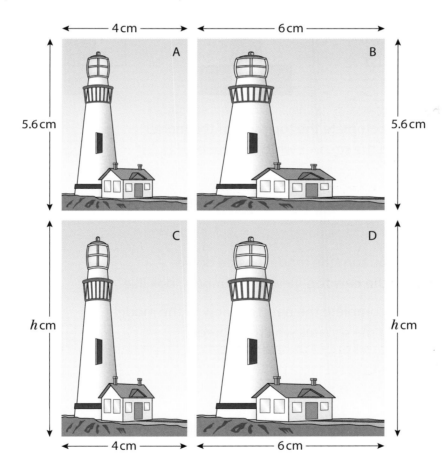

a Picture A can be stretched horizontally to make picture B.
Show that the horizontal factor of enlargement is 1.5.

b Picture A can be stretched vertically to make picture C.
The vertical factor of enlargement is 1.25.
What is the height, h, of picture C?

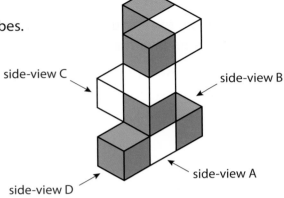

4 *1999 level 6*

The diagram shows a model made with nine cubes.
Five of the cubes are green.
The other four cubes are white.

side-view C

side-view B

side-view A

side-view D

a The drawings below show the four side-views of the model.
Which side-view does each drawing show?

i 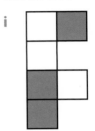 **ii** 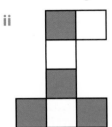 **iii** 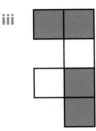 **iv**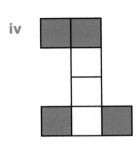

b Copy and complete the top-view of the model
by shading the squares which are green.

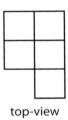

top-view

c Imagine you turn the model upside down.
What will the new top-view of the model look like?

Copy and complete the new top-view of the model
by shading the squares which are green.

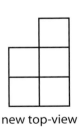

new top-view

5 *GCSE 1387 November 2004*

Calculate the volume of the triangular prism.

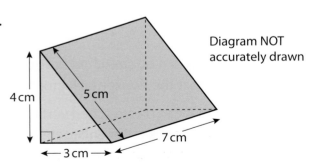

Diagram NOT
accurately drawn

4 cm

5 cm

7 cm

3 cm

6 *GCSE 1387 June 2004*

A can of drink is in the shape of a cylinder. The can has a radius of 4 cm and a height of 15 cm.

Calculate the volume of the cylinder. Give your answer correct to 3 significant figures.

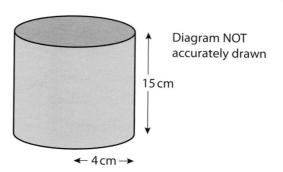

Diagram NOT accurately drawn

15 cm

← 4 cm →

7 *1996 level 6*

This door wedge is the shape of a prism.

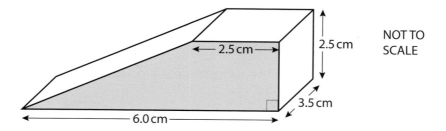

← 2.5 cm →

2.5 cm

NOT TO SCALE

3.5 cm

← 6.0 cm →

a The shaded face of the door wedge is a trapezium. Calculate the area of the shaded face. Show your working.

b Calculate the volume of the door wedge. Show your working.

8 *1996 level 6*

a What is the volume of this standard size box of salt?

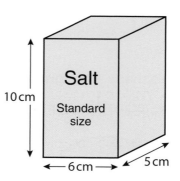

Salt

Standard size

10 cm

← 6 cm → 5 cm

b What is the volume of this special offer box of salt, which is 20% bigger?

20% more

Salt

Special offer

c The standard size box contains enough salt to fill up 10 salt pots. How many salt pots may be filled up from the special offer box of salt?

Extension problems

9 *2001 level 8*

The diagram shows parts of
two circles, sector A and sector B.

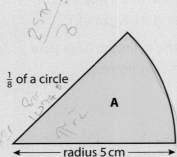
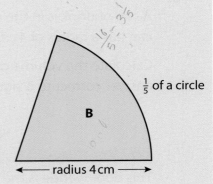

a Which sector has the
   bigger area?
   Show working to explain
   your answer.

$\frac{1}{8}$ of a circle

$\frac{1}{5}$ of a circle

A

B

radius 5 cm

radius 4 cm

b The perimeter of a sector is made from two straight lines and an arc.
   Which sector has the bigger perimeter?
   Show working to explain your answer.

c A semicircle, of radius 4 cm, has the same area as a complete circle of radius r cm.

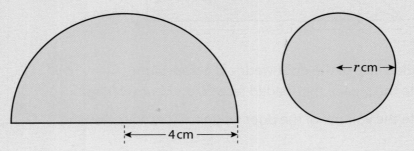

←4 cm→

←r cm→

What is the radius of the complete circle? Show your working.

10 *1998 level 8*

This shape is designed using three semicircles.

The radii of the semicircles are $3a$, $2a$ and a.

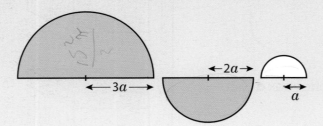

←3a→

←2a→

a

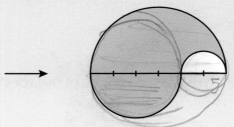

a Find the area of each semicircle, in terms of a and π, and show that the total area of the
   shape is $6\pi a^2$.

b The area, $6\pi a^2$, of the shape is 12 cm².
   Write an equation in the form of $a = \ldots\ldots\ldots$
   Leave your answer in terms of π.
   Show your working and simplify your equation.

Points to remember

- When you **enlarge** a shape, measure distances of the vertices from the centre of enlargement. If C is the centre, for corresponding points P′ and P on the image and object:

  CP′ = scale factor × CP

- **Volume of prism** = area of cross-section × length

- **Arc length** = $\dfrac{\text{angle of arc}}{360}$ × circumference of the circle

- **Area of a sector** = $\dfrac{\text{angle of sector}}{360}$ × area of the circle

5 Grouped frequency

This lesson will help you to:

- interpret scatter graphs and draw lines of best fit;
- represent grouped data, estimate the mean and range and identify the modal class.

Exercise 5A

The **grouped frequency table** shows the times that 50 runners took to complete a 10 km run.

Time (t minutes)	Frequency (f)
$50 \leqslant t < 60$	2
$60 \leqslant t < 70$	8
$70 \leqslant t < 80$	19
$80 \leqslant t < 90$	14
$90 \leqslant t < 100$	7

$50 \leqslant t < 60$ means 50 seconds or more but less than 60 seconds.

Each group is called a **class interval**. There are 2 runners in the class interval $50 \leqslant t < 60$.

In the table, each interval has an equal **class width** of 10 seconds.

The **modal class interval** is the class interval with the highest frequency.
In the table, the modal class interval is $70 \leqslant t < 80$ since the highest frequency is 19 runners.

Estimating the range

The exact time for each runner is not given so you cannot find an exact value for the range.

minimum possible time = 50 minutes
maximum possible time = 100 minutes

Estimated range = maximum possible time − minimum possible time
$$= 100 - 50 = 50 \text{ minutes}$$

Estimating the mean

The exact time for each runner is not given so you cannot find an exact mean time.
To estimate the mean time for the 80 runners, use the middle value of each class interval.

For example:

- Assume that the 2 runners in the class interval $50 \leqslant t < 60$ took on average 55 seconds.
- This gives a total time for these 2 runners of 55×2 seconds.

The calculations for each group of runners are shown in the table.

Midpoint of class (t)	Frequency (f)	$t \times f$
55	2	$55 \times 2 = 110$
65	8	$65 \times 8 = 520$
75	19	$75 \times 19 = 1425$
85	14	$85 \times 14 = 1190$
95	7	$95 \times 7 = 665$
Total	**50**	**3910**

The estimated sum of the times is $110 + 520 + 1425 + 1190 + 665 = 3910$.
The number of runners is $2 + 8 + 19 + 14 + 7 = 50$.

So the **estimated mean time** is $3910 \div 50 = \textbf{78.2 minutes}$.

A **frequency polygon** shows grouped data.

Here is the frequency polygon for the times of the 50 runners.

To draw a frequency polygon:

- plot the frequencies against the midpoints of the class intervals;
- join the points with straight lines.

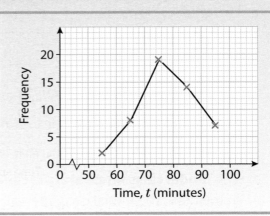

Comparing two sets of grouped data

You can use estimates of the mean and range of sets of grouped data to compare them.

This table shows estimates of the mean and range of the times some runners took to complete a 10 mile run before and after 10 weeks of training.

	Estimate of mean time (minutes)	Estimate of range (minutes)
Before training	78.2	69.6
After training	62.3	68.2

This shows that after 10 weeks of training the average time has improved but the spread of times changed by very little.

This suggests that, on average, each runner improved by approximately the same amount.

You need a copy of **R6.2 Resource sheet 5.2**.

1. A teacher asked 50 pupils in Year 9 how much time they spent on homework last night. This table shows the results.

Time spent on homework (minutes)	Frequency
$0 \leqslant \text{time} \leqslant 30$	6
$30 < \text{time} \leqslant 60$	14
$60 < \text{time} \leqslant 90$	21
$90 < \text{time} \leqslant 120$	9
Total	50

a Use the grid on **Resource sheet 5.2**.
  Draw a frequency polygon to show the results.

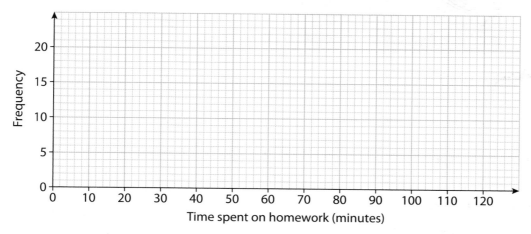

b Show that an estimate of the mean time spent on homework is 64.8 minutes.

② 80 pupils from Jack's school took part in a sponsored swim.

Distance swum (*l* metres)	Frequency
$0 < l \leqslant 100$	12
$100 < l \leqslant 200$	33
$200 < l \leqslant 300$	27
$300 < l \leqslant 400$	6
$400 < l \leqslant 500$	2

The table above shows the results.

a What is the modal class?

b Estimate the mean distance swum by each of the 80 pupils.

c Estimate the range of distances swum.

d Use the grid on **Resource sheet 5.2**. Draw a frequency polygon to show the data.

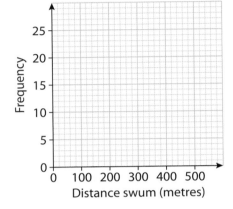

③ 30 students picked strawberries over one weekend. The table shows the money they earned.

Money earned (£)	Frequency
$25 \leqslant earnings < 30$	1
$30 \leqslant earnings < 35$	2
$35 \leqslant earnings < 40$	3
$40 \leqslant earnings < 45$	4
$45 \leqslant earnings < 50$	10
$50 \leqslant earnings < 55$	7
$55 \leqslant earnings < 60$	3

a What is the modal class?

b Calculate an estimate of the mean amount of money earned.

c Calculate an estimate of the range of the amount of money earned.

d Use the grid on **Resource sheet 5.2**. Draw a frequency polygon to show the data.

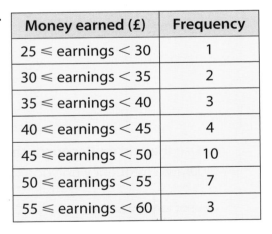

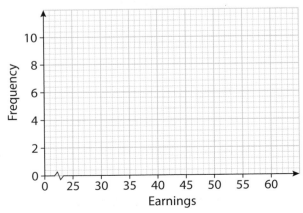

Scatter graphs show whether there is a relationship between two quantities.

For example, this table and the scatter graph below shows the marks of 12 pupils who took a test in science and in maths.

Science mark	5	19	35	7	33	29	23	9	27	36	17	32
Maths mark	6	15	21	10	22	21	18	7	16	25	13	19

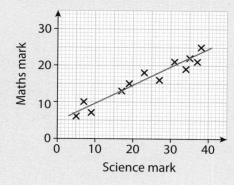

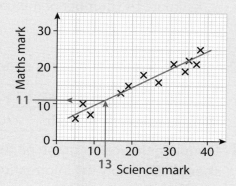

It is possible to draw a straight line which passes near all the points. This line is called a **line of best fit**.

You can use the line of best fit to estimate values. For example, to estimate the maths mark of a pupil whose science mark is 13, draw a vertical line up from 13 to the line of best fit. Then draw a horizontal line across and read off the maths mark, 11.

The pattern of the crosses and the line of best fit on the scatter graph suggest that there is a relationship or **correlation** between the science marks and the maths marks:

   As the science mark increases, the maths mark increases.

When one quantity increases as the other increases, this is called **positive correlation**.

Scatter graphs can suggest other sorts of relationship between two quantities or even that there is no relationship at all.

You need a copy of **R6.2 Resource sheet 5.2**.

(1) *GCSE 1387 June 2007*

Identical candles were lit. The table shows, for 10 of these candles, the number of minutes each candle burnt before it went out and the weight left of each candle when it went out.

Time (min)	29	15	25	50	2	15	7	30	35	35
Weight (g)	8	25	15	2	38	30	28	20	15	12

a Complete the scatter graph on **Resource sheet 5.2**. The first 7 points have been plotted for you.

b Describe the correlation between the time and the weight.

c Draw a line of best fit on the scatter graph.

d A candle burnt for 20 minutes.

   i Use your line of best fit to estimate the weight of this candle when it went out.

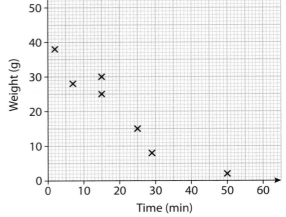

   ii Another candle had a weight of 10 g when it went out. Use your line of best fit to estimate the number of minutes this candle burnt before it went out.

(2) *GCSE 1387 June 2004*

The table shows the number of pages and the weight, in grams, for each of 10 books.

Number of pages	80	130	100	140	115	90	160	140	105	150
Weight (g)	160	270	180	290	230	180	320	270	210	300

a Complete the scatter graph on **Resource sheet 5.2** to show the information in the table. The first 6 points are plotted for you.

b Describe the relationship between the number of pages and the weight of a book.

c Draw a line of best fit on the scatter graph.

d Use your line of best fit to estimate:

   i the number of pages in a book of weight 280 g;

   ii the weight of a book with 120 pages.

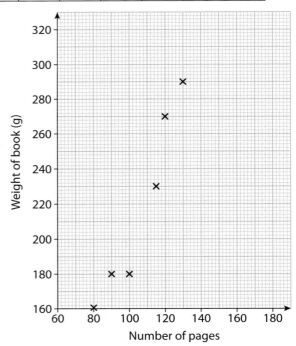

(3) *GCSE 1387 November 2004*

Pablo is an artist. The scatter graph gives information about the area and the cost of some of his pictures.

The table shows the area and the cost of another three of his pictures.

Area (cm²)	2000	2900	3260
Cost (£)	1150	1250	1500

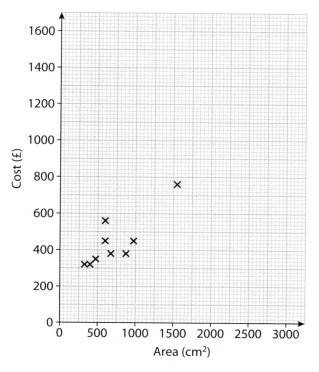

a On the scatter graph on **Resource sheet 5.2**, plot the information from the table.

b Describe the relationship between the area of a picture and its cost.

c Draw a line of best fit on the scatter graph.

d Use your line of best fit to find an estimate of the cost of a picture with area 2500 cm².

e All Pablo's pictures are rectangles. One of his pictures costs £1000. Its length is 48 cm. Use your line of best fit to find an estimate for the width of the picture.

Points to remember

⊙ A **line of best fit** represents the best estimate of the relationship between the two variables on a scatter graph. To draw it, draw a straight line so that the points on the scatter graph are balanced on each side of it.

⊙ To draw a **frequency polygon** for a set of grouped data:
  – plot the frequencies (f) against the midpoints of the class intervals (x);
  – join the points with straight lines.

⊙ The **modal class** is the class interval with the greatest frequency.

⊙ To estimate **the mean of a set of grouped data**:
  – for each interval, work out $x \times f$;
  – find the total of the products $x \times f$;
  – divide by the sum of the frequencies f.

Answers to
How well are you doing?

N6.1 Powers and roots

1   a   4.36   b   7.37

    c   −5.31   d   0.28

2

y	$y + 2$	$y(y + 2)$	
8	10	80	too large
7	9	63	too small
7.2	9.2	66.24	too small
7.3	9.3	67.89	correct

3   a $k = 3, m = 6$ b   16 384

4   For integer values of (x, y) choose any four from:
(2, 6), (4, 3), (8, 2), (−2, 6), (−8, 2)

5   $m = 12, n = 4$

6   5×10^3

7   9.43×10^{12}

A6.1 Expressions and formulae

1   a   No

    b $10y = 238, y = 23.8$

2   $t = 6\frac{1}{4}$

3   a $y^2 − 6y$ b $k^2 + 5k + 6$

4   a   C   b $y^2 + 11y + 18$

5   $c = \dfrac{20 \times 4}{12 + 4} = \dfrac{80}{16} = 5$ ml

N6.2 Proportional reasoning

1

Type of juice	Amount
Orange	$\frac{1}{2} \times 1\frac{1}{2} = \frac{3}{4}$ litre
Cranberry	$\frac{1}{3} \times 1\frac{1}{2} = \frac{1}{2}$ litre
Grape	$\frac{1}{6} \times 1\frac{1}{2} = \frac{1}{4}$ litre
	Total $1\frac{1}{2}$ litres

2   For B, $40 = \dfrac{100}{t}, t = 2\frac{1}{2}$.

    For A, therefore, $s = \dfrac{60}{2\frac{1}{2}} = 24$ km/h.

3   a   6 cm and 10.5 cm

    b   The height of the largest doll has been scaled up by a factor of $\frac{9}{7}$.
The heights of the other dolls are 5.1 cm and 7.7 cm, both correct to 1 decimal place.

4   a 70×1.09

    b   For example, 70×0.9.
What is 70 decreased by 10%?

    c   For example, 70×1.9.
What is 70 increased by 90%?

    d   To decrease by 14%, multiply by 0.86.

5   Tuesday's price is £19.95 × 0.85.
Wednesday's price is:
£19.95 × 0.85 × 0.85 = £14.41 to the nearest penny.

6

Retailers	$\frac{44}{175} = 25.1\%$
Growers	$\frac{5}{75} = 2.9\%$
Others	$\frac{126}{175} = 72\%$

7   2.67 million

S6.1 Enquiry 1

1   a   Month A
Sum of frequencies = 30

    b   B

    c   B
Higher frequencies at higher rainfalls

    d   There is no information in the frequency polygon about rainfall on particular days.

    e   Month A
Range = 25 mm
Median = 9 mm
Mean = 8.8 mm
Month B
Range = 25 mm
Median = 17 mm
Mean = 15.9 mm

    f   The range is the same for both months.
The means and the medians confirm that there was more rain in Month B.
The rainfall did not exceed 25 mm on any day in either month.

2 a

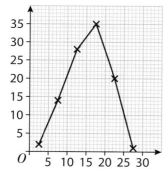

b **i** $15 \leqslant t < 20$ **ii** 15.5 **iii** 16

c 30

3 a Sample restricted to one age group

b Ask people selected at random from a telephone directory.

4 a L

b

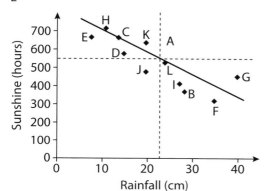

c 470 ± 10 hours

G6.1 Geometrical reasoning

1 4 kites are congruent.

So angle at centre $= 360/4 = 90°$

So $\angle k = (360 - 90 - 40)/2 = 115°$

(opposite angles in a kite)

2 $\angle BCD = \angle x$ (equal angles in isosceles $\triangle$)

$\angle BDC = 180 - 2 \times \angle x$ (sum of angles in $\triangle$)

$\angle BDA = 180 - (180 - 2 \times \angle x) = 2 \times \angle x$

(angles on a straight line)

$\angle y = 2 \times \angle x = 70°$ (equal angles in isosceles $\triangle$)

3 AD = BC (given)

$\angle BAD = \angle ABC$ (given)

AB is common.

ABC is congruent to $\triangle$BAD. (SAS)

4 a AB = AC (tangents are equal)

b OB = OC (radii are equal)

c Both are 90° (tangent perpendicular to radius)

d In quadrilateral OBAC

$360 - 40 - 2 \times 90 = 140°$

e $\angle y = 360 - \angle x - 2 \times 90$ (angles in a quadrilateral)

$\angle y = 180 - \angle x$

$\angle x + \angle y = 180°$

5 $\dfrac{h}{1.8} = \dfrac{6.3}{2.7}$

$h = 4.2\,\text{m}$

A6.2 Linear graphs and inequalities

1 $4x + 3y = 21$

$2x + y = 8$

$4x + 2y = 16$

$3y - 2y = 21 - 16$

$y = 5$

$2x + 5 = 8$

$x = 1.5$

2 7

3 a $y = x^2$

b $x = -5$

c $y = x^2$

d $x + y = 10$ and $y = 2x + 1$

4 a gradient $= -2$, intercept $(0, 8)$

b $y = -x + 8$ or $x + y = 8$

c

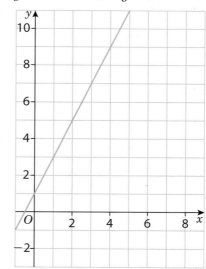

d $y = 2x + 1$

$3y = 6x + 3$

$3y = 4x + 6$

$6x + 3 = 4x + 6$

$2x = 3$

$x = 1.5$

$y = 3 + 1$

$y = 4$

5    $\dfrac{4(7 - 2y)}{12} > 1$

     $28 - 8y > 12$

        $16 > 8y$

          $y < 2$

G6.2 Trigonometry 1

1   84 cm²

2   $a = 6.36$ cm

3   $b = 3.61$ cm

4   $c = 7.26$ cm

5   a   A

       B: $a^2 + c^2 = b^2$

   b   C

       D is not a right-angled triangle.

6   $\cos 3.5° = \dfrac{\text{base}}{10}$

    base $= 10 \times \cos 3.5°$

          $= 9.98$ cm

A6.3 Expressions, equations and graphs

1   a   When x is even $(x - 2)^2$ is even.

   b   Let $x = 2n$

       Then $(2n - 2)^2 \equiv 4n^2 - 8n + 4$ and 2 is a factor.

   c   When x is even $(x - 1)(x + 1)$ is odd.

   d   Let $x = 2m$

       Then $(2m - 1)(2m + 1) \equiv 4m^2 - 1$ and 2 is not a factor.

2   a $a = 1500, b = 20$

   b $\dfrac{3d}{5}$

   c   i $9x - 14$ ii $x^2 + 5x + 6$

      iii $x^2 + 3x - 4$ iv $x^2 - 4x + 4$

3   $18y^2 + 6y = 6y(3y + 1)$

4     $3x + 9y = 120$

      $5x + 5y = 90$

   $15x + 45y = 600$

   $15x + 15y = 270$

        $30y = 330$

          $y = 11$

    $5x + 55y = 90$

          $x = 5$

    $5x + 7y = 35 + 77 = 112$

   The concert will last 112 minutes.

5   A: $2^{(4 - 1)} = 2^3 = 8$

    B: $\dfrac{4^2 - 4 + 2}{2} = \dfrac{14}{2} = 7$

    C: $\dfrac{4(4^2 - 3 \times 4 + 8)}{6} = \dfrac{4(12)}{6} = 8$

6   a $(x - 2)(x + 9)$

   b $(x + 7)(x - 7)$

G6.3 Transformations and loci

1   a   13

   b   7

   c $\sqrt{400} = 20$

   d $\sqrt{85} = 9.2$

2   (7, 3)

3   a   3 (maximum width is 12 cm, which is 3×4 cm)

   b   0.4 (maximum height is 2.7 cm, which is 0.41 $\times$ 6.5); 0.4 $\times$ 6.5 = 2.6 cm

4   Reflection in $x = 0$

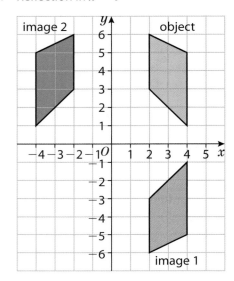

5

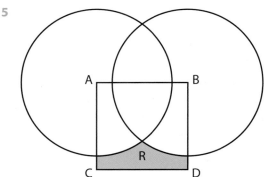

N6.3 Decimals and accuracy

1   The true answer to $28 \div 3$ is $9\frac{1}{3}$ or $9.\dot{3}$. $9.\dot{3}$ is 9.333 333 333…, which is a little bigger than 9.33.

2   a $0.1 \times 0.05 = 0.005$

   b $10 \div 0.1 = 100$

3   a   16   b   30

4 a 92.5 metres

  b 49.5 metres

  c The shortest possible perimeter of the pitch is
$92.5 + 49.5 + 92.5 + 49.5 = 284$ metres.
$3000 \div 284 = 10.56$, so Des must run round
the pitch 11 times.

5 Number of gallons used in one hour
$= 33 \times \frac{5280}{13} = 13\,403.076\,92$ gallons
$13\,000$ gallons to 2 s.f.

S6.2 Probability 1

1 a 0.89

  b Meg 0.89
Ravi 0.85

  c Ravi's results are likely to give a better estimate
as it is based on twice as many trials.

  d $\frac{259}{300} = 0.86$

2 Feb 1950: relative frequency of Labour vote $= 0.46$
May 2001: relative frequency of Labour vote $= 0.31$
Labour won the election of 1950 with 46% of the
vote; they also won in 2001, but this time with only
31% of the vote.

3 0.65

4 a

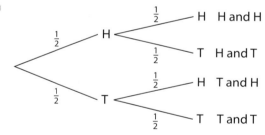

  b A scores 2 points for the outcome **H** and **H**.
There are four equally likely outcomes, one of
which is **H** and **H**.
So the probability that A gets 2 points is $\frac{1}{4}$.

  c B scores exactly 1 point for the outcomes **H**
and **T**, and **T** and **H**. So the probability of this
is $\frac{1}{4} + \frac{1}{4} = \frac{1}{2}$.

5 0.6

G6.4 Measures and mensuration

1

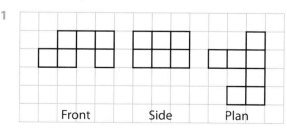

2 167.1 cm

3 a 28.3 cm²   b 24.3 cm

4 a 120 cm³   b 450 cm³

5 Volume $4.5\pi\,\text{cm}^3 = \pi r^2 h$
$= 6.25\pi h$
$h = \frac{4.5\pi}{6.25\pi} = 0.72\,\text{cm}$

S6.3 Enquiry 2

1 Small sample size
People who do not visit newsagent not asked
People who are not shopping on Monday morning
not asked

2 a

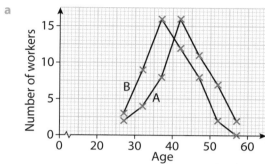

  b On average the workers at Factory B are
younger than those at Factory A.

3 a 2.74 minutes

  b 2.76 minutes

  c For example, use more than one checkout

4 a Positive correlation

  b Graph shows that a poplar with diameter 5 cm
will be about 6 m tall

  c 4.7 m

  d i False   ii False   iii False   iv False

G6.5 Trigonometry 2

1 Area $= \frac{1}{2}$ base $\times$ height
$h^2 = 25^2 - 7^2$
$h = 24\,\text{cm}^2$
Area $= \frac{1}{2} \times 7 \times 24$
$= 84\,\text{cm}^2$

2 $y^2 = 5^2 + 5^2, y^2 = 50, y = \sqrt{50}$

3 a $AC^2 = 6^2 + 8^2$
$AC = \sqrt{100}$
$AC = 10\,\text{cm}$

  b $AD^2 = 6^2 + 10^2$
$AD = \sqrt{136} = 11.7\,\text{cm}$

4 7.8 cm

5 a 17.2 cm   b 35.0°

A6.4 Using algebra

1

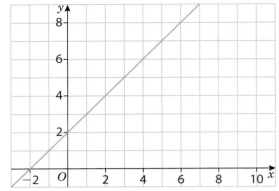

2 $y = 4x + 5$

3 $x = 1, y = -3$

4 a

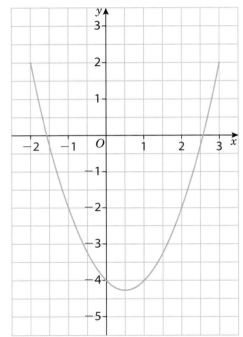

    b i $y = -4.25$ **ii** $x = 2.56$ or $x = -1.56$

5 a

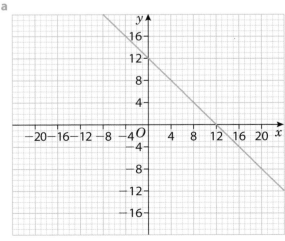

b

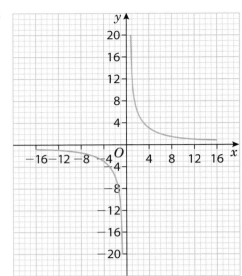

6 $x = -1.85$

7 a 4, 12, 24

    b 220

    c $2n(n + 1)$

8 a The buses passed each other; bus A was going towards Town Hall, bus B towards Red Lion.

    b Bus A passed bus B which had stopped.

    c 17.8 km per hour

    d 5 stops = 10 mins, so the bus was in motion for 17 mins, at an average speed of
$8 \times \frac{60}{17} = 28.2$ km per hour

    e 21.5 km/h $= 21.5 \times \frac{8}{5}$ mph
$= 34.4$ miles per hour

S6.4 Probability 2

1 a No, expected number of sixes = 100

    b **6** and **not 6** at end of each pair of branches
$\frac{1}{6}$ and $\frac{5}{6}$ on all pairs of branches

    c i $\frac{1}{36}$ **ii** $\frac{11}{36}$

2 0.66

3 a The outcome of picking first counter does not affect probability of second.

    b **R** and **B** at end of each pair of branches
$\frac{2}{5}$ and $\frac{3}{5}$ on all pairs of branches

    R and **R**
    R and **B**
    B and **R**
    B and **B**

    c i $\frac{4}{25}$ **ii** $\frac{6}{25}$
    iii $\frac{6}{25}$ **iv** $\frac{9}{25}$

    d $\frac{13}{25}$

    e 240

4 a

		H	H and H and H
	H		
		T	H and H and T
H			
		H	H and T and H
	T		
		T	H and T and T
		H	T and H and H
	H		
		T	T and H and T
T			
		H	T and T and H
	T		
		T	T and T and T

b B scores exactly 2 points from H, H and T, H, T and H or T, H and H, which is $3 \times \frac{1}{8} = \frac{3}{8}$.

N6.4 Using and applying maths

1 The maximum number of digits is 5, from 999×99, which is just less than $1000 \times 100 = 100\,000$.
The minimum number of digits is 4, from $100 \times 10 = 1000$.

2 **a** A is true. If x is even, so is $x - 2$. The square of an even number is even, so $(x - 2)^2$ is even.

b D is true. If x is odd, $x - 1$ is even and $x + 1$ is even. The product of two even numbers is even, so $(x - 1)(x + 1)$ is even.

3 **a** $\dfrac{n}{2n + 1}$ **b** B

4 5 hours 12 minutes

Index